SETS, LATTICES, AND BOOLEAN ALGEBRAS

JAMES C. ABBOTT
Professor of Mathematics
United States Naval Academy

SETS, LATTICES, AND BOOLEAN ALGEBRAS

Allyn and Bacon, Inc. Boston

470 Atlantic Avenue, Boston

Library of Congress Card Number: 69-11623
Printed in the United States of America

PREFACE

THE MOTIVATION FOR THE PRESENT TEXT lies in the theory of sets and various algebraic systems that are derived from it. In recent years the role of set theory has expanded reaching into the lowest level of the curriculum in the elementary grades and extending to new theories concerning the very foundation of mathematics and logic at the advanced graduate level. It has become almost a sine qua non for all branches of mathematics. Almost all present day algebra books begin with a chapter on sets. Courses in analysis beginning with the calculus itself require a basic knowledge of the concepts of set theory in order to properly understand function theory. Probability is almost entirely dependent on set theory, while topology of course rests completely on its foundations. On the other hand, the work of the logicians during the past decade have extended the basic understanding of the subject and offer even more hope for its future. One purpose of the French Bourbaki school is to show how all of mathematics derives its essential justification from the theory of sets.

The purpose of this book is to give a brief picture of this central role of set theory beginning with its axiomatics and leading to various abstract mathematical systems developed from it. Chapter 1 begins with a brief look at the various paradoxes of set theory to see why it is necessary to have an axiomatic treatment. The author is of the opinion that every undergraduate mathematics student should have an opportunity to see how the elementary contradictions of too naïve an approach to sets may be eliminated by a reasonably logic development of its axioms. Therefore, we examine in brief one system of axiomatics that leads to a sufficient body of mathematics free from the taint of contradictions. We choose the Zermelo-Fraenkel Skolem system, but because it is partly inadequate for the modern development of category theory and universal algebra, we also include a brief description of the von Neumann-Bernays-Gödel theory of classes in Appendix 1.

The axioms proceed as far as the axiom of choice in its simplest form, leaving alternate forms until after the introduction of partially ordered sets.

Chapter 2 is devoted to showing how the basic concepts and axioms of Chapter 1 lead to a logic justification of the basic core concepts of the rest of mathematics.

Thus the theory of ordered pairs, cartesian products, relations, functions and operations are all reduced to special kinds of sets. From here it follows that linear algebra, the theory of numbers, functional analysis, topology, etc., all obtain their basic justification from the theory of sets. The abstract concepts of universal algebra, subalgebras, homomorphism and direct products are introduced at this stage in an abstract form and then exemplified throughout the remainder of the text in various specific cases. Chapter 2 then develops the algebra of sets itself based on the axiomatics of Chapter 1 and using the concepts of universal algebra. The remainder of the book then shows how this concrete algebra of sets can be used as a model for the development of abstract algebras leading eventually to Boolean algebra as the final abstract characterization of set algebra.

Chapter 3 is devoted to the simplest form of universal algebra, the theory of sets with the empty set of operations. The morphisms then lead to the theory of cardinality and the arithmetic of cardinal numbers. The second half of the chapter is then spent on examining the situation when either a linear or well-ordering relation is imposed on the system. These alternatives lead to the theory of order types and ordinal numbers, respectively. The complete treatment follows the classical outline of Cantor himself culminating in Zermelo's famous proof of the well-ordering theorem. On the way we examine the process of transfinite induction and definition by transfinite recursiveness.

Chapter 4 begins the development of the second portion of the book which consists of various abstract systems modeled on the specific algebra of sets of Chapter 2. The most general of these is the theory of partially ordered sets which retains only the structure of a partial order based on the concept of set inclusion developed in the first two chapters. Following the general theory, the theory of lattices and semi-lattices follows by imposing restrictions requiring the existence of various least upper and greatest lower bounds. Lattice theory is also presented alternatively as an abstract algebra exemplifying the principles of universal algebra and the two approaches are amalgamated in the general theory of lattices.

Chapter 5 then develops more specific types of lattices with the main emphasis on the modular and distributive cases. The natural culmination of this development is the theory of complemented, distributive lattices which become the central topic of the third part of the book, the theory of Boolean algebras of Chapters 6 and 7.

This theory serves as the abstract characterization of the full algebra of sets and therefore brings us full cycle back to Chapter 2 with the Stone Representation Theorem of every abstract Boolean algebra as a concrete algebra of sets. Thus we proceed from the axiomatic foundations to the concrete algebra of sets to abstract systems of a very general nature at first but gradually narrowing down to an abstraction embodying all of the algebra of sets returning us to the starting point.

For those with an interest in topology Appendix 2 is included to show the relationship of topology to lattice theory in general and to prepare the reader for the last section of Chapter 6 which is the topological form of the representation theory.

Chapter 7 remains as a diversion of our own which generalizes Boolean algebra in a slightly different way. In the development of lattice theory we diverge somewhat from the norm by placing more than usual emphasis on semi-lattices, so that we are prepared for a study of semi-Boolean algebras in Chapter 7. These algebras generalize Boolean algebra omitting the requirement of both a least and greatest element and closure under both the join and meet operations. These systems are modeled on the set theoretic operations of set subtraction and set implication and give rise to a single characterization of the dual algebras of subtraction and implication. The theory thus developed returns us once again to Chapter 1 as an abstract characterization of set theory without need for a universal set. Thus our system is more in keeping with the more modern approach of von Neumann's class theory and category theory in that we don't need a "set of all sets," but merely a class of all sets on which our algebra is defined. Thus we obtain an algebra which serves for full axiomatic set theory, free of the Russell paradox, so that Chapter 7 comes closer to the needs of Chapter 1.

This book was written not so much as a text for one of the traditional courses in college mathematics, but rather to meet the needs of a changing curriculum in which emphasis on abstract mathematics is replacing the role of mathematics as a support function for engineerings and physical sciences. Today following the revolution in school mathematics, the outlook in college mathematics is changing rapidly so that the calculus is now no longer the sole justification for mathematics even amongst the engineers and physicists. Abstract algebra has come into its own, not just as a beautiful theory of interest to pure mathematicians, but as a necessity for understanding the expanding role of mathematics in modern society. The last twenty years has seen the development of a complete new role of the mathematician in such widely diverse fields as computing theory, linguistics, operational analysis, decision theory, etc., in which the calculus is hardly noticed. No longer do we justify college mathematics solely on the applications of calculus to engineering, but abstract mathematics becomes essential in business and management, in economics, in biology, in languages both natural and artificial, and in even psychology and other diverse fields. Therefore, there are newer needs in the college curriculum for more diverse mathematics and a deeper understanding of the meaning of mathematics as an abstract science, not just as a computing tool.

Linear algebra has become a sine qua non while old-fashioned college algebra has almost disappeared from the scene. The present volume follows these trends and presents a deeper look into the foundations of abstract algebra in terms of axiomatic set theory in order to prepare the student for such new and growing fields as category theory and universal algebra. At the same time it offers a diversification of fields so as to be adaptable to many different needs. There are three basic sections devoted to the three subjects of the title closely bound together by the common bond of the algebra of sets, but at the same time sufficiently independent to fit varying requirements. Thus Chapters 1–3 can be used as a brief course in set theory and an introduction to universal algebra, while Chapter 3 carries us through the theory of transfinite numbers. For those not interested in this special topic, however, this chapter can be omitted without breaking the trend of thought of the remaining chapters.

The next three chapters are devoted to lattice theory and its specialization to Boolean algebra. Much of the classical modern algebra is devoted to groups, rings and fields, and their variations. These are mainly algebras with finitary operations and the role of order is secondary. On the other hand in lattice theory, the theory of partially ordered sets is essential. It is this side of modern algebra that is developed here so that the entire book is devoted largely to the study of order relations in mathematics. Unfortunately lattice theory has been somewhat neglected in modern college mathematics particularly in this country, so that lattice theory is less popular than classical abstract algebra. This situation is changing today and this book is intended to help accelerate this change so that the mathematician of the future will be more aware of the role of order in the whole field of mathematics. There are few good texts solely devoted to lattice theory readily available on the American market today. It is hoped that the present book will help to remedy this situation. Of course, Birkhoff's Lattice Theory will remain the bible of all lattice theoreticians for a long time to come, but it is hoped that this text can make some of the material from Birkhoff available at a more elementary level for the college student.

For those whose main interest is lattice theory by itself, Chapters 4–6 can serve this purpose fairly independent of the rest of the book, so that a short course can be developed on these three chapters alone with only occasional references to Chapters 1 and 2. On the other hand, Chapters 6 and 7 are devoted to Boolean algebra as a topic by itself. In fact Boolean algebra constitutes one of the oldest branches of abstract algebra dating from original work of Boole himself. As such it developed quite rapidly and enjoyed considerable favor of mathematicians during the later part of the last century and the early part of this century, but has been somewhat quiescent since. However, recently there has been a revival of interest due to its applications to computer design and electrical analysis. Therefore, there have been many recent books on Boolean algebra mostly in terms of applications to electrical engineering on a fairly elementary level. Particularly since there are so many good books of this type now available, this side of Boolean algebra has been neglected in this volume which puts more emphasis on Boolean algebra as a part of pure mathematics rather than as a tool for engineers. There are perhaps only two advanced books of recent vintage on Boolean algebra as a subject of current research and these are the works of Halmos and Sikorski, so that this book can be taken more as an introduction to these than as preparation for the books on applied Boolean algebra.

In the last chapter, the material is devoted to some new and elementary developments in Boolean algebra from the point of view of abstract algebra. This material was the outgrowth of an undergraduate research seminar and as such is suitable as a reading topic for interested undergraduates who wish to try their hand at something slightly different not readily available in the literature, but sufficiently elementary as to be available at their level. Furthermore, it exemplifies most of the notions of universal algebra and lattice theory developed in the first six chapters. Hence it is an ideal topic for student stimulation on an individual basis with many elementary problems left open. At the same time Boolean algebra and its representation can be obtained as a special case.

The entire book is designed to be as flexible as possible, adaptable within the undergraduate curriculum for a variety of one-semester courses in any of the three major fields of set theory, lattice theory or Boolean algebra. At the same time it is designed to develop the student's own imagination by leaving many special topics to the exercises. Particularly in Chapters 4–7 many important topics have been left to the student as a means of sharpening his research abilities by supplementary reading and self-study. Thus it is hoped to suggest the creative role in mathematics even before entering graduate school. Too often students graduate with majors in mathematics lost in a maze of formulas and techniques without a feel for their science as a living, growing organism. It is hoped that this book may alleviate some of this problem.

The author would like to thank Professor Samuel Holland who read the manuscript and offered valuable suggestions. In addition he would like to thank the following students who helped prepare the materials in Chapter 7: Mr. Paul Kleindorfer, Mr. William Heard, Mr. Donald Pilling, and Mr. Robert Kimble. He would also like to express appreciation to the staff of Allyn and Bacon, Inc., and in particular Miss Beverly Malatesta, for their cooperation in preparing the final manuscript. Finally he would like to thank his wife for her patience during the writing of the entire book.

J. C. Abbott

CONTENTS

3. Transfinite Numbers 64

4. Partially Ordered Sets and Lattice Theory 96

5. Distributive and Modular Lattices 140

6. Boolean Algebra 178

SETS, LATTICES, AND BOOLEAN ALGEBRAS

1

THE AXIOMATICS OF SET THEORY

1-1. RUSSELL'S PARADOX

Up until fairly recently, much of the history of mathematics has been centered around the fundamental concept of number. In fact, mathematics was frequently thought of as the science of numbers, and much of its usefulness revolved around its ability to analyze quantitatively situations occurring elsewhere in life. It was assumed that the concept of number was a primitive notion that we must accept intuitively, and on which the remainder of our science rests. Thus Kronecker states that God gave us the integers, but all the rest was created by man. Even the science of geometry, which was independent of the concept of numbers in Greek mathematics, came under the realm of the science of numbers with Descartes' invention of analytic geometry. However, all this began to change toward the middle and end of the last century when Cantor, Fourier, Peano, Dedekind and others began to find the need for a more exact meaning of the number concept. Spurred on by the study of infinite series and analytic functions, they began to formulate the concept of number in terms of the theory of aggregates. Cantor's results were published in two memoirs in 1895 and 1897, which to this day remain as classics of the beauty of pure mathematics, well worth the reading by all prospective mathematicians (*cf:* Cantor).

At the same time, the success of the axiomatic method within geometry in the solution of Euclid's parallel postulate began to encourage the algebraists to use similar methods in developing an axiomatic approach to the concept of number. Thus Peano was led to a more exact formulation of the integers in his now famous axiomatic treatment of the natural numbers (*cf:* Peano and Dedekind). He based the notion of natural number on that of the function concept, specifically, on the successor function. Later, we shall see how even the function concept can be reduced to a secondary concept within the theory of sets. Meanwhile, Cantor extended the concept of counting number to apply to infinite sets, thus leading to his theory of transfinite numbers. An arithmetic of sets was developed in which sets are combined in various fashions to form new sets. The algebraic rules governing these combinations resemble the arithmetic of numbers and extend in many cases to infinite as well as finite sets. Thus the foundations of mathematics were pushed deeper to rest on the more primitive notion of set.

Even earlier than Cantor and Peano, toward the middle of the nineteenth century, the English logician, George Boole, began to formulate similar laws in an attempt to arithmetize mathematical logic (*cf:* Boole). He considered statements as the fundamental building blocks for a calculus in which they can be combined by the connectives "either. . . or," "both. . . and" and "not." These connectives behave in a fashion similar to the arithmetic operations of addition, multiplication, and subtraction of ordinary numbers, and follow laws similar to those used later by Cantor in his arithmetization of set theory. Thus the theory of Boolean algebra began to develop almost simultaneously as an arithmetic for the theory of sets and the statement calculus. The science of mathematics was broadened to encompass much of mathematical logic, while the notion of number so long dominant in the history of mathematics became a secondary concept, derivable from that of set. Thus Kronecker's concept of mathematics is today replaced by that of N. Bourbaki, who states that "on sait aujourd'hui qu'il est possible. . . de faire dériver presque toute la mathematique actuelle d'une source unique, la Théorie des Ensembles." Today such diverse fields as algebra, geometry, statistics, functional analysis, topology, etc. are all founded on set theory. At the same time, mathematics has become much broader as a pure science as well as in its applications, so that today a mathematician is no longer simply an arithmetician *par excellence*. Systems analysis, graph theory, the theory of automata, mathematical linguistics, etc. now come within the realm of mathematics, not simply as fields for the application of quantitative analysis, but as parts of mathematics independent of the concept of number. Our problem is to trace the various concepts of these different branches of mathematics back to their origins in the theory of sets. We begin in this chapter with the axiomatics of set theory itself in an informal way, so as to understand the logical basis of our subject. Then in Chapter 2 we study briefly how the other central concepts of modern mathematics can be defined in terms of set theory. First we see that the general notion of a relation can be expressed in terms of sets, then that the specific concepts of function and operation are contained within the theory of relations. We study briefly general systems consisting of sets together with relations and operations defined on them. This leads to the study of universal algebra, which is therefore again founded on set theory. We apply it first of all to set theory itself to develop the algebra of sets which is the simplest form of Boolean algebra. In Chapter 3 we study the arithmetic of sets with and without order following the basic outlines of Cantor's original theory of transfinite numbers. In Chapter 4 we generalize the algebra of sets to various abstract algebras which are modeled on different parts of set algebra. In particular, we study the partial order relation of set inclusion and use it to motivate a general theory of partially ordered sets which underlies a very large part of modern mathematics. Specific types of partially ordered sets form the basis of the theory of lattices which occupies most of Chapters 4 and 5. Abstract Boolean algebra as a specific type of a lattice is taken up in Chapter 6. This carries us back to the algebra of sets, since every abstract Boolean algebra turns out to be representable in terms of the algebra of sets. Finally, in Chapter 7 we discuss a special topic which gives a new look to Boolean algebra and suggests further topics for the future. Hence, general set theory serves as the underlying motivating factor for the entire book. However, we conclude with a warning that, although the theory of sets has revolutionized mathematics during the past century, there are indications today that this is not the end, and there are further revolutions to come. The von Neumann theory of classes, discussed briefly in the appendix, the theory of categories, and the new model theory and its divergent forms of set theory indicate that there are further changes in the offing.

We begin this chapter with a study of some of the weaknesses of too naive an approach to set theory, in order to see the need of a more careful examination of its own foundation. In Cantor's papers he recognized that there must be a beginning somewhere, based on an undefined concept. For this purpose, he chose the concept of a set of elements. This concept is primitive in the sense that we do not try to explain it, but, at best, list synonyms such as aggregate, class, collection, family, etc. Cantor himself described a set as a "zusammenfassung zu einem Ganzem," a bringing together into a whole. He thus thought of a set as an abstraction from certain objects according to some common property, all other properties being ignored. The elements with this property are then put together into a set. In this sense he thought of the terms "set" and "property" as being coextensive.

Cantor's theory seemed quite satisfactory, and is so taken today in most elementary mathematics. In fact, Boolean algebra is really much simpler than arithmetic, since the concept of a number requires a second order of abstraction from the objects being numbered. Thus we perform a first abstraction when we collect the objects together into sets, and then perform a second abstraction when we assign numbers to these sets. Set theory therefore basically precedes arithmetic. But it is not that simple when we take a closer look. Hence we begin with a discussion of what is wrong with set theory, in order to understand some of the things that are right with it.

The first difficulty which forced mathematicians to take a closer look at its foundation was due to the English mathematician and philosopher, Bertrand Russell, who posed a paradox within Cantor's set theory. According to the naive or intuitive approach, technically known as "naive set theory," a set is known when some common property of its elements is given. We bring together into the whole exactly those and only those elements which have some prestated property. For example, the set of all men living in the United States singles out those objects which are (*a*) men and (*b*) reside in the United States. Other differences among them, such as height, are ignored. We recognize a member of this set by determining whether or not a given candidate measures up to the condition of membership. Hence, we may associate with this set the property of being a male resident of the United States. Thus it would seem that to determine a set is simply a matter of stating a property which certain objects have in common. It is in this sense that a set is a first order of abstraction from this property. This is the attitude of Cantor; *i.e.*, sets are coextensive with properties and each determines the other. Cantor indicated his sets by the symbolism $\{t|p(t)\}$ where the braces are to be read "the set of all," the vertical bar is to be read "such that," and $p(t)$ is some property which holds for t. Hence "the set of all t such that $p(t)$ is true." We know a set when we can determine for any object whether or not it is an element of the given set. If we designate the set by the letter x and the proposed element by the letter t, then we signify an affirmative answer to our question by the symbolism $t \in x$, "t is an element of x." In the contrary case we write $t \notin x$, "t is not a member of x." $\in$ is therefore a symbol which we write between other symbols as an indication of an answer to a question. We assume that for any two objects, designated by t and x, one or the other of the two symbols $\in$ or $\notin$ belongs between them. Thus we assume that the statement "$t \in x$" is either true or false. That is not to say that we always know which answer is correct, but we merely assume that the question has a definite answer and that they cannot both be true. For example, if $s = \{t| x^t + y^t = z^t\}$, where t, x, y, z are positive integers, then we have no way of knowing for a given integer $n \neq 1, 2$ whether $n \in s$ or $n \notin s$.

We now turn to the case where x and t designate the same object and ask "is $x \in x$ or is $x \notin x$?" There are certainly cases for which $x \notin x$. For example, the set of male residents of the United States is not a male resident of the United States. For this set, certainly $x \notin x$. As another example, we may consider the empty set which has no members (we reserve the specific definition of this set until later, but for the present use it intuitively). We designate it by ϕ. Then $\phi \notin \phi$. Russell now proposes the following property: call a set "normal" if it is not a member of itself. In symbols, x is normal if $x \notin x$. We now collect together those sets which are normal and form a set from them. Designate this set so formed by n. n is not empty, since $\phi \in n$ among other sets. We now inquire into the status of n itself: is n normal? *i.e.*, is $n \notin n$? If the answer is *yes*, then n has the defining property, $n \notin n$. This is a contradiction. Hence we assume n is not normal; *i.e.*, n is not an element of the set n of normal sets: $n \notin n$. But in this case, n now has the defining property necessary to be a member of the set of normal sets; *i.e.*, $n \in n$. Again we have a contradiction, and we are in a quandary. In symbolic notation, if $n = \{x|x \notin x\}$, then replacing x by n we have $n \in n \leftrightarrow n \notin n$. (The symbol $\leftrightarrow$ is to be read "if and only if.") The word "paradox" is used to describe Russell's example in the hope that it is only a semantic problem and can be explained by semantics. In fact, it is a true antinomy. It was first published in 1903 (*cf*: Russell). Other antinomies were also discovered even earlier by Burali-Forti and Cantor himself, but both of these require some knowledge of the cardinal and ordinal numbers, and are omitted here. We return to them in Chapter 3. The antinomies caused considerable consternation and reëxamination within mathematics for some years. In fact, there are still many questions that have not yet been completely resolved, and there is still considerable controversy among mathematicians concerning the foundations of the subject.

The essential difficulty is that we are trying to use the word "set" in too broad a sense, and have allowed a self-contradiction to creep in. The solution is to limit the use of the term "set" by specific rules. Therefore, we must spell out just what we will accept as sets. This turns out to be a rather lengthy task, but one that the young mathematician should face at some time. Once he has had some familiarity with elementary set theory as well as other fields of mathematics, he should pause long enough to examine its foundations. This is the purpose of the present discussion. We shall not try to give a completely rigorous development of the axioms of set theory and their ramifications. Such a task is much too long for a brief introduction like this, and would take an entire volume in itself. The reader interested in more details is advised to consult the bibliography for additional material. Our purpose is mainly to outline how the axioms are intertwined with working mathematics, so that the beginner may have a greater respect for the subject of set theory and its applications to applied mathematics.

There are two general approaches to the answer to what sets will be acceptable. The first is that of Zermelo (1908), later modified by Fraenkel and Skolem and properly known as Zermelo-Fraenkel-Skolem Set Theory (*cf*: Zermelo and Fraenkel). This is the one that we will discuss here. The second is more recent, perhaps more sophisticated, and somewhat more general. It is due to von Neumann (1925), with modifications by Bernays and Gödel. We give a brief account of it in the appendix. (Otherwise, *cf*: von Neumann.) In the second approach, a careful distinction is made between two different types of objects—sets and classes. Sets may be elements of classes, but classes are never elements of sets; *i.e.*, they are ineligible for elementhood. The system permits a universal class to which all sets belong, but this class is not a set. It is in this way that the Russell antinomy is avoided. Both the Zermelo and von Neumann approaches have the essential feature that they carefully delineate exactly what objects shall be acceptable as sets. This is therefore the task we now undertake; *i.e.*, to spell out specifically what the term "set" shall encompass. We shall state certain axioms concerning the behavior of sets and the elementhood relation and postulate the existence of whatever sets are necessary. In particular, we eliminate the possibility of a set which contains every other set. Our purpose is to create enough sets for the usual developments of most of present-day mathematics, but not so many as to lead to an obvious antinomy. Whether there are non-obvious antinomies we leave to the future. Furthermore, just how many and what axioms are sufficient to create enough sets for present-day mathematics is also very much of an open question. Only recently, Cohen (1963) has shown the independence of certain axioms from others which had previously been thought to be dependent (*cf:* Cohen). Hence, it is still unknown today just how far the axioms must go to satisfy various mathematicians. The answer depends on what is desirable to include as theorems in mathematics; so that there is not just one single set theory, but many different ones, some of which permit more results than others. For the present, we shall merely describe those basic axioms necessary to develop the algebra of sets and its generalizations to partially ordered sets, lattices and Boolean algebras.

EXERCISES

1. An adjective is called "heterological" if it does not have the property that it denotes. Which of the following words are heterological: "English," "Anglais," "Français," "monosyllabic," "polysyllabic," "heterological"?
2. Can you determine the truth or falsity of the statement: "This statement is false"? (The paradox of the liar.)
3. In a certain village in Lower Slobovia, a law was passed requiring the village barber to "shave those and only those who do not shave themselves." Explain the fate of the barber. (The paradox of the Village Barber.)

1-2. SET EQUALITY

Having stated some of the difficulties of the naive approach to set theory, we can now proceed to state some of the axioms of the Zermelo-Fraenkel-Skolem school, with slight variations. Since these are the axioms on which much of modern mathematics can be constructed, we shall try to point out how the various parts of mathematics stem from this beginning. However, since we have abandoned the idea that sets can be taken as self-explanatory undefined primitives, it is necessary to explain where the foundations themselves rest. In the first place, as the underlying discipline we shall assume elementary logic. To go much farther into the background would require an analysis of the rules of logic by which proofs in set theory are justified. However, once again, this would take us far afield from our immediate purpose. Hence we shall make free use of the laws of the predicate calculus, although we shall occasionally explain how these rules are used to justify steps in some of the proofs. As such, our approach is closest to what is known as "informal axiomatics." We use words of the English language to describe the axioms and make free use of the calculus of logic to manipulate sequences of statements in so-called informal proofs. A really careful analysis would go much deeper into what is known as "formal axiomatics," in which words are suppressed and only logical symbols involved, following rules of some meta-logic for their manipulation. We leave these formal developments to the logicians (*cf:* Morse).

As a starting point, we shall consider certain objects or entities which we designate by $x, y, z, \ldots$. We tacitly assume the existence of such objects. In addition we have two primitive symbols, $=$ and $\in$, which we place between the object symbols from time to time in accordance with certain specified rules. These rules become the axioms of set theory. An object which precedes the symbol $\in$ is then called an **element**, and an object which follows it is called a **set**. We say that ***t* is an element of *x*** or a **member** of x if the statement $t \in x$ is true. Thus, whether an object is to be considered as an element or a set depends solely on whether it occurs as an antecedent or a consequent of the $\in$ symbol. We therefore speak of an element only in connection with a set; *i.e.*, elements are elements of sets and do not appear independently of their containing sets. Similarly, with one exception to be introduced later (the empty set), a set exists only in reference to the elements belonging to it. However, a set may itself occur in a different situation as an element of some larger set; *i.e.*, the same entity may appear at one time as an antecedent of $\in$ and elsewhere as a consequent. Thus we may have both $t \in x$ and $x \in y$. Some authors prefer to distinguish between elements and sets by using different type for each. Thus lower case is used for elements and upper case for sets, while families of sets are indicated by script, etc. Later in Chapters 2–7 we shall follow this custom, but in the strict treatment of axiomatic set theory it is important not to distinguish elements from sets since the same object will occur in both roles. It is at this point that the von Neumann-Bernays-Gödel approach differs quite widely from that of the Zermelo-Fraenkel theory. In the von Neumann theory the only objects considered are classes, and there are no individuals other than these classes. The relation of elementhood is defined between certain pairs of classes, and a class which is an element of some other is called a set. All other classes are non-sets. Thus a set is simply a class which appears as an antecedent for the $\in$ relation. The universal class is an example of a non-set. We give a brief description of the principal differences between these two versions of set theory in the appendix. For the remainder of this chapter, we continue with the Zermelo-Fraenkel theory.

The first axiom of set theory governs the use of the symbol $=$. It is simply restated from logic. In fact, it is left by many as part of the underlying logic rather than as an axiom of set theory. From this second point of view, equality is simply a symbol for logical identity which needs no further explanation. We write $x = y$ when x and y are different symbols for the same logical entity. Thus when we write $1 + 1 = 2$, $1 + 1$ and 2 are simply different notations for the same concept. Equality is then a symbol for replacement, and when we have a statement we may replace any symbol by any other symbol which repesents the same object. On the other hand, we may consider $=$ as a separate primitive notion and state certain rules for its use. These are given in axiom I (which would otherwise be a theorem).

I. Axiom of Equality. *If x, y, z are any three sets, then*

(i) $x = x$	*(Reflexive),*
(ii) $x = y$ *implies* $y = x$	*(Symmetric),*
(iii) $x = y$ *and* $y = z$ *imply* $x = z$	*(Transitive).*

Our second axiom governs the relation between the $=$ symbol and the $\in$ symbol. In two parts, it states that we may replace equals for equals on either side of the $\in$ symbol. Thus if t is an element of y and $t = x$, then x is also an element of y. Similarly, if t is in the set x and $x = y$, then t is in y. The $\in$ symbol is therefore indifferent to distinct symbols for the same object. Formally, we have:

II. Axiom of Substitution. *If t, x, and y are sets, then*

(i) $t = x$ *and* $x \in y$ *imply* $t \in y$,
(ii) $t \in x$ *and* $x = y$ *imply* $t \in y$.

Surprisingly enough, we cannot deduce from these two axioms alone the fact that two sets which contain exactly the same elements are equal. However, it is certainly desirable that if two sets are consequents for exactly the same antecedents, then they should be the same set. Hence we add a third axiom that states just this condition. It essentially says that a set is determined when its elements are known; *i.e.*, a set extends over its elements. Hence it is known as the axiom of extension.

III. Axiom of Extension. *If x, y, and t are sets and if $t \in x$ if and only if $t \in y$, then $x = y$.*

This axiom is sometimes taken as a definition for set equality when equality is not a primitive concept at the outset. We shall find it very useful when it is desired to establish the equality of two sets. In the next section we reformulate it in a slightly different notation.

1-3. SET INCLUSION

At this point, we interrupt the listing of the axioms in order to introduce a new secondary symbol and establish its properties. We say that a set x is **contained in** a set y, if every element of x is at the same time an element of y. We write $x \subseteq y$ and call x a **subset** of y and y a **superset** of x. Formally, our definition states:

Definition 1-1. *$x \subseteq y$ if and only if $t \in x$ implies $t \in y$.*

Note that both the antecedent and consequent of the $\subseteq$ symbol are sets, not elements. That is, since both x and y occur as consequents of $\in$ in the definition, they both play the role of sets. In particular, we do not write $x \subseteq y$ if x is an element of y, but only if x is a subset of y. Later we shall speak of the set whose only element is x and write $\{x\}$ for this set. It then becomes proper to write $\{x\} \subseteq y$ if $x \in y$. Using the new symbol, we can now write its properties in the form:

Theorem 1-1. *If x, y, and z are sets, then*

(*i*) $x \subseteq x$ (*Reflexive*),
(*ii*) $x \subseteq y$ *and* $y \subseteq x$ *imply* $x = y$ (*Anti-symmetric*),
(*iii*) $x \subseteq y$ *and* $y \subseteq z$ *imply* $x \subseteq z$ (*Transitive*).

Proof.

(*i*) follows trivially, since $t \in x$ implies $t \in x$.
(*ii*) is simply axiom II restated using definiton 1-1. We leave (*iii*) to the exercises.

If $x \subseteq y$ but $x \neq y$, then we say that x is a **proper subset** of y and write $x \subset y$. Hence $x \subset y$ if $t \in x$ implies $t \in y$. and there exists an element s such that $s \notin x$ and $s \in y$.

Our next axiom of set theory imposes a further condition on set inclusion. We give a special case first. If x and y are two sets, then we wish to establish the existence of a third set z sufficiently large as to contain both x and y as subsets; *i.e.*, such that $x \subseteq z$ and $y \subseteq z$. In terms of the primitive symbol $\in$, we say that given x and y there exists z such that $t \in x$ or $t \in y$ imply $t \in z$. Note that the implication is only required to go one way; *i.e.*, we do not require that $t \in z$ imply that either $t \in x$ or $t \in y$. z is therefore a superset of both x and y, but may not necessarily be unique; *i.e.*, z may contain other elements in neither x nor y, and there may be different sets satisfying these requirements. We say that z is an **upper bound** for both x and y in that it contains both. Hence we call our new axiom the axiom of upper bounds. In more general situations, we are not simply given two sets for which to find a superset, but an entire collection of sets. Thus if x is a collection of sets, then we postulate the existence of a set z such that if y is any set in the collection x, then $y \subseteq z$. If x were a finite collection, we could obtain the desired set z by iteration from the case of two sets, but this is not generally possible. Hence we state our axiom in its more general form as:

IV. Axiom of Upper Bounds. *If x is any set, then there exists a set z such that if $t \in y$ for some $y \in x$, then $t \in z$.*

Note in particular that we do not postulate the existence of an upper bound for *all* sets, but only for *some* particular collection of sets. If there were an upper bound set for all sets, then this set would be exactly that set of all sets which led us to the Russell paradox.

EXERCISES*

1. Prove: $(x \subseteq y) \wedge (y \subseteq z) \Rightarrow (x \subseteq z)$.
2. Prove: $(x \subset y) \wedge (y \subseteq z) \Rightarrow (x \subset z)$.
3. Prove: $(x \subset y) \wedge (y \subset z) \Rightarrow (x \subset z)$.
4. Prove: $x \not\subset x$.
5. Prove: $(x \subset y) \Rightarrow (y \not\subset x)$.
6. Prove: $(x \in y) \wedge (t = x) \wedge (s = y) \Rightarrow (t \in s)$.
7. Prove: $(x = y) \wedge (z = y) \Rightarrow (x = z)$.
8. Prove: $(x = y) \wedge (y \neq z) \Rightarrow (x \neq z)$.
9. Prove: $(x = y) \wedge (y \subseteq z) \Rightarrow (x \subseteq z)$.
10. Discuss: $(x \neq y) \wedge (y \notin z) \Rightarrow (x \notin z)$.
11. Discuss: $(x = y) \wedge (y \notin z) \Rightarrow (x \notin z)$.
12. Prove: $(x \subseteq y) \wedge (y \subseteq z) \wedge (x \neq z) \Rightarrow (x \subset y) \vee (y \subset z)$.
13. Prove: $(x \subset y) \Rightarrow (x \subseteq y) \wedge (y \not\subset x)$.
14. Prove: $(x = y) \wedge (y \subset z) \Rightarrow (x \subset z)$.
15. Prove: $(x \subseteq y) \wedge (y \subseteq z) \wedge (z \subseteq w) \Rightarrow (x \subseteq w)$.
16. Prove: $(x \subset y) \wedge (y = z) \Rightarrow (x \subset z)$.
17. If x and y are two sets such that $(t \in x) \Rightarrow (t \notin y)$, then we call x and y **disjoint.** Prove that disjointness is symmetric with respect to x and y; *i.e.*, $(t \in y) \Rightarrow (t \notin x)$.

*In the following we adopt the notations of logic where $\Rightarrow$ is used for "implies," $\Leftrightarrow$ is used for "if and only if," $\forall$ is used for "for all," $\exists$ is used for "there exists," $\vee$ is used for "either...or..., and $\wedge$ is used for "both...and."

1-4. THE AXIOM OF ABSTRACTION

Our next step is to return to Russell's antinomy to find a way to avoid it. Following the outline in section 1-1, we let $p(t)$ be any property of an object t. By this we mean any statement that can be made about t in the language of logic; *i.e.*, a sentence involving t as a free variable, which is either true or false. Refer to any good text on logic for a more complete explanation of these terms. We write $\vdash p(t)$ or simply $p(t)$ to mean that the statement at hand is true and $\sim p(t)$ if it is false. If now x is any set, we postulate the existence of a subset within x containing exactly those elements t of x for which $p(t)$ is true. Our axiom is called the axiom of abstraction in deference to Cantor, since it abstracts from x those elements with the given property. It states:

V. Axiom of Abstraction. *For each set x and for every statement $p(t)$, there exists a set z such that $t \in z$ if and only if $t \in x$ and $p(t)$.*

We designate the set z postulated by this axiom by the brace notation explained in section 1-1:

$$z = \{t|(t \in x) \wedge p(t)\}$$

The key to the axiom is the limitation to the elements of a given set x. It singles out of x just those elements with the specified property. Hence it is also known as the "Ausorderungs axiom" (the singling-out axiom). To see how it avoids the Russell paradox, let $p(t)$ stand for the statement: $(t \notin t)$. We then designate by n the set of all elements t in a given set x with the property $p(t)$; *i.e.*, $n = \{t|(t \in x) \wedge (t \notin t)\}$. As before, we inquire as to the status of n. First we assume $n \in n$. Then $n \in x$ and $n \notin n$, which is a contradiction. Therefore, we try $n \notin n$. If also $n \in x$, then n qualifies for membership in n, so that we have the contradiction, $n \in n$. But this time we are left with a third alternative, namely, $n \notin x$, and this is not a contradiction. We have avoided the Russell paradox by the trick of applying the property only to elements of x. To leave out reference to x invites trouble. We note, however, that in referring to sets defined by some $p(t)$, we do leave out specific mention of x when it is clearly understood just what set we are working in. This axiom is one of the most powerful to date, and permits us to construct many of the sets required in Boolean algebra as well as a large portion of the rest of mathematics.

As an example, let x be the set of all U. S. male residents, and let $p(t)$ be the property of being over six feet tall. Then the set $y = \{t|(t \in x) \wedge p(t)\}$ is the set of all U. S. male residents over six feet tall. It does not include Europeans over six feet tall, but is a subset of x. Again, let $\mathbf{R}$ be the set of real numbers. Then the set of real roots of the quadratic equation $x^2 - 3x + 2$

$= 0$ is designated by $\{x|(x \in \mathbf{R}) \wedge (x^2 - 3x + 2 = 0)\}$. We abbreviate it by $\{x|x^2 - 3x + 2 = 0\}$ when the parent set $\mathbf{R}$ is clearly understood. A further abbreviation is simply $\{1, 2\}$. In this final form the number of elements is finite, and the set is designated simply by listing the elements enclosed by braces. This same technique is also used even for infinite sets where a sample list of elements is given, leaving it to the imagination to supply the property $p(t)$ as well as the parent set x. Thus $\{0, 2, 4, 6. . .\}$ would probably mean the subset of the set of natural numbers which are divisible by 2. On the other hand, the practice of abbreviation can sometimes be dangerous. The set $\{x|x^2 + 1 = 0\}$ is ambiguous unless we known the parent set of which it is a subset. Thus in $\mathbf{R}$, there are no elements of our set, while in $\mathbf{C}$, the set of complex numbers, this set is $\{i, -i\}$.

As a further example of the usefulness of the axiom of abstraction, we can now introduce the intersection and difference of two sets x and y. Thus:

Definition 1-2. *If x and y are any two sets, then the set $x \cap y = \{t|(t \in x) \wedge (t \in y)\}$ is called the* **intersection** *or* **meet** *of x and y.*

Definition 1-3. *The set $x - y = \{t|(t \in x) \wedge (t \notin y)\}$ is called the* **difference** *of x and y.*

The intersection of x and y is therefore the set of elements common to x and y and is a subset of both x and y. Its existence as a set is guaranteed by the axiom of abstraction applied to either x or y. Clearly $x \cap y$ is symmetric in x and y. On the other hand, the difference $x - y$ is a subset of x whose existence is again guaranteed by the axiom of abstraction applied to x. It is also a subset of x, but is not generally a subset of y, nor is $x - y$ symmetric in x and y. In the special case where $x = y$, the difference $x - y = x - x$ defines the null set. Alternatively, the null set is characterized by:

Definition 1-4. *The set $\phi = \{t|(t \in x) \wedge (t \notin x)\}$ is called the* **null set** (the empty set).

Since $(t \in x)$ is in contradiction to $(t \notin x)$, there are no elements in ϕ. Hence ϕ is not a consequent of the $\in$ symbol for any elements, and therefore should not qualify as a set. Consequently, we must extend the scope of the term "set" to encompass the null set.

We next note that ϕ was defined in terms of some specific set x, which therefore acts as a parameter in the definition. Hence we should properly write ϕ_x for $x - x$. However, if y is any other set, then we can prove that $\phi_x \subseteq y$. Referring to definition 1-1, $x \subseteq y \leftrightarrow (t \in x) \Rightarrow (t \in y)$. But since there are no elements t such that $t \in \phi_x$, the statement $(t \in \phi_x)$ is always false. But in logic the statement "p implies q" is true whenever p is false. Therefore $\phi_x \subseteq y$, for any set y. If now $\phi_y = y - y$, then $\phi_x \subseteq \phi_y$. But by a similiar argument, $\phi_y \subseteq \phi_x$, so that if we apply the axiom of extension to the null set, then $\phi_x = \phi_y$. We can summarize these results in the form of a theorem:

Theorem 1-2.

(*i*) *For all objects* t, $t \notin \phi$.
(*ii*) *For all sets* x, $\phi \subseteq x$.
(*iii*) *The null set is unique.*
(*iv*) $\phi = \{t | t \neq t\}$.

Condition (*iii*) states that conditions (*i*) and (*ii*) essentially characterize the null set. (*iv*) is an alternative definition frequently used by many mathematicians. For a proof of (*iv*) we refer to the exercises. As an example, if $\mathbf{R}$ is the set of real numbers, then the null set is given by $\phi = \phi_{\mathbf{R}} = \{x | (x \in \mathbf{R}) \wedge x^2 + 1 = 0\}$. On the other hand, if $\mathbf{Q}$ is the set of rationals, then $\phi = \phi_{\mathbf{Q}} = \{x | (x \in \mathbf{Q}) \wedge (x^2 = 2)\}$.

The final concept that we introduce in this section is that of the union of two sets. In this case, the axiom of abstraction is insufficient by itself, since the union of two sets is not generally a subset of either. But we can make use of the axiom of upper bounds, which guarantees the existence of a set z that contains both x and y. We can therefore apply the axiom of abstraction to z, using the property $(t \in x) \vee (t \in y)$ to abstract a subset of z containing exactly the elements which belong to either x or y. We therefore are assured of the existence of the union of two sets as given in the following definition.

Definition 1-5. *If* x *and* y *are two sets and* z *is any set such that* $x, y \subseteq z$, *then the set* $x \cup y = \{t | (t \in z) \wedge ((t \in x) \vee (t \in y))\}$ *is called the* **union (join)** *of* x *and* y.

Again $x \cup y$ is symmetric in x and y. In the next chapter we shall return to the study of these sets given by definitions 1–2 through 1–5 and develop an algebra for them.

1-5. THE PAIR SET AXIOM

At the present state of development we have been careful to limit the concept of set so as to avoid the antinomies of Russell. However, we have no guarantee that the entire theory is not vacuous; that is, we have no guarantee of the existence of any sets at all. Even the null set was defined only as a subset of some other set.

Assuming that x and y are any two objects, we shall postulate that we can form a set out of them. We have tacitly assumed the existence of objects. The proposed set will therefore contain x and y but no other elements. Hence an object t is in the required set if and only if either $t = x$ or $t = y$. Formally:

VI. Axiom of Pair Sets. *For all objects x and y there exists a set z such that $t \in z$ if and only if either $t = x$ or $t = y$.*

We again use the brace notation and designate this set by $z = \{x, y\}$. Note that the pair set $\{x, y\}$ does not depend on the order in which x and y are written down; *i.e.*, $\{x, y\} = \{y, x\}$. This follows from the axiom of extent, since every element of $\{x, y\}$ is an element of $\{y, x\}$, and conversely. Thus $t \in \{x, y\}$ if and only if either $t = x$ or $t = y$. But by the commutative law for "either $\cdots$or" from logic, this is equivalent to either $t = y$ or $t = x$. Hence $t \in \{y, x\}$ and therefore $\{x, y\} \subseteq \{y, x\}$. Similarly, $\{y, x\} \subseteq \{x, y\}$ and therefore $\{x, y\} = \{y, x\}$. We have carried out the details of this little proof to show how the axioms of logic and the earlier axioms enter into basic proofs.

There is of course nothing to restrict x and y to being distinct objects; *i.e.*, they may be distinct symbols for the same object. In this case, we simply write $\{x\}$ instead of $\{x, x\}$ and call this set the *singleton* set (unit set) generated by x. In general, any element repeated in a list of elements of a set may be dropped without changing the set. Later we shall see that this is not true for ordered sets. Note again that we must be careful to distinguish between x and $\{x\}$. It is proper to write $x \in \{x\}$ but not $x = \{x\}$ or $x \subseteq \{x\}$.

It is now possible to assert the existence of sets containing either zero, one or two elements. In fact, following Cantor, we use the sets ϕ, $\{x\}$, and $\{x, y\}$ for $x \neq y$ to define the first three natural numbers, zero, one and two. In particular, Cantor takes x to be the null set itself, y the singleton ϕ, and $\{x, y\} = \{\phi, \{\phi\}\}$. Thus he defines $0 = \phi$, $1 = \{\phi\}$ and $2 = \{\phi, \{\phi\}\}$. To form a set of three elements, we now form the singleton $\{2\} = \{\{\phi, \{\phi\}\}\}$. We then form the union of 2 and $\{2\}$, thereby obtaining a set with three distinct elements which we now define to be the natural number 3; *i.e.*, $3 = \{\phi, \{\phi\}, \{\phi, \{\phi\}\}\}$. This process may be continued to obtain any finite natural number. Thus if n is a natural number already defined, then we form the set $\{n\}$ and take its union with n. The set so obtained is called the **successor** of n and written n^*; *i.e.*, $n^* = n \cup \{n\}$. In this way we obtain the sequence of natural numbers. However, we still do not know that there is a single set which contains *all* the natural numbers as elements. For this purpose, we shall need a new axiom which we add in section 1-7.

EXERCISES

1. Prove: $(x \subseteq \phi) \Rightarrow (x = \phi)$.
2. Prove: $x \in \{t\} \Rightarrow x = t$.

3. Prove: $x \subseteq \{t\} \Rightarrow (x = \{t\}) \vee (x = \phi)$.
4. Prove: $x \in \{s, t\} \Rightarrow (x = s) \vee (x = t)$.
5. Prove: $\{s, t\} = \{t\} \Rightarrow s = t$.
6. Prove: $\{x, y\} = \{s, t\} \Rightarrow [(x = s) \wedge (y = t)] \vee [(x = t) \wedge (y = s)]$.
7. Prove: $\{x, x, x\} = \{x, x\} = \{x\}$.
8. Prove: $\{x, y, x\} = \{x, y\}$.
9. Show that if y is any subset of x, then $y = \{t | (t \in x) \wedge p(t)\}$ for some property $p(t)$. Hence any subset is given by the axiom of abstraction.
10. Prove: $\phi \subseteq \{\phi\}$.
11. Prove: If x is any set, then x and ϕ are disjoint.
12. Prove that $\{t | (t \in x) \wedge p(t)\}$ is unique.
13. Prove: If x is disjoint from x, then $x = \phi$ (disjointness is never reflexive for $x \neq \phi$).

1-6. THE AXIOM OF REGULARITY

In the discussion of Russell's paradox, we introduced the concept of a normal set as a set which was not $\in$-related to itself; *i.e.*, x was normal if $x \notin x$. The possibility of abnormal sets satisfying $x \in x$ was left open. In general such possibilities are undesirable, although there are no restrictions within our axiom system to eliminate them. A new axiom is needed. It is called the axiom of regularity, thereby implying that it limits the kind of sets available to some kind of regular or normal sets. It guarantees, first, against the reflexivity of the $\in$ relation. However, it is also not desirable to permit symmetry in $\in$; *i.e.*, we wish to rule out $x \in y$ and $y \in x$, simultaneously. Using brace notation to list the elements of a set, we wish to rule out the possibility that $x = \{y, \ldots\}$ where y is itself a set with x as an element; *i.e.*, $y = \{x, \ldots\}$ or $x = \{\{x, \ldots\}, \ldots\}$. In such cases the set x is defined in terms of itself in a circular fashion. Generalizing this situation, we put an injunction against the possibility that $x_1 \in x_2, x_2 \in x_3, \ldots, x_{n-1} \in x_n$, and $x_n \in x_1$. The result is accomplished by assuming that if x is any non-empty set, then there will be at least one element (set) y in x such that y contains no elements which belong to x. Sets with this property are called **regular**. Thus x is regular if x contains some set disjoint from itself. The axiom of regularity states that every set is regular.

VII. Axiom of Regularity. *For every set $x \neq \phi$ there exists $y \in x$ such that $t \in x$ implies $t \notin y$.*

Note that we do not state that every element of x is disjoint from x but only that there is *some* such element. We do not rule out the possibility that

$\in$ be transitive; *i.e.*, $t \in x$ and $x \in y$ as well as $t \in y$. In fact, we make considerable use of such sets later. What we do eliminate is abnormal sets in the sense of Russell as stated in the following theorem.

Theorem 1-3. *For all sets x, $x \notin x$.*

Proof. Let x be any set and form the singleton $\{x\}$; *i.e.*, the set such that $t \in \{x\}$ if and only if $t = x$. Apply the axiom of regularity to this set. Then there exists $y \in \{x\}$ such that $t \in \{x\}$ implies $t \notin y$. But $y \in \{x\}$ implies $y = x$. Hence $t \in \{x\}$ implies $t \notin x$. Finally, since $x \in \{x\}$, we may replace t by x and obtain $x \notin x$.

EXERCISES

1. Prove: $x \in y$ implies $y \notin x$ (Hint: consider $\{x, y\}$).
2. Prove: $\{x\} \notin x$.
3. Prove: $\forall x, \exists y$ for which $y \notin x$.
4. Prove: $(x \in y) \wedge (y \in z) \Rightarrow (z \notin x)$.
5. Prove: $x \neq \{x\}$ for all sets x.
6. Show that there cannot exist a set of all sets.

1-7. THE AXIOM OF INFINITY AND THE POWER SET AXIOM

In section 1-5 we saw how axioms I-IV enabled us to create sets of one, two, . . . , n elements for any finite n. However large these sets may be, they are still finite (by the definition of "finite"*), so that there is nothing in the axioms thus far to justify the existence of infinite sets. That is not to say that there is not enough mathematics dealing with finitely constructable sets to be interesting. There are, in fact, schools of mathematics who do not accept *arbitrary* infinite sets, However, many mathematicians find infinite sets sufficiently desirable to include some axiom asserting their existence. We shall follow this lead, thus maintaining our attitude of creating sets wherever we deem them desirable and see no immediate contradictions. Thus our next axiom postulates the existence of infinite sets in such a way as to permit the construction of the set of all natural numbers. We shall assume the reader is familiar with the development of the natural number system starting with Peano's axioms and using inductive sets (*cf:* MacLane and Birkhoff). Our purpose here is only to examine how Peano's axioms may by derived from the

*See also Chapter 3.

axioms of set theory. Thereby we hope to indicate the central role of set theory behind the number system.

The Peano postulates are based on the notion of a successor to a natural number. Our first step is therefore to introduce the concept of successor in terms of set theory. As in section 1-5, this is to be a set which contains all the elements of some given set x plus some extra element not in x. For this element we choose the singleton $\{x\}$, relying on the axiom of regularity to insure against the possibility that $\{x\}$ is already an element of x. We leave it to the exercises to show that there exists a set whose elements are exactly those of x plus $\{x\}$. We then formally define:

Definition 1-6. *If x is any set, then the set $x^* = \{t|(t \in x) \vee (t = \{x\})\}$ is called the* **successor** *to x.*

The axiom of infinity now states that if x_0 is any set, then there exists a set z such that x_0 belongs to z, and if x belongs to z, then x^* belong to z.

VIII. Axiom of Infinity. *If x_0 is a set, then there exists z such that (i) $x_0 \in z$ and (ii) $x \in z$ implies $x^* \in z$.*

We call the set z **the inductive set generated by x_0**. We then associate the names *one* with x_0, *two* with x_0^*, *three* with x_0^{**} etc., thereby generating the natural numbers. The axiom of infinity then guarantees there is a set which contains all the natural numbers. If we wish to be specific, we frequently take x_0 as the null set as in section 1-5. At this point in the development, we are now in a position to establish the existence of the complete system of natural numbers, as is done in algebra. The next step would then be to enlarge the system to the system of integers, positive, zero, and negative, and from them the rationals and the reals. This is more properly the subject of introductory analysis and will not be developed here. However, it does show how a goodly and non-contradictory portion of numerical mathematics is founded.

Our only difficulty remaining for the time is to guarantee the existence of enough sets for the algebra of sets which will lead to Boolean algebra. Axiom V assured the existence of a subset of any given set corresponding to any given property. However, it did not guarantee that the collection of all subsets of a given set itself qualified as a set. We therefore introduce a new axiom for this purpose.

IX. **Power Set Axiom.** *If x is any set, then there exists a set z such that $t \in z$ if and only if $t \subseteq x$.*

The set z postulated by this axiom contains every subset of x as an element. It is called the **power set of x** and designated by $\mathfrak{P}(x)$. If x is a finite set with

n elements, then we can show that $\mathfrak{P}(x)$ contains 2^n elements. Hence we also write 2^x when designating $\mathfrak{P}(x)$. This statement is also true even when x is infinite, although we postpone the details to Chapter 3.

With the introduction of the power set axiom we can next introduce set operations and be assured that the proper sets exist. This will be the subject of the next chapter. Thus with the use of axioms I-IX we can lay the foundations for much of modern mathematics. We shall show how many of the more common concepts of elementary mathematics can be developed from this foundation, in sections 1-9 and 1-10. Meanwhile, in the next section, we introduce one final axiom that is needed in many branches of mathematics, but is of a much more controversial nature than those introduced up to this point.

EXERCISES

1. Prove that if x is any set, then there exists a set whose elements are those of x plus the singleton $\{x\}$.
2. Show that if x contains n elements (finite), then there are 2^n subsets of x.
3. Show that n and n^* are distinct.
4. Determine the power set of each of the following sets:
   (*a*) ϕ,
   (*b*) $\{\phi\}$,
   (*c*) $\{\phi, \{\phi\}\}$,
   (*d*) $\{\phi, \{\phi\}, \{\{\phi\}\}\}$.
5. Determine the power set of $\{a, b, c, d\}$.
6. Describe $\mathfrak{P}(\mathfrak{P}(\phi))$, $\mathfrak{P}(\mathfrak{P}(\{\phi\}))$.
7. If x has n elements, how many elements are there in $\mathfrak{P}(\mathfrak{P}(x))$?
8. If x is any set, prove that its successor x^* is unique.
9. Prove that if x and y are two sets such that $x^* = y^*$, then $x = y$.
10. Prove that ϕ is not the successor of any set; *i.e.*, $x^* \neq \phi$ for any set x.

1-8. THE AXIOM OF CHOICE

Before discussing the applications of the axioms of set theory to the construction of the more common concepts of everyday mathematics, we introduce one final axiom at this point. Of all the axioms, this one is the most discussed. We will merely state one form of it here and leave alternative forms to a later chapter (*cf:* section 4-12), as well as most of the applications. Briefly, it states that if we have a non-empty collection of disjoint sets, also non-empty, then we can form a new set which will contain one and only one element from each of the given sets. Hence, the axiom permits us to choose a set of representative elements, one each from a collection of disjoint sets. If both the collection of sets is finite and each of the sets in the collection is finite, then there is no problem. The difficulty arises in dealing with infinite sets. In this case, an infinite number of selections must be made simultaneously with no special property available to make the selection. For this reason the axiom of abstraction cannot be used, and none of the other axioms leads to a satisfactory solution. Apparently a new axiom is therefore needed. It is called the axiom of choice and states:

X. **Axiom of Choice.** *If x is any non-empty collection of pairwise disjoint non-empty sets, then there exists a set z such that z contains one and only one element from each of the sets in x.*

The element selected from a given set is called its representative and z is called a **complete set of representatives** from the collection x. The axiom was first formulated by Zermelo in 1904, although some forms of it had been used previously. Since then many theorems have been discovered whose proofs depend on this axiom, and which in turn can be used to derive the axiom with the aid of the other axioms. Hence these "theorems" are in effect equivalent forms of the axiom. Testimony to the significance of this axiom lies in the fact there are now over 100 different equivalent forms which have appeared in the literature (*cf:* Rubin and Rubin). In the early history, many attempts were made to derive the axiom as a theorem from the other axioms. A milestone was reached in 1930 when Gödel proved the consistency of the axiom in the sense that it cannot lead to any contradictions not already inherent in the axioms of the natural number system (*cf:* Newman and Nagel). Consequently, most working mathematicians have been willing to accept it and theorems derived from it. More recently, further spectacular results were obtained by Cohen in 1963 when he proved the independence of the axiom of choice from the other axioms (*cf:* Cohen). Thus it is not possible to derive it as a theorem within the more limited set theory given by axioms I–IX. In general, a proof in mathematics is called effective if it does not involve the axiom of choice or any of its equivalents. Thus an effective theorem is one that follows from axioms I–IX. Some schools of mathematics, in particular the intuitionists, do not accept proofs based on the axiom of choice, so that effective mathematics is essentially the portion which is accepted by intuitionists and others alike. Other axioms have also been discovered that lie somewhere between the axiom of choice and axioms I–IX in strength. In Cohen's most recent results he has also shown that some of these are independent, so that at just what point the axiomatization of set theory is complete is still very much an open question. In fact, it becomes somewhat a matter of choice at what point to stop adding axioms. We assume enough to be able to prove those theorems of mathematics which we wish to hold, as long as there are no apparent contradictions. We shall therefore leave the development of the axioms and turn to some applications (*cf:* Scott). In particular, in the next chapter we shall show how many of the elementary concepts of mathematics can be developed and justified within the bounds of set theory. The axiom of choice will be used as it is deemed necessary.

2

THE ALGEBRA OF SETS

2-1. ORDERED PAIRS AND CARTESIAN PRODUCTS

In Chapter 1 we discussed the axiomatics of set theory in an informal manner, showing how the axioms enable us to create enough sets on a non-contradictory basis sufficient for the foundations of most of modern mathematics. The purpose of the present chapter is to show how the central concepts of working mathematics stem directly from set theory, and how the axioms justify their use. In particular, much of analysis and many other parts of mathematics depend to a large extent on the concept of a function. We shall show how this concept arises as a special case of the more general concept of a relation between sets, and how the notion of a relation is a special type of set. We shall also see how the concept of an operation in algebra is a special type of function, and therefore also definable as a special kind of set. In general, algebra is concerned with algebraic systems which consist of a set together with a family of operations. In this way, the whole field of algebra comes within the realm of set theory. We examine how the basic concepts common to all algebraic systems arise and how they interrelate. This subject is known as universal algebra, and is the main topic of the first part of the chapter. The second half is devoted to applying these concepts as well as the results of Chapter 1 to the development of an algebra of set theory itself.

Since it is our contention that most of mathematics is concerned with sets except for the occasional use of classes in the von Neumann sense (*cf:* Appendix 1), in the future we shall consider that all objects are sets. For example, we shall speak of the natural numbers as special kinds of sets. However, we also revert to the more conventional notation using different type for different hierarchies of sets. We use lower case letters to denote basic elements, capitals for sets of these elements, and script for families of sets. Furthermore, having completed our formal discussion of the axioms of set theory, we shall relax our approach somewhat and take a semi-axiomatic point of view in the future.

The first concept that we shall need is that of an ordered pair of elements, x and y. We have already seen that the pair set generated by these elements was independent of the order of the elements; *i.e.*, the sets $\{x, y\}$ and $\{y, x\}$ are the same set by axiom II. To introduce an order between the elements, we need to distinguish one of them from the other to act as a first; the remaining one will then be the second. Thus to form an ordered pair, we first form the unordered pair set and then distinguish one of them. The result is an ordered pair which we write as $\langle x, y\rangle$ to distinguish it from the unordered pair $\{x, y\}$. We make the following definition:

Definition 2-1. *If x and y are two sets, then the pair set $\{\{x, y\}, x\}$ is called the* **ordered pair** *and designated by $\langle x, y\rangle$. x is called the first and y the second.*

We note that the definition does not require that x and y be distinct. Thus if x and y are the same element, then the ordered pair becomes $\langle x, x\rangle$. In this case the situation is different from that of the pair set $\{x, x\}$. The pair set $\{x, x\}$ reduces to the singleton $\{x\}$ as we have already seen, but the ordered pair does not reduce to a single element; it is the pair set $\{\{x, x\}, x\}$ that consists of two distinct elements, since $\{x, x\} = \{x\}$ and x are distinct by the axiom of regularity.

The concept of an ordered pair as expressed purely in terms of set theory is due to von Neumann and Wiener.

We can now show that two ordered pairs $\langle x, y\rangle$ and $\langle u, v\rangle$ are equal if and only if their first and second elements are equal separately.

Theorem 2-1. *If x and y are two sets, then $\langle x, y\rangle = \langle u, v\rangle$ if and only if $x = u$ and $y = v$.*

Proof. By definition $\langle x, y\rangle = \{\{x, y\}, x\}$ and $\langle u, v\rangle = \{\{u, v\}, u\}$. But $\{\{x, y\}, x\} = \{\{u, v\}, u\}$ if and only if either (*i*) $\{x, y\} = \{u, v\}$ and $x = u$ or (*ii*) $\{x, y\} = u$ and $\{u, v\} = x$. In case (*i*) $\{x, y\} = \{u, v\}$ implies either (*ia*) $x = u$ and $y = v$ or (*ib*) $x = v$ and $y = u$. Case (*ia*) agrees with our contention. In case (*ib*) we have $x = y = u = v$, which also agrees with the theorem. In case (*ii*) $x = \{u, v\}$ implies $u \in u$. But this is contrary to the axiom of regularity.

The ordered pair concept can be extended to that of an ordered triple and an ordered n-tuple in several ways. Thus we may define the **ordered triple** $\langle x_1, x_2, x_3\rangle$ whose elements are x_1, x_2 and x_3 in terms of the ordered pair $\langle\langle x_1, x_2\rangle, x_3\rangle$ whose first element is the ordered pair $\langle x_1, x_2\rangle$. Alternatively, it may be defined directly in terms of unordered sets as $\langle x_1, x_2, x_3\rangle = \{\{x_1, x_2, x_3\}, \{x_1, x_2\}, x_3\}$. We leave it as an exercise to show that these two definitions are equivalent, and that two ordered triples are equal if and only if their respective first, second and third elements are equal. We use induction to extend the concept to **ordered *n*-tuples**. Thus we define

$$\langle x_1, x_2, \ldots, x_n \rangle = \langle\langle x_1, x_2, \ldots, x_{n-1}\rangle, x_n\rangle$$

where the right hand side is a pair set whose first element is an ordered $(n-1)$-tuple. Again the important property that $\langle x_1, x_2, \ldots, x_n\rangle = \langle y_1, y_2, \ldots, y_n\rangle$ if and only if $x_i = y_i \; \forall \; i$ follows by induction. We call the x_i the coordinates of the *n*-tuple. For the sake of completeness, we define an ordered one-tuple as the singleton $\{x\}$ and write $\langle x\rangle$.

We use the concept of ordered pair to define our next concept, which is that of the cartesian product of two sets. It is simply the set of all ordered pairs taken from the two sets as given by the following definition.

Definition 2-2. *If X and Y are two sets, then the set $X \times Y = \{z | (\exists\, x \in X) \wedge (\exists\, y \in Y) \wedge (z = \langle x, y\rangle)\}$ is called the* **cartesian product** *of X and Y. If X or Y is empty, then $X \times Y = \emptyset$.*

The nomenclature is taken from the fact that if X and Y are the x-and y-axes of analytic geometry, then $X \times Y$ is the cartesian plane. Thus if x-and y are real numbers, then $\langle x, y\rangle$ is a point in the real plane with coordinates x and y. More generally, if X and Y are subsets of the set of real numbers, then $X \times Y$ is a subset of the plane. Figure 2-1(*a*), for example, shows the

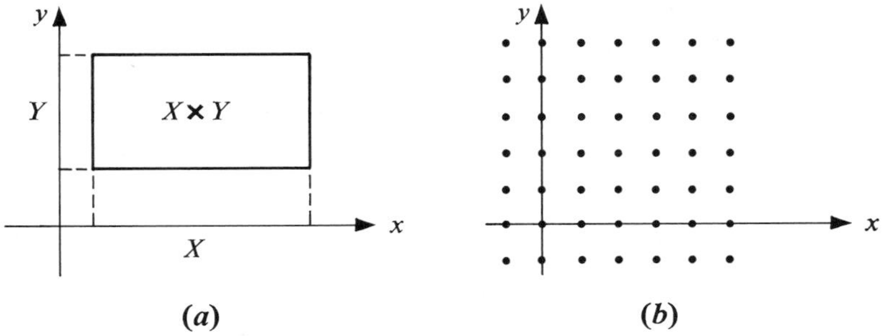

FIGURE 2-1

case where X and Y are intervals of the x-and y-axes. In this case $X \times Y$ is the rectangular region shown. Figure 2-1(*b*) shows the cartesian product of the set $\mathbf{Z}$ of integers with itself; it is simply the set of points with both coordinates integral.

To establish the existence of the cartesian product of two sets requires the axiom of upper bounds, the axiom of abstraction, the pair set axiom, and the power set axiom.

Theorem 2-2. *If X and Y are two sets, then their cartesian product $X \times Y$ is a set.*

Proof. The cartesian product of X and Y is the set of all ordered pairs $\langle x, y \rangle$ where $x \in X$ and $y \in Y$. But the ordered pair $\langle x, y \rangle$ is defined as the set $\{\{x, y\}, x\}$. Hence it is necessary to show that there exists a set which contains all pair sets of the form $\{x, y\}$ where $x \in X$ and $y \in Y$. To establish this result, we first form the set z which contains all the elements of X and Y, using the upper bound axiom. The set $\{x, y\}$ will be an element of the power set of z; *i.e.*, $\{x, y\}$ is a subset of z. But the existence of the power set of z is already guaranteed by the power set axiom. We now have to abstract from z the set of all possible pairs $\{x, y\}$ with $x \in X$ and $y \in Y$, using the axiom of abstraction. We can then repeat the entire process to obtain the set of ordered pairs $\{\{x, y\}, x\}$. The set so obtained is the desired cartesian product set.

Using the concept of ordered n-tuple we can extend the concept of cartesian product to any (finite) number of factors. Thus if $X_1, X_2, \ldots, X_n$ are n sets, then their cartesian product $X_1 \times X_2 \times \cdots \times X_n$ is the set of all n-tuples $\langle x_1, x_2, \ldots, x_n \rangle$ where $x_i \in X_i$. It will be empty if and only if some X_i is empty. As a short hand we use the notation $\Pi_i X_i$ or $\prod_{i=1}^{n} X_i$. The X_i need not all be distinct and, in fact, may all be equal. In this case we write X^n. For example if $\mathbf{R}$ is the set of real numbers, then $\mathbf{R}^2$ is the set of real number pairs; *i.e.*, the real plane. Similarly, $\mathbf{R}^n$ is the set of real number n-tuples. This is the set of points of real euclidean n-space, or may also be thought of as the elements of a real n-dimensional vector space. On the other hand, if $\mathbf{C}$ is the set of complex numbers, then $\mathbf{C}^n$ is the set of complex n vectors. Later we shall extend the concept of cartesian product to an arbitrary number of factors, possibly infinite. The concept of cartesian product is basic to many branches of mathematics, and for example, brings the subjects of analytic geometry and vector spaces into the domain of set theory. As far as numbers go, we may extend the set of real numbers to that of the complex numbers by defining a complex number as an ordered pair of real numbers. The set of all complex numbers is then nothing more than the cartesian product of the reals with itself, although the definitions of the operations on complex numbers must be defined. We return to this point after we have discussed operations. Our next concept, that of relation, is also definable in terms of cartesian products.

EXERCISES

1. Prove: $\langle x, y \rangle = \langle y, x \rangle \Rightarrow y = x$.
2. Prove: $\langle x, x \rangle = \{\{x\}, x\}$.

3. Prove: $\langle x, y\rangle = \langle u, u\rangle \Rightarrow x = y$.
4. Using the definition of an ordered triple $\langle x, y, z\rangle$ as $\langle\langle x, y\rangle, z\rangle$, show that $\langle x, y, z\rangle = \langle u, v, w\rangle \Rightarrow x = u, y = v$, and $z = w$.
5. Show that the definitions of ordered triple given by $\langle\langle x, y\rangle, z\rangle$ and $\{\{x, y, z\}, \{x, y\}, x\}$ are equivalent.
6. Prove that two n-tuples are equal if and only if corresponding coordinates are equal.
7. Show that $\{x\} \times \{y\} = \{\langle x, y\rangle\}$.
8. If $X = \{a, b, c\}$ and $Y = \{1, 2, 3, 4\}$, list all elements of (a) $X \times Y$, (b) $Y \times X$, (c) $X \times X$, (d) $Y \times Y$.
9. Show that if X has m elements and Y has n elements, then $X \times Y$ has mn elements.
10. If $\mathbf{R}$ is the set of reals, $\mathbf{Q}$ the set of rationals, $\mathbf{Z}$ the set of integers and $\mathbf{N}$ the set of natural numbers, describe the sets: (a) $\mathbf{R} \times \mathbf{N}$, ($b$) $\mathbf{Q} \times \mathbf{Z}$, ($c$) $\mathbf{N} \times \mathbf{R}$, ($d$) $(\mathbf{R} \times \mathbf{R}) \times \mathbf{N}$.
11. In what sense may $(X \times Y) \times Z$ and $X \times (Y \times Z)$ be identified?
12. Prove that if $X \subseteq Y$, then $X \times Z \subseteq Y \times Z$.
13. Prove that $X \times Y = Y \times X \Rightarrow$ either $X = \emptyset$, $Y = \emptyset$ or $X = Y$.
14. Show that if $X = \{x \in \mathbf{R} \mid 0 \leq x < 2\pi\}$, then $X \times X$ represents the points of a torus.

2-2. RELATIONS

One of the most important concepts of modern mathematics is that of a relation between the elements of one set and those of another. Thus if X and Y are any two sets, then we may specify a relation between them by simply naming which elements of X are related to corresponding elements of Y. But a related pair of elements is an ordered pair $\langle x, y\rangle$ where $x \in X$ and $y \in Y$. Therefore we know a relation between X and Y when we can determine for any ordered pair $\langle x, y\rangle$ whether x is related to y or not. Those pairs for which the answer is in the affirmative form a subset of the cartesian product $X \times Y$, which completely determines and is determined by the given relation. Hence distinct relations from a set X to a set Y are completely determined by distinct subsets of $X \times Y$. We call the subset G_ρ of $X \times Y$ which determines the relation the **graph** of the relation. A relation ρ is therefore completely determined when the sets X and Y are given and the graph G_ρ is specified. Formally we have:

Definition 2-3. *A* **relation** *ρ is an ordered triple $\rho = \langle X, Y, G_\rho\rangle$ where X and Y are any two sets and G_ρ is any subset of $X \times Y$. We call ρ a* **relation**

from X to Y (or a relation between X and Y). We write $x\rho y \Leftrightarrow \langle x, y\rangle \in G_\rho$. *If* $X = Y$, *then we call* $\rho = \langle X, X, G_\rho\rangle$ *a* **relation within X**.

We note that many authors tend to fix X and Y and then identify ρ with its graph G_ρ.

The set of points x in X for which there exists an element y in Y such that $\langle x, y\rangle \in G_\rho$ is called the **domain** of ρ, and designated by D_ρ; *i.e.*, $D_\rho = \{x \in X \mid \exists\, y \in Y \wedge \langle x, y\rangle \in G_\rho\}$. Similarly the set of elements y of Y for which there exists elements x in X such that $x\rho y$ is called the **range** of ρ, designated by R_ρ; *i.e.*, $R_\rho = \{y \in Y \mid (\exists\, x \in X) \wedge (\langle x, y\rangle \in G_\rho)\}$. Note that $D_\rho \subseteq X$ and $R_\rho \subseteq Y$, while $G_\rho \subseteq D_\rho \times R_\rho$. None of these inclusions is required to be an equality. In general if R_ρ is a proper subset of Y, then we call Y the **codomain** of ρ. Unfortunately, there is no commonly accepted term to designate the set X in cases where $X \neq D_\rho$.

As an example, let X and Y be subsets of **R** so that they can be represented by points on an x- and y-axis system. $X \times Y$ is represented by a rectangular region in the plane. The graph of ρ will now be any subset G_ρ of this rectangle. The domain will be the projection of the graph onto the x-axis, while the range will be the projection onto the y-axis as shown in figure 2-2(b).

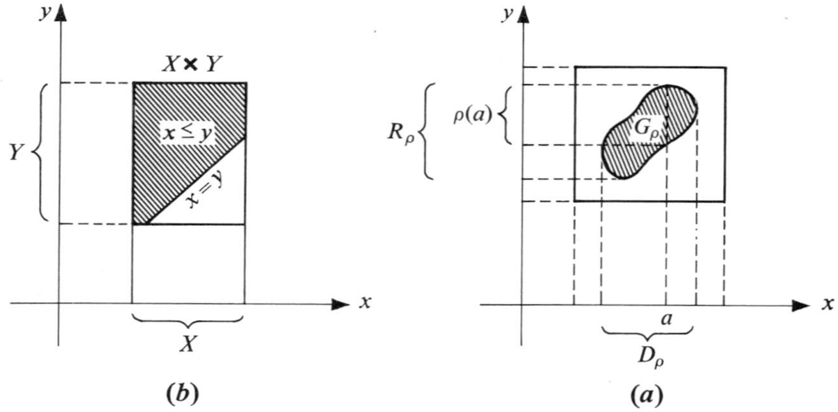

FIGURE 2-2

For example, the equality relation is the set of pairs $\langle x, y\rangle$ where $x = y$. Its graph is simply those points lying on the diagonal $x = y$ within the region representing $X \times Y$ as in (a) of figure 2-2. This may be the empty set, if the sets X and Y are disjoint. One of the most important cases is when $X = Y$, wherein both the domain and range are all of X. This relation is denoted by

Δ_X or id_X and is called the **identity on X**. We write $x = y$ for $\langle x, y\rangle \in \Delta_X$. As a further example, the inequality relation $\leq$ within $\mathbf{R}$ is the set of ordered pairs $\langle x, y\rangle$ for which $x \leq y$ and its graph is the set of points above the diagonal $x = y$ as shown in figure 2-2(*a*).

Since a relation from X to Y is determined by any subset of $X \times Y$, then the set of all relations is simply the power set of $X \times Y$. We designate this set by $\mathfrak{R} = \mathfrak{P}(X \times Y)$. As special examples other than those already discussed, we may consider the null set and the universal set, $X \times Y$. In the first of these no element of X is related to any element of Y, and this relation is called the **null relation**, ϕ. At the other extreme, the set $X \times Y$ defines the **universal relation** μ in which every element of X is related to every other element of Y. Since we are dealing with subsets, we can also apply the other terms of set theory. For example, we say that a relation ρ is a subrelation of σ if $\langle x, y\rangle \in \rho$ implies $\langle x, y\rangle \in \sigma$. In this case we also say that ρ is a **restriction** of σ or that σ is an **extension** of ρ. Thus $\leq$ is an extension of $<$, since $x < y$ implies $x \leq y$. Similarly, it is an extension of $=$. We can also speak of the **union** of two relations simply by applying the concept of union to the graphs as sets. Thus $\leq$ is the union of $<$ and $=$. Similarly, $=$ is the intersection of $\leq$ and $\geq$. Later we shall develop an algebra for sets, so that we can also speak of the algebra of all relations within a given set.

More generally, we use the concepts of extension and restriction of relations even when the relations are not between the same sets. Thus if $\rho = \langle X, Y, G_\rho\rangle$ and $\sigma = \langle U, V, G_\rho\rangle$ are any two relations, then we call ρ an **extension** of σ or σ a **restriction** of ρ if $U \subseteq X$, $V \subseteq Y$ and $G_\sigma \subseteq G_\rho$. We write $\sigma \subseteq \rho$. For example, if $U \subseteq X$, then the identity on X is an extension of the identity of U; *i.e.*, $\Delta_U = \langle U, U, \{\langle x, x\rangle | x \in U\}\rangle \subseteq \Delta_X = \langle X, X, \{\langle x, x\rangle | x \in X\}\rangle$. If $U \subseteq X$ and $\rho = \langle X, Y, G_\rho\rangle$ is any relation from X to Y, then we write $\rho|_U$ for the relation defined on U into Y whose graph is the subset of G_ρ corresponding to those elements of G_ρ whose first element lies in U. We call $\rho|_U$ the restriction of ρ to U. Its graph is $\{\langle x, y\rangle | \langle x, y\rangle \in G_\rho \text{ and } x \in U\}$.

As a further example, consider the circular relation within the real numbers whose graph is the set of points $\{\langle x, y\rangle | x^2 + y^2 = 1\}$; *i.e.*, $\rho = \langle \mathbf{R}, \mathbf{R}, \{\langle x, y\rangle | x^2 + y^2 = 1\}\rangle$. ρ is a relation within $\mathbf{R}$ whose domain and range are both the set $D_\rho = R_\rho = \{x | -1 \leq x \leq 1\}$. If $X = \{x \in \mathbf{R} | -1 \leq x \leq 1\}$, then ρ is an extension of $\sigma = \langle X, X, \{\langle x, y\rangle | x^2 + y^2 = 1\}\rangle$ which has exactly the same graph as ρ. $\sigma = \rho|_X$ is then the restriction of ρ to X.

A further variation of this example is given by the semi-circular relation τ defined from $X = \{x \in \mathbf{R} | -1 \leq x \leq 1\}$ into $\mathbf{R}$ given by $\tau = \langle X, \mathbf{R}, \{\langle x, y\rangle | y = \sqrt{1 - x^2}\}\rangle$. The domain is still X but the range is now $Y = \{y \in \mathbf{R} | 0 \leq y \leq 1\}$. This relation is an extension of the relation $\langle X, Y, \{\langle x, y\rangle | y = \sqrt{1 - x^2}\}\rangle$.

Given a relation $\rho = \langle X, Y, G_\rho\rangle$ from X to Y, then ρ induces two additional relations between the power sets of X and Y. We first consider any subset

A of X and let $A_* = \{y \in Y \mid \exists\, x \in A \wedge \langle x, y\rangle \in G_\rho\}$. A_* is defined for every $A \in \mathfrak{P}(X)$ and is an element of $\mathfrak{P}(Y)$. Hence the relation $\rho_* = \langle \mathfrak{P}(X), \mathfrak{P}(Y), \{\langle A, A_*\rangle | A \in \mathfrak{P}(X)\}\rangle$ is a relation between $\mathfrak{P}(X)$ and $\mathfrak{P}(Y)$ defined on all of $\mathfrak{P}(Y)$. We call A_* the **image of A under ρ**. In particular, if $A = \{a\}$ is a singleton set, then $\{a\}_*$ is called the **image of a**. We note that many authors use the same notation for ρ and the induced relation ρ_*. They also write $A_* = \rho(A)$ and $\{a\}_* = \rho(a)$. In this notation the range of ρ is simply $R_\rho = \rho_*(X) \subseteq Y$.

In a similar fashion, if B is any subset of Y, then we define $B^* = \{x \in X \mid \exists\, y \in B \wedge \langle x, y\rangle \in G_\rho\}$. The relation $\rho^* = \langle \mathfrak{P}(Y), \mathfrak{P}(X), \{\langle B, B^*\rangle | B \in \mathfrak{P}(Y)\}\rangle$ is then an induced relation from all of $\mathfrak{P}(Y)$ into $\mathfrak{P}(X)$. We call B^* the **inverse image of B** under ρ. Again, more popular usage is to write ρ^{-1} for ρ^*, designating $B^* = \rho^{-1}(B)$ and $\rho^*(\{b\}) = \rho^{-1}(b)$.

If $\rho = \langle X, Y, G_\rho\rangle$ is any relation from a set X to a set Y, then the relation $\rho^{-1} = \langle Y, X, \{\langle y, x\rangle | \langle x, y\rangle \in G_\rho\}\rangle$ is called the **inverse** or converse of the relation ρ. It is a relation from Y to X whose graph is the set of ordered pairs of the graph of ρ with reversed order.

As an example we consider the relation $\leq$ between real numbers; *i.e.*, within the set $\mathbf{R}$ of all real numbers. The inverse of $\leq$ is then the relation $\geq$ defined by $x \geq y \leftrightarrow y \leq x$. Within the power set $\mathfrak{P}(\mathbf{R})$, if ρ is the relation $\leq$ for reals, then ρ induces the relation in which $\rho(a) = \{y | \langle a, y\rangle \in \rho\} = \{y | a \leq y\}$. This set is the set of all elements greater than or equal to a and is also called the **principal filter generated by a** in $\mathbf{R}$. In Chapter 4 we shall study such sets in greater detail. On the other hand, the set $\rho^{-1}(a) = \{x | x \leq a\}$ is the set of all elements less than or equal to a. It is called the **principal ideal generated by a** in $\mathbf{R}$. Furthermore, if A is any subset of $\mathbf{R}$, then $A_* = \rho_*(A) = \{y | (\exists\, x \in A) \wedge (x \leq y)\}$, while $\rho^*(A) = \{x | (\exists\, y \in A) \wedge (x \leq y)\}$. For example, if $A = \{1/n | n \in \mathbf{P}\}$ ($\mathbf{P}$ is the set of positive integers), then $\rho_*(A) = \{x | 1/n \leq x \text{ for some } n\} = \{x | 0 < x\}$ is the set of positive reals. Furthermore, the set $\rho^*(A) = \{x | (\exists\, y \in A) \wedge (x \leq y)\} = \{x | x \leq 1\}$. The concept of a relation as extended to the power sets of X and Y is most commonly used in connection with the special case of functions which we discuss in the next section.

The final concept which we need in connection with relations is that of the composition of two relations. First we define the composite of two ordered pairs of the form $\langle x, y\rangle$ and $\langle y, z\rangle$ where the second element of the first pair is the same as the first element of the second pair. In this case we call the ordered pair $\langle x, z\rangle$ the **composite** of $\langle x, y\rangle$ and $\langle y, z\rangle$ and write $\langle x, z\rangle = \langle x, y\rangle \circ \langle y, x\rangle$. If now ρ is a relation from X to Y and σ is a relation from Y to Z, then the set of composites of pairs from ρ and σ forms a relation from X to Z (possibly empty). This relation is written $\rho \circ \sigma$ so that the formal definition becomes:

Definition 2-4. *If ρ is a relation from a set X to Y and σ is a relation from Y to Z, then the relation $\rho \circ \sigma = \langle X, Z, G_{\rho\circ\sigma}\rangle$ whose graph is $G_{\rho\circ\sigma} = \{\langle x, z\rangle | (\exists\, y \in Y) \wedge (\langle x, y\rangle \in \rho) \wedge (\langle y, z\rangle \in \sigma)\}$ is called the* **composite** *of ρ and σ.*

The domain of $\rho \circ \sigma$ is then a subset of D_ρ while its range is a subset of R_σ. Furthermore, it is the null relation unless $R_\rho \cap D_\sigma \neq \emptyset$. One of the principal properties of the composition of relations is that it is associative in the following sense:

Theorem 2-3. *If ρ, σ and τ are three relations from sets X to Y, Y to Z, and Z to W, then the composite relations $\rho \circ (\sigma \circ \tau)$ and $(\rho \circ \sigma) \circ \tau$ are equal.*

Proof. (exercise).

As a second example, if we consider the identity relation Δ_Y on Y, then $\rho \circ \Delta_Y = \rho$, while the identity Δ_X satisfies $\Delta_X \circ \rho = \rho$ where ρ is a relation from X to Y.

EXERCISES

1. If $X = \{0, 1, 2, 3\}$ describe the sets determined by the relations (*a*) $x < y$, (*b*) $x = y$, (*c*) $x > y$ and (*d*) $x = y + 1$. Draw the graph of each of these relations.
2. Describe the set of all possible relations on the set $\{0, 1\}$.
3. How many distinct relations can be defined on a set of n elements?
4. Describe the relation $\subseteq$ for the power set of $X = \{1, 2, 3\}$.
5. Which of the following are extensions of others: (*a*) "similar to," (*b*) "congruent to," and (*c*) "equal to" within the set of triangles in the plane?
6. Draw the graphs and determine the domain and range of the following relations in $\mathbf{R}$: (*a*) $x^2 + y^2 = 1$, (*b*) $x^2 + y^2 < 1$, (*c*) $y = \sqrt{1 - x^2}$, (*d*) $x^2 = y^2$, (*e*) $x^2 + y^2 = 0$.
7. If $\mathbf{N}$ is the set of natural numbers and $|$ is the relation "divides," what is the image of a fixed integer, n? What is its inverse image?
8. Prove Theorem 2-2.
9. If ρ is any relation, prove that $(\rho^{-1})^{-1} = \rho$.
10. If ρ and σ are two relations, prove that $(\rho \circ \sigma)^{-1} = \sigma^{-1} \circ \rho^{-1}$.
11. *A relation ρ on a set X is called* **reflexive** *if and only if $x\rho x\ \forall\, x \in X$. Show that ρ is reflexive if and only if ρ is an extension of the identity on X, i.e., $\Delta_X \subseteq \rho$.*
12. *A relation ρ on a set X is called* **symmetric** *if $x\rho y \Rightarrow y\rho x$. Show that ρ is symmetric if and only if $\rho = \rho^{-1}$.*

13. *A relation is called* **transitive** *if* $x\rho y$ *and* $y\rho z \Rightarrow x\rho z$. *Show that* ρ *is transitive if and only if* $\rho \circ \rho \subseteq \rho$.

14. Draw the graphs of the relations $\leq$ and $\geq$ in **R** and determine the images of the following sets under $\leq$: (*a*) $\{0\}$, (*b*) $\{0, 1\}$, (*c*) $\{x \mid 0 < x < 1\}$. Find the inverse of the set $\{2\}$ under $\leq$.

15. If U is a fixed set and $\subseteq$ is the relation of inclusion in $\mathfrak{P}(U)$, what is the image of a fixed set A under $\subseteq$? What is its inverse image?

2-3. FUNCTIONS

We are now in a position to define one of the central concepts of modern mathematics, the concept of a function. A function from X to Y is a relation in which each element of the domain is related to one and only one element of the range; *i.e.*, it is defined for all x in X and it is single-valued, as given by the following definition.

Definition 2-5. *A relation* $f = \langle X, Y, G_f \rangle$ *from a set* X *to a set* Y *is called a* **function** if (*i*) $D_f = X$ and (*ii*) $\langle x, y \rangle \in f$ and $\langle x, z \rangle \in f$ imply $y = z$.

Since functions are relations, all the terminology and discussion concerning relations also apply to functions. Thus we speak of the graph of a function, its domain and range, the inverse of a function, extensions and restrictions of functions, and the composition of two functions.

We note that there was complete symmetry between the sets X and Y in the definition of a relation between X and Y. This symmetry does not carry over to the special case of functions, as indicated in definition 2-5. First, we require that a function be defined for every element of X, so that the domain of f is all of X. No such restriction is desirable for arbitrary relations, for if relations are always defined over all of X, then the null relation would be ruled out except in the case where X itself is the empty set. Since we will want to form a Boolean algebra out of the family of all relations from X to Y, *every* subset of $X \times Y$ must define a relation, not simply those for which $\mu_\rho = X$. In the case of functions, on the other hand, there seems to be no particular value in considering functions for which the domain is a proper subset of X.

The second restriction on the concept of function is more fundamental. It requires that a function be single-valued. Single-valuedness is again not symmetric with respect to X and Y; *i.e.*, there may be distinct pairs $\langle x_1, y \rangle$ and $\langle x_2, y \rangle$ with the same second element and belonging to the same function. This means that, although we can always define the inverse of a function in the sense of an inverse relation, the inverse need not itself be a function; *i.e.*, it may not be single-valued.

As with relations, every function $f = \langle X, Y, G_f \rangle$ from a set X to a set Y induces two additional functions between the power sets $\mathfrak{P}(X)$ and $\mathfrak{P}(Y)$, respectively. The fact that the induced relations f_* and f^* are functions follows from the definition, since $f_*(A) = \{y \in Y \mid \exists\, x \in A \wedge \langle x, y \rangle \in G_f\}$ and $f^*(B) = \{x \in X \mid \exists\, y \in B \wedge \langle x, y \rangle \in G_f\}$ show that f_* and f^* are defined and unique for each $A \in \mathfrak{P}(X)$ and $B \in \mathfrak{P}(Y)$. The popular notation is to designate $f_*(A)$ by $f(A)$ and $f^*(B)$ by $f^{-1}(B)$. In particular, if $A = \{a\}$ is a singleton, then we write $f(a)$ for $f_*(A)$ and call $f(a)$ the **image of *a* under *f*** or the **value of *f* at *a***. The fact that f is a function simply means that $f(a)$ *is a singleton in* $\mathfrak{P}(Y)$. We also write $y = f(x)$, if y is the value of f at x. An alternative notation is $x \xrightarrow{f} f(x)$ and we say that f is **mapped** into $f(x)$ under f. In this terminology f is called a **mapping**; *i.e.*, a mapping associates with each element of X a unique element of Y. Again, we indicate that f is a mapping from a set X to a set Y by the further notation: $f\colon X \rightarrow Y$ where X and Y are the domain and codomain of f. The range of f is then the subset of Y given by $R_f = f(X)$; *i.e.*, $f_*(X)$.

In our example of a function from **R** to **R** the distinguishing feature of a function appears in the form that a "vertical line" will cut the graph in at most one point as shown in figure 2-3(a). Furthermore, given any x in D_f,

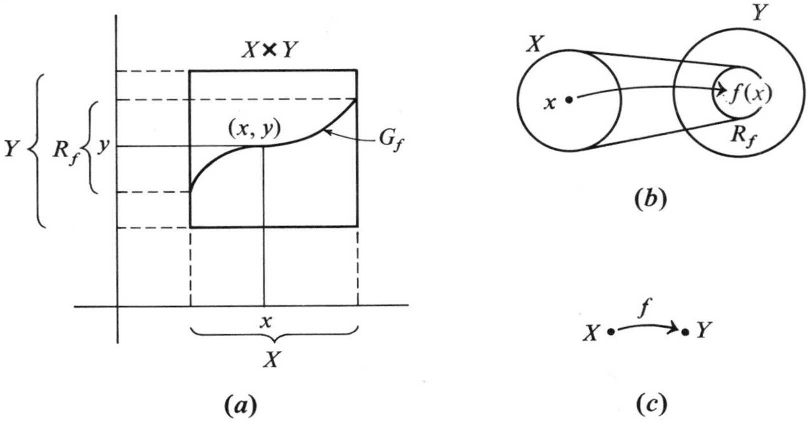

FIGURE 2-3

we project upward to this point of the graph and then project horizontally onto the y-axis to obtain the value $y = f(x)$ in R_f. The graph therefore serves as an intermediary in determining the value to be associated with a generic element of X. We say that f maps x to y and call f a mapping.

Furthermore, we also represent f by simply showing X and Y and connecting points of X in D_f to the corresponding value in Y by an arrow as shown in figure 2-3(b). In this type of figure the graph is omitted, and Venn diagrams are used to show X, Y, D_f and R_f. Generally we simplify the diagram and represent X and Y by points. This type of diagram is particularly useful when it is desired to show the composite of two functions. If f is a function from X to Y and g is a function from Y to Z, then we can form the composite of f and g, which will be a function from X to Z as shown in figure 2-4(a). We say that such a diagram is **commutative.** More complicated

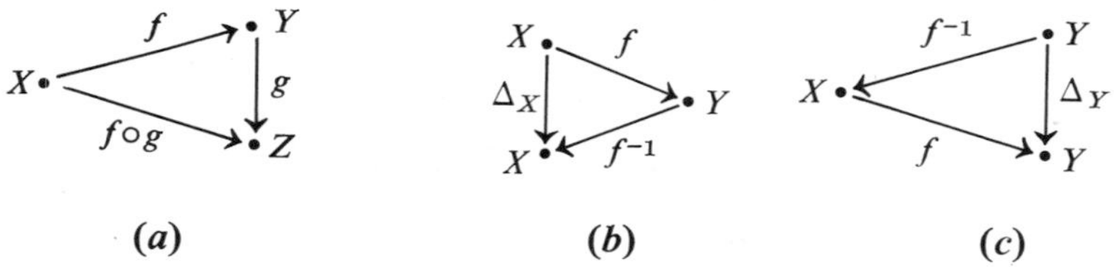

FIGURE 2-4

diagrams occur when more than two functions are involved. The composite of f and g is, of course, defined by $f \circ g = \{\langle x, z\rangle | (\exists\, y \in Y) \wedge (y = f(x)) \wedge (z = g(y))\}$. We also write $z = g(f(x)) = (f \circ g)(x)$.*

In general, the inverse of a function may not be a functional relation. Thus the squaring function for the real numbers given by $f = \{\langle x, x^2\rangle | x \in \mathbf{R}\}$ or $f(x) = x^2$ determines an inverse relation f^{-1}, but this relation is not a function since there may be distinct numbers whose squares are equal. The graph of this function is a parabola and every vertical line cuts the graph in one point, but a horizontal line may cut it at two or more distinct points. The case in which the inverse of a function is itself a function is particularly important. Such functions are called **one-to-one** functions. Hence a one-to-one function is one such that $\langle x_1, y\rangle \in f$ and $\langle x_2, y\rangle \in f$ imply $x_1 = x_2$. This will be the case if and only if the composite of f and f^{-1} is the identity on X; *i.e.*, $f \circ f^{-1} = \Delta_X$. Here f^{-1} means the relation which is inverse to f restricted to R_f; *i.e.*, if $f = \langle X, Y, G_f\rangle$ and $\rho = \langle Y, X\{\langle x, y\rangle | \langle y, x\rangle \in G_f\}\rangle$ then $f^{-1} = \rho^{-1}|_{R_f}$. We also call such a function **injective** or an **injection** of X into Y. The diagram of figure 2-4(b) will then be commutative.

On the other hand, a function with domain $D_f = X$ whose range is all of Y is called an **onto** mapping or a **surjection**. In this case $f(X) = Y$ and the composite of f^{-1} and f is the identity on Y; *i.e.*, $f^{-1} \circ f = \Delta_Y$. This is the

*The reversal of order can be avoided if we indicate the image of x under f by xf, in which case $x(f \circ g) = (xf)g$.

case if the diagram of figure 2-4(c) is commutative. Finally, if f is both injective and surjective, then it is called a **bijection;** *i.e., a bijection is a one-to-one, onto map.* Both diagrams (b) and (c) are then commutative, while f satisfies $f \circ f^{-1} = \Delta_X$ and $f^{-1} \circ f = \Delta_Y$. We say that f is **invertible** and call f^{-1} the *inverse function* of f. Finally, if X and Y are the same set, then an invertible function is called a **permutation.**

As an example of an injective mapping, let X be a subset of Y. Then the mapping $\{\langle x, x\rangle | x \in X\}$ maps X one-to-one into Y and is called the **inclusion** map of X into Y. It is a restriction of the identity Δ_Y on Y and is equal to the identity on X.

If f is a function defined over the positive integers $\mathbf{P}_n = \{1, 2, \ldots, n\}$ into a set X, then we frequently write $f(i)$ as x_i and call f an **indexing function.** The range of f can then be written as an n-tuple or n-vector $\langle x_1, x_2, \ldots, x_n\rangle$. Similarly, if the domain is the set of all positive integers $\mathbf{P}$, then a function defined over $\mathbf{P}$ determines an (infinite) **sequence** in X given by $\langle x_1, x_2, x_3, \ldots\rangle$. More generally, if I is any set and f is a function with domain I, then we can write the values of f as x_α with $\alpha \in I$ and again think of R_f as a set indexed by the set I. Of course, any set can be thought of as an indexed set by simply using the identity function and indexing X by its own members. Thus we can write any set as $\{\alpha_\alpha | \alpha \in I\}$.

The class of *all functions defined on a set X into a set Y is now denoted by* Y^X. If X and Y are finite with n and m elements respectively, then Y^X will contain m^n elements, since there will be n possible choices for the values of each of the m elements of X. We shall return to a study of Y^X in the next chapter when we consider exponentiation for sets.

One of the principal advantages of considering a function as an indexing function is that it enables us to extend the notion of a cartesian product of sets to an arbitrary indexed family of sets. Thus if $\mathfrak{F} = \{X_\alpha | \alpha \in I\}$ is an indexed family of sets, then the cartesian product over I is the set of functions defined on I with values x_α at α where $x_\alpha \in X_\alpha$. Such a function is defined on the index set I into the union $\mathbf{U}_\alpha X_\alpha$ of all the X_α's. Its graph is the set of pairs $\{\langle\alpha, x_\alpha\rangle | \alpha \in I, x_\alpha \in X_\alpha\}$. We write such a product as $\Pi_\alpha X_\alpha$ or $\prod_{\alpha \in I} X_\alpha$. The elements of this product are designated by $\{x_\alpha | \alpha \in I\}$, which is a natural generalization of the notion of a sequence defined over the natural numbers. In particular, if all the X_α are equal to some fixed set X, then $\Pi_\alpha X_\alpha$ reduces to X^I, which is again a generalization of exponentiation as a product of terms all equal. The principal problem concerning an arbitrary cartesian product is its existence. Certainly if one of the X_α is empty, then the product will also be empty. Again, this generalizes the fact that the product of numbers is zero if and only if one of the factors is zero. It remains therefore to consider the case when all the X_α are non-empty, assuming also I is non-empty. First of all, we may consider the X_α as pairwise disjoint sets, since distinct sets have distinct indices. It is then a case of establishing the existence of a function defined on the family of sets $\{X_\alpha\}$, whose values lie in X_α. But this is exactly the axiom of choice. Therefore, the axiom of choice can be stated in the form that the cartesian product of a non-empty family of non-empty sets will itself be non-empty. The axiom of choice is therefore alternatively called the **multiplicative axiom**, and a set of representatives for a family of pairwise disjoint sets is called a **choice function**. We note also that the requirement for disjointness can be dropped, since we can always make the sets disjoint by indexing them. Hence the axiom of choice can be stated in the apparently weaker, but actually equivalent form:

Multiplicative Axiom: *If $\mathfrak{F}$ is any non-empty family of sets, each of which is non-empty, then there exists a function f which assigns to each $X \in \mathfrak{F}$ an element $x = f(X)$ in X.*

EXERCISES

1. Show that the following are functions, determine their domains and ranges. Which are 1-1? Draw their graphs:
   (*a*) $f = \{\langle x, |x|\rangle | x \in \mathbf{R}\}$ ($|x|$ is the absolute value of x),
   (*b*) $\phi = \{\langle x, \tan x\rangle | x \in \mathbf{R}\}$,
   (*c*) $g = \{\langle x, y\rangle | y = x + \sqrt{1 - x^2}\}$,
   (*d*) $h = \{\langle x, y\rangle | y = x$ if x is rat. and $y = -x$ if x is irrat.$\}$,
   (*e*) $\sigma = \{\langle 0, 0\rangle, \langle 1, 1\rangle, \langle 2, 2\rangle\}$.
2. Show that if $f = \{\langle \log x, x\rangle | x \in \mathbf{R}\}$ and $g = \{\langle x, e^x\rangle | x \in \mathbf{R}\}$, then $f = g$.
3. In a computer, the sine function is stored as a table of values. What is the relation between this function and the function $\{\langle x, \sin x\rangle | x \in \mathbf{R}\}$?
4. How many functions can be defined on X to X if $X = \{0, 1\}$? Graph each of them. Which ones are one-to-one? onto?
5. Determine the domain and range, and describe the function $\{\langle\langle x, y, z\rangle, x\rangle | x, y, z \in \mathbf{R}\}$.
6. Graph the function $f = \{\langle x, y\rangle | x \in \mathbf{R}, y = [x]\}$ where $[x]$ stands for the largest integer less than or equal to x. Describe the domain and range of f.
7. Graph the functions $f = \{\langle t^2 + 1, t^2 - 1\rangle | t \in \mathbf{R}\}$ and $g = \{\langle x, x - 2\rangle | x \in \mathbf{R}\}$. Compare f and g.
8. What is the relationship between the functions $\{\langle x, y\rangle | x, y \in \mathbf{R}$ and $x + y = 1\}$ and $\{\langle \sin^2 \theta, \cos^2 \theta\rangle | \theta \in \mathbf{R}\}$?
9. Graph the function $f = \{\langle\langle x, y\rangle, [x + y]\rangle | x, y \in \mathbf{R}\}$.
10. Let ρ be a relation from X to Y and G_ρ its graph. Show that the mappings π_x: $\langle x, y\rangle \to x$ and π_y: $\langle x, y\rangle \to y$ are functions. π_x and π_y are called the **first** and **second projections** from G_ρ to X and Y, respectively.
11. Show that if f is a function from X to Y, then π_x^{-1} is a functional relation and that $f = \pi_y \circ \pi_x^{-1}$.

12. If f is a function of X into Y, show that f is 1-1 if and only if there exists a function g in Y onto X such that $f \circ g = \Delta_X$ is the identity on X. g is called a **left inverse** of f.

13. If f is a function of X into Y, show that f is onto if and only if there exists a function h such that $h \circ f = \Delta_Y$ is the identity map on Y. h is called a **right inverse** of f.

14. If f is a function on X, show that f is 1-1 and onto if and only if f has both a right and left inverse and they are equal. f is then called **invertible** and f^{-1} is a one-to-one function on Y onto X satisfying $f \circ f^{-1} = \Delta_X$ and $f^{-1} \circ f = \Delta_Y$.

15. If f is a function on X into Y and $A \subseteq B \subseteq X$, show that $f_*(A) \subseteq f_*(B)$. Show that if $f_*(A) = f_*(B)$ whenever $A = B$, then f is 1-1.

16. If f is a function on X into Y and $A \subseteq B \subseteq Y$, show that $f^*(A) \subseteq f^*(B)$. Show that if $f^*(A) = f^*(B)$ whenever $A = B$, then f is onto.

17. If f is a function on X into Y and $A \subseteq X$, then show that $A \subseteq f^*(f(A))$. Furthermore, show that if $A = f^*(f_*(A)) \; \forall \; A \subseteq X$, then f is 1-1.

18. If f is a function on X into Y, and $A \subseteq Y$, then $f_*(f^*(A)) \subseteq A$ and $f_*(f^*(A)) = A \; \forall \; A \subseteq Y$ implies f is onto.

19. If f is a map on X into Y, g a map on Y into Z, show that $(g \circ f)^{-1} = f^{-1} \circ g^{-1}$.

20. Show that composition of functions is associative, *i.e.*, if f is a function on X into Y, g a function on Y into Z, and h a function on Z into W, then $f \circ (g \circ h) = (f \circ g) \circ h$.

2-4. EQUIVALENCE RELATIONS

In this section we discuss an important type of relation called an equivalence relation. As the name suggests, an equivalence relation is a generalization of the concept of equality. In the special case of equality of sets, we showed in section 1-2 that set equality was reflexive, symmetric and transitive. In general, these same three properties characterize the more general relation of equivalence.

Definition 2-6. *A relation* $\equiv$ *on a set* X *is called an* **equivalence relation** *if it satisfies:*

(*i*) $x \equiv x$ (reflexive),
(*ii*) $x \equiv y \Rightarrow y \equiv x$ (symmetric),
(*iii*) $x \equiv y$ and $y \equiv z \Rightarrow x \equiv z$ (transitive).

Here we have replaced the usual symbol ρ for a relation by the more specific symbol $\equiv$ suggesting a generalization of $=$.

Our first example of an equivalence relation is the case of set equality for the set of subsets of some given set X. In section 2-2 we have already verified (*i*)–(*iii*). Here again we consider only subsets of some specific set; *i.e.*, the domain is the power set of X.

As a less "trivial" example we let **Z** be the set of integers and let m be a fixed element of **Z**. We then define $x \equiv y$ (or $x \equiv y \bmod m$) if and only if $x - y$ is divisible by m; *i.e.*, $m|x - y$ or $x - y = km$ for some $k \in \mathbf{Z}$. It is left as an exercise to show that congruence modulo m satisfies (*i*)–(*iii*). For example if $m = 5$, then $2 \equiv 7$, $3 \equiv 13$, etc.

The importance of an equivalence relation lies in the fact that it permits us to divide up the elements of X into non-overlapping subsets which exhaust X. We call such a division a partition of X. Thus a *partition* of a set X is a set of subsets of X such that each element of X lies in one and only one subset. If x is an element of X, then we designate the subset containing x by $\bar{x}$ and the class of subsets by $\bar{X}$. Hence $\bar{x} = \{t|t \equiv x\}$. The statement $t \equiv x$ is therefore equivalent to the statement $t \in \bar{x}$. We then have the following theorem:

Theorem 2-4. *If* $\equiv$ *is an equivalence relation on a set* X, *then the set* $\bar{X}$ *of subsets* $\bar{x} = \{t|(t \in X) \wedge (t \equiv x)\}$ *is a partition of* X. *Conversely, every partition of* X *determines an equivalence relation on* X *such that* $x \equiv y$ *if and only if* x *and* y *lie in the same partition of* X.

Proof. It is clear that every x belongs to some partition, namely x, since $x \equiv x$ by (*i*). We now use (*i*)–(*iii*) to show that if x and y are elements of X, then either $\bar{x} = \bar{y}$ or $\bar{x}$ and $\bar{y}$ have no elements in common. Let $\bar{x}$ and $\bar{y}$ have an element t in common. Then $t \in \bar{x}$ implies $t \equiv x$ and $t \in y$ implies $t \equiv y$. But $t \equiv x$ implies $x \equiv t$ and $x \equiv t$ together with $t \equiv y$ imply $x \equiv y$. Thus $x \in \bar{y}$. Next $t \in \bar{x}$ implies $t \equiv x$, while $x \equiv y$ implies $t \equiv y$ or $t \in \bar{y}$. Thus $\bar{x} \subseteq \bar{y}$. Similarly, $\bar{y} \subseteq \bar{x}$ and therefore, by extensionality, $\bar{x} = \bar{y}$. We leave the converse to the exercises.

If x is any element of X, then we call the set $\bar{x}$ of elements equivalent to x, the **coset** generated by x or the **equivalence class** of x (congruence class, residue class). The set $\bar{X}$ of such classes is called the **quotient system** of X modulo $\equiv$ and written $X/\equiv$ (residue class system). Hence within $\bar{X}$ equality of cosets replaces equivalence of elements within X; *i.e.*, $\bar{x} = \bar{y} \leftrightarrow x \equiv y$. A subset of X consisting of one and only one element from each coset is called a **complete set of representatives of** X **mod** $\equiv$. (Its existence will, in general, require the axiom of choice.) In our example above, the coset $\bar{5}$ is the set of elements . . . $-5, 0, 5, 10, \ldots$; *i.e.*, the set of multiples of 5. Thus $\bar{5} = \bar{0} = \overline{10}$, etc. On the other hand, $\bar{1} = \{\ldots -4, 1, 6, 11, \ldots\}$. The quotient system has five elements; *i.e.*, $\bar{\mathbf{Z}} = \{\bar{0}, \bar{1}, \bar{2}, \bar{3}, \bar{4}\}$ and is therefore a finite set, whereas **Z** was of course infinite. Thus $\bar{\mathbf{Z}}$ is a considerably simpler set than **Z**. We write $\bar{\mathbf{Z}} = \mathbf{Z} \bmod 5$ to show the dependence on the particular equivalence relation involved. A complete set of representatives for $\bar{\mathbf{Z}}$ mod 5 would be $\{1, 2, 3,$

4, 5}, for example. Later when we study algebraic systems in more detail, we shall show how an algebraic structure can be imposed on $\bar{X}$ in terms of some given structure within X.

We note that in this particular example, we did not actually have to invoke the axiom of choice for selecting a complete set of representatives. Thus we can choose a set of representatives by a fixed construction; namely, choose the set 1, 2, 3, 4, 5. An example which does require the axiom of choice is given by defining the relation $a \equiv b$ if and only if $a - b$ is rational where a and b are any two real numbers. Again this relation is an equivalence relation which partitions the real numbers into non-overlapping cosets. However, we know of no specific formula which will pick exactly one element form each coset. The axiom of choice must be used.

EXERCISES

1. Prove the second half of Theorem 2-3.
2. Show that equivalence mod m is an equivalence relation.
3. Define $x \equiv y \bmod 1$ in **R** if and only if $x - y$ is an integer. Show that congruence mod 1 is an equivalence relation, determine the quotient structure and give a complete set of representatives.
4. Show that the relation "is congruent to" is an equivalence relation in the set of all triangles in the plane. What is the nature of the quotient set in this case?
5. If F is the set of real-valued functions defined over the interval $0 \leq x \leq 1$ and $f \equiv g \Leftrightarrow f(0) = g(0)$ for $f, g \in F$, show that $\equiv$ is an equivalence relation and determine $F/\equiv$.
6. Prove that a relation ρ which is reflexive is an equivalence relation if and only if $x\rho y$ and $x\rho z$ imply $y\rho z$.
7. Show that if ρ is a relation which is symmetric and transitive in X, then ρ is an equivalence relation if for every $x \in X$ there exists $y \in X$ such that $x\rho y$.
8. Give examples of relations on a set X which are (a) reflexive but not symmetric or transitive, (b) symmetric but not reflexive or transitive, (c) transitive but not reflexive or symmetric.
9. Give examples of relations which are (a) reflexive and symmetric but not transitive, (b) reflexive and transitive but not symmetric, (c) symmetric and transitive but not reflexive.

15. Show that the relation "is parallel to" is an equivalence relation in the set of lines in the plane and describe the quotient structure.

11. In the set **R**, let $x \equiv y$ if and only if x and y have the same integral part; *i.e.*, $[x] = [y]$. Show that this is an equivalence relation, describe the quotient structure and give a complete set of representatives. (Compare with exercise 3).
12. Show that the relation $x \equiv y \Leftrightarrow x - y \in$ **Q** is an equivalence relation in the set **R** of reals (**Q** is the set of rationals).

2-5. UNIVERSAL ALGEBRA

One of our main topics for this chapter involves a synthesis of all the concepts developed thus far. It is that of an algebraic system. By this we mean a set X on which are defined certain relations and operations. In specific cases, these operations and relations satisfy certain limiting postulates which are the axioms of the system. However, many general results and concepts apply without regard to these specific limitations imposed by the postulates, and the study of these general results constitutes what is known as universal algebra. The general subject dates back to Whitehead's original treatment of Universal Algebra, but did not develop greatly until the 1930's, when Birkhoff achieved some results valid for all algebraic systems. Since then the field has expanded rapidly, culminating more recently in the works of P. M. Cohen, G. Grätzer, J. Schmidt and others, so that is is now a recognized branch of mathematics (see bibliography). Here we shall attempt no more than a brief introduction to the subject.

We begin with a discussion of the concept of an operation within a set X. First, a **binary operation** is nothing more than a function from the cartesian product $X \times X$ into X. Thus it assigns a single element in X to every pair of elements of X. If $\langle x, y\rangle$ is an ordered pair of elements of X, then we designate the result of operating on them by an operation ϕ by $x\phi y$ instead of the functional notation $\phi(x, y)$. For example, within the set $\mathbf{N}$ of natural numbers we designate the operation of addition by $x + y$, and for each $x, y \in \mathbf{N}$, $z = x + y$ is again an element of $\mathbf{N}$. Multiplication is also an operation defined for every pair of natural numbers, but subtraction is only defined for certain pairs; *i.e.*, $x - y$ is defined if $y \leq x$. Hence subtraction in $\mathbf{N}$ does not qualify as a binary operation, but is called a **partial operation**. Similarly, within the real numbers, division is defined for all pairs $\langle x, y\rangle$ for which $y \neq 0$.

The concept of a binary operation extends to n-ary operations. First of all, a **unary operation** is nothing more than a function from X into X. For example, the absolute value function defines the operation $x \rightarrow |x|$ which assigns to each $x \in \mathbf{R}$ its absolute value. Similarly, complementation assigns to each subset of a set U its complement, and is therefore a unary operation. We can now define a ternary operation as a mapping from X^3 into X; *i.e.*, as a mapping from triples $\langle x_1, x_2, x_3\rangle$ of elements of X into single elements. In this case the sandwich notation used for binary operations breaks down, and we revert to the functional notation, writing $\phi(x_1, x_2, x_3)$. More generally, an ***n*-ary operation** *is a mapping from* X^n into X written $\phi(x_1, x_2, \ldots, x_n)$. For the sake of completeness we define a **nullary operation** as a constant or fixed element of X. Note that a binary operation determines a ternary relation. Thus if $z = \phi(x, y)$ designates a binary operation, then ϕ determines the relation $\{\langle x, y, z\rangle | z = \phi(x, y)\}$. Therefore, we could dispense with operations entirely and deal only with relations. However, it is generally more convenient to work with the operations separately.

In general, the most important aspect of operations from the point of view of universal algebra is simply to know the arity of them; *i.e.*, nullary, unary binary, etc. An **algebra** *is* now *a pair* $\langle A, \mathfrak{F} \rangle$ *where A is any set, known as the* **carrier**, *and* $\mathfrak{F}$ *is a family of operations.* The **type** of the algebra is simply a list of the arities of the various operations in $\mathfrak{F}$. The simplest example is a **groupoid**, which is a set G with a single binary operation defined on it. We designate it by $\langle G, \circ \rangle$ where $x \circ y$ is the binary operation. It has type $\langle 2 \rangle$. From the class of all groupoids, we can select a subclass consisting of those which satisfy certain equational laws. Thus a **semigroup** is a groupoid in which the associative law: $x \circ (y \circ z) = (x \circ y) \circ z$, always holds. Such a subclass is called an **equational class** of the algebra $\langle G, \circ \rangle$, or a **variety.** In general, most of the commonly studied varieties of algebras are of this sort *i.e.*, equational classes of algebras of a certain type. Our next example is that of a semigroup with an identity. An **identity** e is a constant or nullary operation which satisfies $x \circ e = e \circ x = x \ \forall \ x \in G$. Such a system is called a **monoid** and written $\langle G, \circ, e \rangle$. It has type $\langle 2, 0 \rangle$; *i.e.*, has a binary and a nullary operation and is an equational class of algebras of this type.* From the class of monoids, we obtain the groups by requiring that every element x have an inverse x^{-1} which satisfies $x \circ x^{-1} = x^{-1} \circ x = e$. The mapping $x \rightarrow x^{-1}$ is then a unary operation, so that a **group** is an algebra of type $\langle 2, 0, 1 \rangle$ with a binary, a nullary and a unary operation. It is therefore designated by $\langle G, \circ, e, ^{-1} \rangle$. On the other hand, it is also possible to characterize a group entirely in terms of a single ternary operation, so that we may also consider it as having type $\langle 3 \rangle$. Still another way to characterize a group is by a set G with a family of unary operations which are the mappings $x \rightarrow y \circ x = L_y(x)$, where L_y stands for left multiplication by y. We then have a family of left multiplications indexed by G itself. In this case we write $\langle G, \mathfrak{L} \rangle$, where $\mathfrak{L}$ is the set of all left multiplications. Its type is then $\langle 1, 1, \ldots \rangle$ where the number of operations depends on the size of G and may well be infinite. The associative law now takes the form $L_{xy} = L_y \circ L_x$ where $\circ$ is now a compostion of operators; *i.e.*, under L_{xy}, z maps onto $(xy)z$, where under $L_y \circ L_x$, it maps first onto yz and then onto $x(yz)$. Here we omitted the operation symbol for the group and wrote xy for $x \circ y$.

The next example is that of a **ring** which is a commutative group with respect to addition, satisfies the distributive law for multiplication over addition, and is associative under multiplication. From our point of view, it is an algebra $\langle R, +, 0, -, \circ \rangle$ of type $\langle 2, 0, 1, 2 \rangle$. Finally a *ring with identity* is a ring with a multiplicative identity e. Hence it has type $\langle 2, 0, 1, 2, 0 \rangle$.

In general, the study of universal algebra is concerned with sets and operations which are defined on all of the carrier and which are finitary. Recently,

*Note that in describing the type, we could just as easily write $\langle 0, 2 \rangle$ as $\langle 2, 0 \rangle$.

extensions have been made to partial operations and infinitary operations, but they will not concern us here.

2-6. SUBALGEBRAS

The first important concept of universal algebra is that of a subalgebra. Thus if $\langle A, \mathfrak{F} \rangle$ is an algebra of a given type, then a subalgebra is a subset of A which is an algebra of the same type under the same operations as A. If B is a subset of the carrier A, then B is said to be **closed under an operation** ϕ of $\mathfrak{F}$ if $x_1, x_2, \ldots, x_n \in B$ imply $\phi(x_1, x_2, \ldots, x_n) \in B$. If B is closed under all the operations of $\mathfrak{F}$, then $\langle B, \mathfrak{F} \rangle$ is called a **subalgebra** of $\langle A, \mathfrak{F} \rangle$. It clearly has the same type as $\langle A, \mathfrak{F} \rangle$. For example, a subset H of a groupoid $\langle G, \circ \rangle$ determines a subgroupoid if $x, y \in H$ imply $x \circ y \in H$. Similarly, if $\langle G, \circ, e \rangle$ is a semigroup with identity; *i.e.*, a monoid, then a subset must be closed under $\circ$ as well as contain e to be a submonoid. But if we consider $\langle G, \circ \rangle$ only with respect to its being a groupoid, then we require only that H be closed under $\circ$. $\langle H, \circ \rangle$ will then be a subgroupoid but not necessarily a submonoid. We therefore see from this example that the term subalgebra is meaningless unless the type of the algebra at hand is clearly understood. For example, if we use the term subgroup, it must mean that the subset H is closed under the same binary operation, contains the identity of the group, and contains the inverse of each of its elements. Every submonoid of a subgroup is not necessarily a subgroup. We note, however, that a subset H of a group $\langle G, \circ \rangle$ will be a subgroup if the single condition $x, y \in H$ implies $x \circ y^{-1} \in H$ is satisfied (exercise).

We note finally that if $\langle B, \mathfrak{F} \rangle$ is a subalgebra of an algebra $\langle A, \mathfrak{F} \rangle$ and $\langle A, \mathfrak{F} \rangle$ belongs to an equational class of algebras, then $\langle B, \mathfrak{F} \rangle$ will belong to this same class. For if the elements of A satisfy some equation, then the elements of B, being also in A, will satisfy the same equation. Hence equational classes are preserved under the process of taking subalgebras. For example, a subsemigroup of a semigroup is still a semigroup; *i.e.*, the associative law holds for elements in the subsystem, since they are also members of the parent system.

2-7. MORPHISMS

The next concept of importance in universal algebra is that of a homomorphism. If $\langle A, \mathfrak{F} \rangle$ and $\langle B, \mathfrak{F} \rangle$ are two algebras of the same type defined on carrier sets A and B respectively, then a mapping f from A to B is called a homomorphism if it preserves all the operations of $\mathfrak{F}$. Thus, if ϕ is an n-ary operation in $\mathfrak{F}$, then f is a **homomorphism** it if satisfies: $f(\phi(x_1, x_2, \ldots, x_n)) = \phi(f(x_1), f(x_2), \ldots, f(x_n))$. For example, if $\circ$ is a binary operation, then $f(x \circ y) = f(x) \circ f(y)$. As was the case with subalgebras, homomorphisms can only be defined with specific reference to the type of the algebra involved. For example, if f is a mapping from a set G to a set H and $\langle G, \circ, e, ^{-1}\rangle$ and $\langle H, *, e', ^{-1}\rangle$ are groups, then in order that f be a homomorphism, it is necessary that (*i*) $f(x \circ y) = f(x)*f(y)$, (*ii*) $e' = f(e)$ and (*iii*) $(f(x))^{-1} = f(x^{-1})$. If condition (*i*) only is satisfied, then f is merely a groupoid homomorphism, not a group homomorphism. Thus the word "homomorphism" must always be qualified. We shall see further examples in the following chapters.

As was the case for mappings in general, a homomorphism may be either injective, surjective or bijective. If f is an injective homomorphism from an algebra $\langle A, \mathfrak{F}\rangle$ into an algebra $\langle B, \mathfrak{F}\rangle$, the image set of A will be a one-to-one image of A. We call such a homomorphism a **monomorphism** and say that $\langle A, \mathfrak{F}\rangle$ is **embedded in** $\langle B, \mathfrak{F}\rangle$. Next, if f is an onto map; *i.e.*, a surjection, then we call f an **epimorphism.** In this case the entire algebra $\langle B, \mathfrak{F}\rangle$ is called a **homomorphic image** of $\langle A, \mathfrak{F}\rangle$. Finally, if f is a bijection; *i.e.*, a one-to-one onto map, then it is called an **isomorphism.** In this case the structures of $\langle A, \mathfrak{F}\rangle$ and $\langle B, \mathfrak{F}\rangle$ are indistinguishable except for notation. Again we warn that the term "structure" used here refers to the specific family $\mathfrak{F}$ of operations. Two groups may be isomorphic either from the standpoint of groupoids or from the standpoint of groups, so that when we say they are identifiable in structure we refer to the structure given.

Within the class of homomorphisms we again distinguish two special cases. First, if $A = B$, then a homomorphism is called an **endomorphism;** *i.e.*, an endomorphism is a many-one map of an algebra A into itself preserving the operations. Second, if f is an isomorphism of A onto itself, then it is called an **automorphism.** In this case, the reader may verify that the composition of two automorphisms is again an automorphism. Furthermore, the associative law holds for composition, and the identity mapping serves as an identity automorphism. Finally, the inverse of an automorphism is again an automorphism, so that the set of all automorphisms on a given algebra $\langle A, \mathfrak{F}\rangle$ forms a group, called the **automorphism group of A.**

Note that homomorphisms preserve equational classes of algebras. For example, if the associative law holds in $\langle A, \mathfrak{F}\rangle$, then it will hold in any homomorphic image, since $f(x) \circ (f(y) \circ f(z)) = f(x) \circ (f(y \circ z)) = f(x \circ (y \circ z)) = f((x \circ y) \circ z) = (f(x) \circ f(y)) \circ f(z)$. Therefore, any image of an associative system will also be associative.

EXERCISES

1. Show that a mapping f from a group $\langle G, \circ, e, ^{-1}\rangle$ onto a group $\langle H, \circ, e', ^{-1}\rangle$ is a homomorphism if $f(x\circ y^{-1}) = f(x)\circ(f(y))^{-1}$.
2. Show that for one-to-one mappings between groups, it is sufficient that a mapping be a groupoid isomorphism in order to be a group isomorphism; *i.e.*, if f preserves $\circ$, it will also preserve the identity and inverses. Show by example that this is not the case for arbitrary homomorphisms.
3. Show that the inverse of an isomorphism is also an isomorphism.
4. Show that the mapping $z \to iz$ is a group isomorphism from the additive group of the complex numbers into itself, but is not a ring isomorphism.
5. Show that the mapping $\theta \to e^{i\theta}$ is a homomorphism of the real numbers under addition onto the complex numbers with modulus 1 under multiplication.
6. Let P be the set of polynomials over the real numbers with degree 2 or less. Let V_3 be real vector space of dimension 3. Determine an isomorphism between P and V_3.
7. Show that the set of mapping X^X of a set X onto itself is a semi-group under composition.
8. Show that every monoid $\langle G, \circ, e\rangle$ is isomorphic to a submonoid of $\langle G^G, \circ, \Delta_G\rangle$ under composition.
9. Prove that every group is isomorphic to a subgroup of permutations on its carrier set (Caley's representation theorem).
10. Show that if f is a homomorphism of an algebra $\langle A, \phi\rangle$ onto an algebra $\langle B, \phi\rangle$ and $\langle A_1, \phi\rangle$ is a subalgebra of $\langle A, \phi\rangle$, then the image of A_1 under f is a subalgebra of $\langle B, \phi\rangle$; *i.e.*, homomorphisms preserve subalgebras.
11. Repeat the last exercise for the inverse image of a subalgebra of $\langle B, \phi\rangle$.
12. Show that the set $\mathbf{N}$ of natural numbers is a semigroup under the operation $n \circ m = \max\{n, m\}$. It is a group? a monoid?
13. Let $\langle G, \circ\rangle$ be a semigroup. Define by induction the mapping $\phi_{n+1}(x_1, x_2, \ldots, x_n) = \phi_m(x_1, x_2, \ldots, x_n) \circ x_{n+1}$. Prove by induction that the general associative law holds: $\phi_{n+m} = \phi_n \circ \phi_m$. Note that for ordinary addition or multiplication, $\phi_n(x_1, x_2, \ldots, x_n)$ becomes $\sum_{i=1}^{n} x_i$ or $\prod_{i=1}^{n} x_i$. Interpret these results for the case $x_i = x \; \forall \, i$.
14. Prove that the set of automorphisms of a group onto itself is a group.
15. Classify the following as to semigroup, monoid or group: (*a*) $\langle \mathbf{N}, +\rangle$, (*b*) $\langle \mathbf{N}, \cdot\rangle$, (*c*) $\langle \mathbf{Z}, +\rangle$, (*d*) $\langle \mathbf{Z}, \cdot\rangle$, (*e*) $\langle \mathbf{R}, +\rangle$, (*f*) $\langle \mathbf{Q}, \cdot\rangle$, (*g*) $\langle\{-1, 1\}, \cdot\rangle$, (*h*) $\langle\{-1, 0, 1\}, +, 0\rangle$.
16. Show that the empty set is a subalgebra of an algebra $\langle A, \mathfrak{F}\rangle$ if and only if $\mathfrak{F}$ contains no nullary operations.
17. Show that the singleton $\{0\}$ is a subsemigroup of $\langle \mathbf{Z}, \cdot, 1\rangle$ but that it is not a submonoid.

18. Show that the set of invertible elements of a monoid forms a submonoid which is a group (an element x is invertible if there exists an element x^{-1} such that $x \circ x^{-1} = x^{-1} \circ x = e$.).

2-8. CONGRUENCE RELATIONS

Closely connected to the concept of a homomorphism is that of a congruence relation. If $\langle A, \mathfrak{F} \rangle$ is an algebra of a given type, then a **congruence relation** is an equivalence relation on A with the substitution property for each operation in $\mathfrak{F}$; *i.e.*, elements may be substituted for congruent elements in any operation, thereby generating congruent elements. Specifically, if θ is a congruence relation and ϕ is an operation in $\mathfrak{F}$, then $x_i \equiv x_i'(\theta)$ implies $\phi(x_1, x_2, \ldots, x_n) \equiv \phi(x_1', x_2', \ldots, x_n')(\theta)$. Again it is important to note that a congruence relation is always defined in terms of some special type of algebra. For example, in a group congruence, θ, we must have $x \equiv x'(\theta)$ and $y \equiv y'(\theta)$ implying $x \circ y \equiv x' \circ y'(\theta)$ and $x^{-1} \equiv (x')^{-1}(\theta)$, whereas if the first of these conditions alone is satisfied, then the relation θ is merely a groupoid congruence. We also note that, as was the case with subalgebras and homomorphisms, congruences preserve equations.

The importance of congruence relations is that they enable us to create new and frequently simpler algebras out of given ones and, at the same time, preserve equational classes. Thus if $\langle A, \mathfrak{F} \rangle$ is an algebra of specified type and θ is a congruence relation on A, then, since θ is an equivalence relation, it partitions A into non-overlapping cosets or congruence classes. As before, we write $\bar{A} = A \bmod \theta$ or A/θ for the collection of cosets where $\bar{x} = \{t | t \equiv x(\theta)\}$ is the coset containing x. We can now define operations on $\bar{A}$ corresponding to the operations on A. Thus if ϕ is an n-ary operation, we define $\phi(\bar{x}_1, \bar{x}_2, \ldots, \bar{x}_n) = \overline{\phi(x_1, x_2, \ldots, x_n)}$ to be the coset containing $\phi(x_1, x_2, \ldots, x_n)$. If now $x_1', x_2', \ldots, x_n'$ are any elements of $\bar{x}_1, \bar{x}_2, \ldots, \bar{x}_n$, respectively, then we have $x_i \equiv x_i'(\theta)$ for $i = 1, 2, \ldots, n$. Now, since θ is a congruence relation, $\phi(x_1, x_2, \ldots, x_n) \equiv \phi(x_1', x_2', \ldots, x_n')(\theta)$. Hence $\overline{\phi(x_1, x_2, \ldots, x_n)} = \overline{\phi(x_1', x_2', \ldots, x_n')}$. This fact implies that the definition of $\phi(\bar{x}_1, \bar{x}_2, \ldots, \bar{x}_n)$ is independent of the particular set of representatives chosen; *i.e.*, ϕ is a well-defined operation on $\bar{A}$. Therefore, $\langle \bar{A}, \mathfrak{F} \rangle$ is an algebra of the same type as $\langle A, \mathfrak{F} \rangle$. We call it the **quotient algebra** (factor algebra), $A \bmod \theta$.

The next step is to show that A/θ is a homomorphic image of A. Specifically, we let f_θ be the mapping which maps each element into its coset; *i.e.*, f_θ maps $x \rightarrow \bar{x}$. The every definition of the operations in A/θ guarantees that the operations are preserved under this map, so that f_θ is a homomorphism of $\langle A, \mathfrak{F} \rangle$ onto (epimorphism) $\langle A/\theta, \mathfrak{F} \rangle$. We call f_θ the **natural homomorphism** associated with θ. Hence any congruence relation θ on an algebra $\langle A, \mathfrak{F} \rangle$ determines an associated homomorphism, f_θ.

Conversely, if we are given a homomorphism f on an algebra $\langle A, \mathfrak{F} \rangle$, then f will determine a congruence relation θ_f on A given by $x \equiv y(\theta_f) \leftrightarrow f(x) = f(y)$. We leave it as an exercise to verify that θ is indeed a congruence relation. The congruence classes are then just the sets of inverse images of individual elements of the range of f; *i.e.*, if $\bar{x}$ is the coset containing x, then $\bar{x} = \{t | t \equiv x(\theta_f)\} = \{t | f(t) = f(x)\} = f^*(f(x))$. The final result is to show that the correspondences $f \rightarrow \theta_f$ and $\theta \rightarrow f_\theta$ form a bijection between the class of homomorphisms and the class of congruence relations on $\langle A, \mathfrak{F} \rangle$. We must show that $\theta_{f_\theta} = \theta$ and $f_{\theta_f} = f$. We leave this point to the exercises.

As a corollary, we have the following theorem.

Theorem 2-5. *If f is a homomorphism from an algebra $\langle A, \mathfrak{F} \rangle$ onto an algebra $\langle B, \mathfrak{F} \rangle$ of the same type and θ_f is the associated congruence relation, then A/θ is isomorphic to B.*

The situation is illustrated in figure 2-5. Here f is the given homomorphism from A onto B (epimorphism), θ is the congruence relation associated with f, and f_θ the natural homomorphism of A onto A/θ. The theorem states that there exists an isomorphism g from A/θ onto B such that the diagram is commutative; *i.e.*, f can be written as the composition of f_θ and $g, f = f_\theta \circ g$. Thus the theory of homomorphisms and the theory of congruence relations are essentially but two different aspects of the same subject.

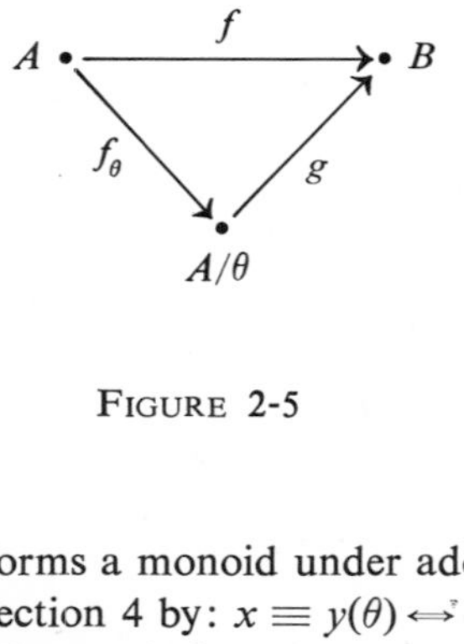

FIGURE 2-5

As an illustration of the preceding theorem we consider the set of natural numbers which forms a monoid under addition and 0; *i.e.*, $\langle \mathbf{N}, +, 0 \rangle$. Let θ be defined as in section 4 by: $x \equiv y(\theta) \leftrightarrow$ either $x - y = 5k$ or $y - x = 5k$ for some $k \in \mathbf{N}$. Then as before the cosets are the five equivalence classes, $\bar{0}, \bar{1}, \bar{2}, \bar{3}, \bar{4}$ where $\bar{3}$, for example, consists of $\{3, 8, 13, \ldots\}$; *i.e.*, all natural numbers with remainder 3 when divided by 5. It is an exercise to show that θ has the substitution property with respect to addition; *i.e.*, $n \equiv n'$ and $m \equiv m' \Rightarrow n + m \equiv n' + m'$. Note that it is not necessary to verify the substitution property with respect to a nullary operation. We now define addition in $\mathbf{N}$ mod $5 = \mathbf{N}/\theta$ by writing $\bar{n} + \bar{m} = \overline{n + m}$; *i.e.*, addition mod 5. Under this definition $\mathbf{N}/\theta$ becomes a monoid with identity $\bar{0}$. Finally, the mapping $n \rightarrow \bar{n}$ is the natural homomorphism of $\langle \mathbf{N}, +, 0 \rangle$ onto $\langle \mathbf{N}/\theta, +, \bar{0} \rangle$.

2-9. DIRECT PRODUCTS

Our final concept of universal algebra is that of the direct product of a set of algebras of the same type. We first consider the case of two algebras $\langle A, \mathfrak{F}\rangle$ and $\langle B, \mathfrak{F}\rangle$. We form the cartesian product of the carrier sets A and B obtaining the set $C = A \times B$. C consists of all ordered pairs $\langle x, y\rangle$ where $x \in A$ and $y \in B$. If ϕ is any n-ary operation belonging to $\mathfrak{F}$, then we define a corresponding operation ϕ on $A \times B$ by $\phi(\langle x_1, y_1\rangle, \langle x_2, y_2\rangle, \ldots, \langle x_n, y_n\rangle) = \langle \phi(x_1, x_2, \ldots, x_n), \phi(y_1, y_2, \ldots, y_n)\rangle$. Thus operations are defined on $A \times B$ by applying the original operations in $\mathfrak{F}$ to each coordinate separately. The resulting algebra $\langle A \times B, \mathfrak{F}\rangle$ is called the **direct product** of $\langle A, \mathfrak{F}\rangle$ and $\langle B, \mathfrak{F}\rangle$. The algebras $\langle A, \mathfrak{F}\rangle$ and $\langle B, \mathfrak{F}\rangle$ are called the **factor algebras** of $\langle A \times B, \mathfrak{F}\rangle$.

As an example, let $\langle \mathbf{R}, +, 0, -\rangle$ be the additive group of the real numbers. The direct product of this system with itself will be the set of ordered pairs of real numbers $\langle x, y\rangle$ where addition is defined by $\langle x_1, y_1\rangle + \langle x_2, y_2\rangle = \langle x_1 + x_2, y_1 + y_2\rangle$, the additive identity is the pair $\langle 0, 0\rangle$ and the additive inverse of $\langle x, y\rangle$ is $\langle -x, -y\rangle$. The resulting direct product is the system $\langle \mathbf{R}^2, +, \langle 0, 0\rangle, -\rangle$ which is itself an additive group. It is quite clear that the associative law for addition in $\langle \mathbf{R}, +, 0, -\rangle$ will then apply within the direct product. Similarly, the commutative law for addition as the direct product is also derivable from the commutative law within the reals.

More generally, any equational laws which apply to the algebras $\langle A, \mathfrak{F}\rangle$ and $\langle B, \mathfrak{F}\rangle$ will also apply within their direct product. Therefore, equational classes of algebras are preserved by the formation of direct products. Summarizing, we see that equational classes of algebras are preserved under the three processes of forming subalgebras, forming homomorphic images and forming direct products. One of the most important theorems of universal algebra is the converse of this result. This theorem is due to Birkhoff and states that if a class of algebras is preserved under subalgebras, homomorphic images and direct products, then it is an equational class of algebras. We shall not attempt to prove it here.

In the example above we defined the direct product of two additive groups and showed that it was an additive group. We can use this same technique to define ordinary two-dimensional real vector space as a direct product of the reals with themselves, provided we first define scalar multiplication operations within $\mathbf{R}$ itself. Thus for each c in $\mathbf{R}$ we define a (left) multiplication operation by $L_c\colon x \to cx$. We then treat the reals as an additive group with an infinite set of unary operations $\{L_c\}_{c \in \mathbf{R}}$. These operations then induce similar left multiplication operations on $\mathbf{R}^2$ given by $L_c\colon \langle x, y\rangle \to \langle cx, cy\rangle$. The resulting direct product algebra $\langle \mathbf{R}^2, +, \langle 0, 0\rangle, -, \{L_c\}_{c \in \mathbf{R}}\rangle$ is then the usual two dimensional vector space over the reals, V_2. It has type $\langle 2, 0, 1; 1, 1, 1, \ldots \rangle$.

We can extend the concept of direct product to any finite number of factors, simply by defining all operations on the cartesian product coordinatewise. We then write $\langle \prod_{i=1}^{n} A_i, \mathfrak{F} \rangle$ for the direct product of n similar type algebras. The condition of finiteness is also unnecessary if we use the definition of cartesian product for an arbitrary indexed set of algebras of the same type. Thus the elements of $\Pi_\alpha A_\alpha$; $\alpha \in I$ are functions defined on I with values in A_α for each $\alpha \in I$. To extend operations from the A_α, we simply again define the function x on I to $\{A_\alpha\}$ coordinatewise; *i.e.*, if $\phi(x_1, x_2, \ldots, x_n)$ is an n-ary operation, we define $x(\alpha) = \phi(x_1(\alpha), x_2(\alpha), \ldots, x_n(\alpha))$ where the operation ϕ here operates in A_α. The function defined over all $\alpha \in I$ is then an element of $\Pi_\alpha A_\alpha$ and defines an operation ϕ on $\Pi_\alpha A_\alpha$; *i.e.*, for each α the operation is performed as in A_α, and then the results form an element of the direct product. For example, the addition of two α-tuples would be defined by $\langle x_\alpha \rangle + \langle y_\alpha \rangle = \langle x_\alpha + y_\alpha \rangle$.

The importance of the direct product is its relation to homomorphisms. We define the **projection maps** of an ordered pair in $A \times B$ by $\pi_1(\langle x, y \rangle) = x$ and $\pi_2(\langle x, y \rangle) = y$; *i.e.*, π_1 maps an ordered pair onto its first coordinate, while π_2 maps it onto its second coordinate. In the example above π_1 and π_2 are the vertical and horizontal projections from the cartesian product onto the x and y axes respectively. If now $\circ$ is a binary operation, then $\pi_1(\langle x_1, y_1 \rangle \circ \langle x_2, y_2 \rangle) = \pi_1(\langle x_1 \circ x_2, y_1 \circ y_2 \rangle) = x_1 \circ x_2 = \pi_1(x_1, y_1) \circ \pi_1(x_2, y_2)$, so that π_1 preserves $\circ$. Similarly, any projection will preserve the operations of the algebra in question, so that they will be homomorphisms. The corresponding cosets of the associated congruence relation will then be the "horizontal" and "vertical" lines respectively, within $A \times B$; *i.e.*, if θ_1 and θ_2 are the congruences determined by π_1 and π_2, then $\langle x_1, y_1 \rangle \equiv \langle x_2, y_2 \rangle (\theta_1) \longleftrightarrow x_1 = x_2$ and $\langle x_1, y_1 \rangle \equiv \langle x_2, y_2 \rangle (\theta_2) \longleftrightarrow y_1 = y_2$.

EXERCISES

1. Show that if f is a homomorphism on an algebra $\langle A, \mathfrak{F} \rangle$ and θ_f is defined by $x \equiv y(\theta_f) \longleftrightarrow f(x) = f(y)$, then θ_f is a congruence relation on $\langle A, \mathfrak{F} \rangle$.
2. If θ is a congruence relation on an algebra $\langle A, \mathfrak{F} \rangle$, f_θ is the associated natural homomorphism, and θ_{f_θ} is defined as in exercise 1, show that $\theta_{f_\theta} = \theta$; *i.e.*, $x \equiv y(\theta_{f_\theta}) \longleftrightarrow x \equiv y(\theta)$.
3. Prove Theorem 4.
4. Given algebras $\langle A, \mathfrak{F} \rangle$ and $\langle B, \mathfrak{F} \rangle$ and a homomorphism f from A to B, let θ_A be any congruence relation on A such that $\theta_A \subseteq \theta_f$; *i.e.*, $x \equiv x'(\theta_A) \Rightarrow f(x) =$

$f(x')$. Show how f induces a congruence relation on B by defining $y \equiv y'(\theta_B) \Leftrightarrow f^{-1}(y) \equiv f^{-1}(y')(\theta_A)$.

5. Using the preceding exercise, show that h may be defined in such a way that the diagram of figure 2-6 is commutative.

6. If f is a homomorphism of $\langle A, \mathfrak{F}\rangle$ into $\langle B, \mathfrak{F}\rangle$, show that f can be written as the composite of an epimorphism, f_θ, into A/θ followed by an isomorphism g onto the range of f, R_f, followed by an inclusion, i, into B; *i.e.*, the diagram of figure 2-7 is commutative.

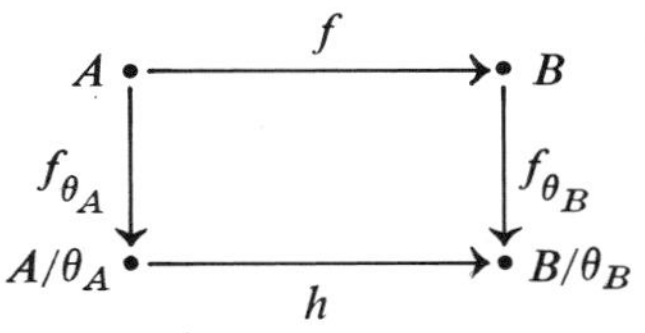

FIGURE 2-6

7. Given the additive group $\langle \mathbf{Z}, +, 0, -\rangle$ define $x \equiv y \bmod m$ (for fixed m)$\Leftrightarrow m|x - y$, ($|$ is "divides"). Show that this relation is a congruence relation. Show that the set of integers $\{x|x \equiv 0 \bmod m\}$ is a subgroup of $\mathbf{Z}$. Show that if addition is defined by $\bar{x} + \bar{y} = \overline{x + y}$ where $\bar{x}$ is the coset containing x, then $\mathbf{Z}$ mod m becomes a group homomorphic to $\mathbf{Z}$ whose identity is the subgroup.

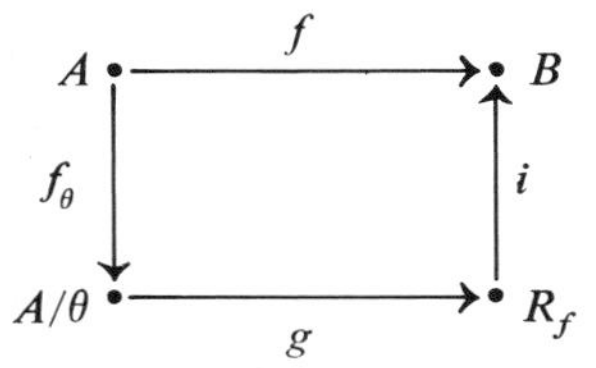

FIGURE 2-7

8. Extend the results of exercise 7 to include multiplication so that the homomorphism is a ring homomorphism.

9. Show that the general projection map π_α of a direct product $\Pi_\alpha A_\alpha$ of a family of algebras, $\langle A_\alpha, \mathfrak{F}\rangle$ onto the factor algebra $\langle A_\alpha, \mathfrak{F}\rangle$ given by $\pi_\alpha \langle x_\alpha\rangle = x_\alpha$ is a homomorphism.

10. If $\langle A, \mathfrak{F}\rangle$ and $\langle B, \mathfrak{F}\rangle$ are two algebras and π_1 is the projection of $\langle A \times B, \mathfrak{F}\rangle$ onto $\langle A, \mathfrak{F}\rangle$ and θ_1 is the associated congruence on A, then A/θ_1 is isomorphic to B.

11. How can the results of the preceding exercise be extended to the case of three factors?

2-10. THE ALGEBRA OF SETS

Having developed the theory of sets from an axiomatic point of view in Chapter 1 and having discussed some of the basic concepts of universal algebra in the early parts of this chapter, we can now combine these two topics to develop an algebra for sets. The basic purpose of Chapter 1 was to axiomatize the theory of sets to guarantee the existence of enough sets to serve the purposes of elementary mathematics. Then in this chapter we have shown how the basic concepts of relation, function, operation, etc., can be developed out of axiomatic set theory leading to universal algebra. It is our purpose now to develop an algebra for set theory itself, in which we begin with a fixed set (universe) U and then take $\mathfrak{P}(U)$ as the carrier of an algebra. We define various operations on $\mathfrak{P}(U)$ which convert $\mathfrak{P}(U)$ into an algebra whose properties we then investigate. The resulting algebra is called the Boolean algebra of sets. Later, in Chapter 6, we shall define an abstract Boolean algebra modeled on the algebra of sets and which, in turn, can be represented within the algebra of sets. Chapters 4 and 5 are devoted to other algebraic systems which are based on various portions of the algebra of sets, but do not in general characterize all of set algebra. Finally, Chapter 7 indicates an algebra which extends to the class of all sets (in the sense of von Neumann), but for the present we shall limit ourselves to subsets of a fixed set.

The operations of set theory are all definable in terms of the elementhood relation for set theory by using the logical connectives "and," "or" and "not." We let $p(x)$ be the statement "$x \in A$," and then form compound statements from primitive statements of this type. We can then use the axiom of abstraction applied within our fixed set U, to establish the existence of various subsets of U which depend on given sets, $A, B, \ldots$. We thereby define various nullary, unary and binary operations on the elements of the power set $\mathfrak{P}(U)$. Thus all our operations depend on the axioms of Chapter 1, using the underlying logic.

We first define the nullary operations of the algebra of sets corresponding to the fixed sets $\emptyset$ and U. $\emptyset$ is the empty set defined by:

$\emptyset = \{x \in U | x \notin U\}$, while U is the set given by:

$U = \{x \in U | x \in U\}$. Since these have already been discussed in Chapter 1, we proceed next to the unary operations.

To obtain the various unary operations, we let A be any subset of U; *i.e.*, element of $\mathfrak{P}(U)$, and we let $p(x)$ be the statement "$x \in A$." Then, by use of the connectives of logic, we can obtain four compound statements, $p(x)$, $\sim p(x)$, $p(x) \wedge (\sim p(x))$, and $p(x) \vee (\sim p(x))$. These give rise to four sets, $A, A', \emptyset$ and U, respectively; *i.e.*, $A = \{x | p(x)\}$, $A' = \{x | \sim p(x)\}$, etc. Of these, the only one that needs discussing is the operation $A \rightarrow A'$ of complementation. We repeat its basic properties from Chapter 1:

Theorem 2-6. 1. $A'' = A$,
2. $\emptyset' = U$,
3. $U' = \emptyset$.

We now consider binary operations defined on two subsets A and B of U. Thus we let p and q be the statements "$x \in A$" and "$x \in B$". Using negation alone, we can form the statements $\sim p$ and $\sim q$. We then can combine these with p and q to form four mutually exclusive and exhaustive cases using $\sim$ and $\wedge$. These are $p \wedge q, p \wedge \sim q, \sim p \wedge q$, and $\sim p \wedge \sim q$. (We omit

Table 2-1.

	Logical statement	Symbol	Operation	Venn Diagram
1	—	$\emptyset$	null set	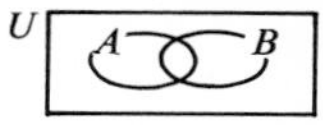
2	$p \wedge q$	$A \cap B$	intersection	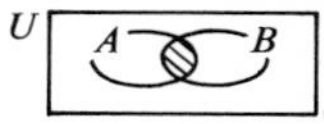
3	$p \wedge \sim q$	$A - B$	difference	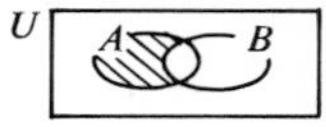
4	$\sim p \wedge q$	$B - A$	difference	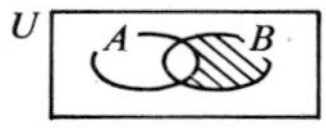
5	$\sim p \wedge \sim q$	$A \mid\uparrow B$	joint denial	
6	$(p \wedge q) \vee (p \wedge \sim q)$	A	first selector	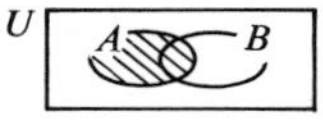
7	$(p \wedge q) \vee (\sim p \wedge q)$	B	second selector	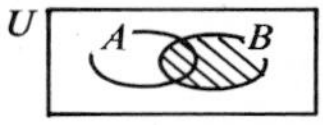
8	$(p \wedge q) \vee (\sim p \wedge \sim q)$	$A \leftrightarrow B$	equivalence	
9	$(p \wedge \sim q) \vee (\sim p \wedge q)$	$A \Delta B$	symmetric difference	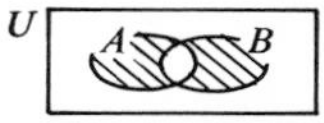
10	$(p \wedge \sim q) \vee (\sim p \wedge \sim q)$	B'	second complement	
11	$(\sim p \wedge q) \vee (\sim p \wedge \sim q)$	A'	first complement	
12	$(p \wedge q) \vee (p \wedge \sim q) \vee (\sim p \wedge q)$	$A \cup B$	union	
13	$(p \wedge q) \vee (p \wedge \sim q) \vee (\sim p \wedge \sim q)$	$B \rightarrow A$	implication	
14	$(p \wedge q) \vee (\sim p \wedge q) \vee (\sim p \wedge \sim q)$	$A \rightarrow B$	implication	
15	$(p \wedge \sim q) \vee (\sim q \wedge q) \vee (\sim p \wedge \sim q)$	$A \mid B$	Shoeffer stroke	
16	$(p \wedge q) \vee (p \wedge \sim q) \vee (\sim p \wedge q) \vee (\sim p \wedge \sim q)$	U	universal set	

parentheses around $\sim p$). Finally, we can combine any subset of these four cases under $\vee$, thereby obtaining sixteen distinct statements formed from the primitives, p and q, by means of $\sim$, $\wedge$, and $\vee$. We list these in a table, which shows, in addition, symbols and names for the resulting operations. We also include Venn diagrams in which U is indicated by a rectangle, and A and B are represented by overlapping Euler circles with the region corresponding to the given operation shaded.

Each of the statements in column 1 is formed from p and q by means of the logical connectives, and therefore determines a subset of U by virtue of the axiom of abstraction. They therefore define sixteen distinct binary operations; *i.e.*, they define mappings from the set of ordered pairs of subsets of U into subsets of U. The first and last determine the **null** and **universal sets** and have already been dsicussed under nullary operations. Operations numbered 6 and 7 assign to the ordered pair $\langle A, B\rangle$ of sets either the first or second. Hence they are called **selector operations**. Similarly, operations 10 and 11 select the **complement** of B or A respectively. They can also be generated by composing the binary selector operations with the unary operation of complementation; *i.e.*, A' is obtained as a binary operation by selecting A from the pair $\langle A, B\rangle$ and then applying complementation as a unary operation. The two most commonly used binary operations are numbers 2 and 12, which are the already familiar operations of Chapter 1, **intersection** and **union**. As stated there, they can be given more simply by $A \cap B = \{x \in U | (x \in A) \wedge (x \in B)\}$ and $A \cup B = \{x \in U | (x \in A) \vee (x \in B)\}$. They thus correspond directly to the logical connectives, $\wedge$ and $\vee$. Next, the **difference** operations 3 and 4 are also the same as those given in Chapter 1, where we used the simpler characterization $A - B = \{x \in A | x \notin B\}$. In this form it is also the same as the *relative complement of B with respect to A*; *i.e.*, $A - B = B'_A$. Operations 13 and 14 are dual to subtraction (a notion to be made more precise later), and are known as **implication**, again terminology that will be evident shortly. Number 9 is called the **symmetric difference** since it is the union of $A - B$ and $B - A$, and is therefore symmetric in A and B. It is also known as the **"exclusive or"** operation, since it gives all elements in either A or B, but not both. In contrast, the union operation gives all elements in A or B, or possibly both, and is known as **"inclusive or."** The dual to symmetric difference is the operation of **equivalence** which we have denoted by $A \leftrightarrow B$. This is not to be confused with an equivalence *relation* which is a relation, whereas $A \leftrightarrow B$ is a binary operation. It is the set of all elements either in both A and B or in neither. Therefore, an element x behaves equivalently with respect to both A and B, which may help explain the terminology. Finally, 5 and 15 are less commonly used operations. Their names are due to Shoeffer, who first investigated them thoroughly. The first, the double stroke, is also known as **joint rejection**, since it is the complement of elements in either A or B; *i.e.*, consists of elements in neither A nor B.

2-11. PROPERTIES OF SET OPERATIONS

The fundamental properties of the various set operations may now be obtained by applying the laws of logic to the definitions. For example, the commutative laws for union and intersection follow directly from the corresponding laws for the logical connectives, "or" and "and." Thus $A \cup B = \{x \in U | (x \in A) \vee (x \in B)\} = \{x \in U | (x \in B) \vee (x \in A)\} = B \cup A$; *i.e.*, the commutative law of $\cup$ follows from commutativity of $\vee$. Similarly, the operations of union and intersection are both associative and idempotent. We omit further proofs and summarize the basic properties of these two operations in the following theorem:

Theorem 2-7. 1. $A \cup B = B \cup A$,
$A \cap B = B \cap A$ (*commutativity*),
2. $A \cup (B \cup C) = (A \cup B) \cup C$,
$A \cap (B \cap C) = (A \cap B) \cap C$ (*associativity*),
3. $A \cup A = A$,
$A \cap A = A$ (*idempotence*),
4. $A \cup (A \cap B) = A = A \cap (A \cup B)$ (*absorption*),
5. $A \cup (B \cap C) = (A \cup B) \cap (A \cup C)$,
$A \cap (B \cup C) = (A \cap B) \cup (A \cap C)$ (*distributivity*).

The next theorem relates the union and intersection operations to the nullary and unary operations, $\emptyset$, U, and $'$.

Theorem 2-8. 1. $A \cup \emptyset = A$ (*identity*),
$A \cap \emptyset = \emptyset$ (*zero*);
2. $A \cup U = U$ (*zero*),
$A \cap U = A$ (*identity*);
3. $(A \cup B)' = A' \cap B'$,
$(A \cap B)' = A' \cup B'$ (*de Morgan's laws*);
4. $A \cup A' = U$,
$A \cap A' = \emptyset$.

Here an element is an **identity** (neutral element) for a binary operation if combining it with an arbitrary element leaves the element fixed; *i.e.*, an identity e for an operation $\circ$ satisfies

$$a \circ e = e \circ a = a \ \forall \ a \in A$$

where A is the carrier of the algebra. Similarly, a **zero** element is an element which combines with any other element to give the zero; *i.e.*, 0 is a zero if it satisfies:

$$a \circ 0 = 0 \circ a = 0 \ \forall \ a \in A.$$

The third set of equations of theorem 7 are known as de Morgan's laws, having been known as early as 1840 by the English logician. They enable us to express either union or intersection in terms of the other and complementation. Thus we may write

$$A \cup B = (A' \cap B')'$$

and

$$A \cap B = (A' \cup B')'.$$

We could have derived the properties of complementation and union, for example, from the properties of the underlying logical connectives, and then defined intersection in terms of them and derived the properties of intersection from those of union and complements. For example, the commutative law for intersection can be derived from the corresponding commutativity of union using the de Morgan laws. Furthermore, the following theorem shows that all the other binary operations can also be defined purely in terms of either union or intersection and complementation, so that no further reference need be made to the underlying logic involving the elementhood relation.

Theorem 2-9. 1. $A \cap B = (A' \cup B')'$,
2. $A \cup A' = U$,
3. $A \cap A' = \emptyset$,
4. $A - B = A \cap B'$,
5. $A \rightarrow B = A' \cup B$,
6. $A \parallel B = (A \cup B)'$,
7. $A \mid B = (A \cap B)'$,
8. $A \,\Delta\, B = (A \cap B') \cup (A' \cap B)$,
9. $A \leftrightarrow B = (A \cap B) \cup (A' \cap B')$.

Theorem 2-9 shows now all the properties of all the set operations are essentially derivable from those of union and complement.

A stronger result may be obtained by starting with the single binary operation, Shoeffer's stroke. We may define complementation by $A' = A|A$, which follows from 7 of theorem 2-9 by letting $A = B$. Intersection can then be characterized by the complement of stroke; *i.e.* as $A \cap B = (A|B)' = (A|B)|(A|B)$. We can apply theorem 2-9 to obtain all the other operations in terms of stroke. In fact, Shoeffer has shown that, starting with the properties of stroke alone, all other properties of all the other operations can be derived. On the other hand, it is also known that similar results cannot be achieved with any of the other operations except double stroke.

Strictly speaking, we must take care of what the phrase "defined in terms of" means. Thus if we take the strict view of universal algebra and consider operations as functions from A^n into A for an algebra $\langle A, \mathfrak{F} \rangle$ and permit only composition of functions, then we must qualify Shoeffer's results. If f is a binary operation on $\mathfrak{P}(U)$, then it is a mapping from $\mathfrak{P}(U) \times \mathfrak{P}(U)$ into $\mathfrak{P}(U)$; *i.e.*, a set of pairs of the form $\langle\langle A, B\rangle, C\rangle$ where A and B are arbitrary subsets of U or elements of $\mathfrak{P}(U)$. The function f is then defined by $f = \{\langle\langle A, B\rangle, C\rangle | A, B \in \mathfrak{P}(U)\}$. We call f a two-place function on $\mathfrak{P}(U)$ into $\mathfrak{P}(U)$. For example, the operation corresponding to set union is given by $U = \{\langle\langle A, B\rangle, C\rangle | C = A \cup B, A, B \in \mathfrak{P}(U)\}$. If now g and h are two further binary operations (two-place functions) on $\mathfrak{P}(U)$, then we define a composition of them with f by:

$$\langle g, h\rangle \circ f = \{\langle\langle A, B\rangle, C\rangle | \exists D, E \in \mathfrak{P}(U), \langle\langle A, B\rangle, D\rangle \in g, \langle\langle A, B\rangle, E\rangle \in h,$$

and $\langle\langle D, E\rangle, C \in f\}$.

In the more conventional, functional value notation we would read: $D = g(A, B)$, $E = h(A, B)$, and $C = f(D, E)$ or $f(D, E) = f(g(A, B), h(A, B))$. For example, the first and second selector functions corresponding to operations 6 and 7 of Table 2-1 are written as:

$$s_1 = \{\langle\langle A, B\rangle, A\rangle | A, B \in \mathfrak{P}(U)\}$$

and

$$s_2 = \{\langle\langle A, B\rangle, B\rangle | A, B \in \mathfrak{P}(U)\}.$$

Similarly, the stroke operation and the intersection become:

$$st = \{\langle\langle A, B\rangle, A|B\rangle | A, B \in \mathfrak{P}(U)\}$$

and

$$i = \{\langle\langle A, B\rangle, A \cap B\rangle | A, B \in \mathfrak{P}(U)\}$$

where $A|B$ and $A \cap B$ are defined by Table 2-1. In this case, intersection can be defined in terms of stroke alone, using binary composition as defined above. Thus

$$i = \langle st, st\rangle \circ st.$$

Again using functional notation, this reads:

$$i(A, B) = st(st(A, B), st(A, B)) = (A|B)|(A|B)$$

as we saw above. However, the complementation operations 10 and 11, cannot be expressed in terms of stroke alone by means of binary composition. Thus the first and second complementation operations are given by:

$$p_1 = \{\langle\langle A, B\rangle, A'\rangle | A, B \in \mathfrak{P}(U)\}$$

and

$$p_2 = \{\langle\langle A, B\rangle, B'\rangle | A, B \in \mathfrak{P})U(\}.$$

To obtain, say, p_1 from st we must now employ the first selector operation along with binary composition; *i.e.*,

$$p_1 = \langle s_1, s_1\rangle \circ st,$$

Again, in functional notation this becomes:

$$p_1(A, B) = st(s_1(A, B), s_1(A, B)) = st(A, A) = A|A = A'.$$

Similarly, $p_2 = \langle s_2, s_2\rangle \circ st$. Thus we note that p_1 as a binary or two-place function is not definable in terms of *st* alone without the use of the selector operations. Similarly, we may express the union function in terms of the selector operations and stroke, but not in terms of stroke alone; *i.e.*,

$$u = \langle\langle s_1, s_1\rangle \circ st, \langle s_2, s_2\rangle \circ st\rangle \circ st.$$

We leave the verification to the exercises (*cf:* Menger).

We next study briefly the operation of subtraction. We note that it can be characterized in terms of intersection and complementation by $A - B = A \cap B'$. Hence its properties may be derived from those of intersection and complementation. The principal properties are given in the following theorem.

Theorem 2-10. 1. $A - (B - A) = A$,
2. $A - (A - B) = B - (B - A)$,
3. $(A - B) - C = (A - C) - B$,
4. $A - U = \emptyset$.

Proof. 1. $A - (B - A) = A \cap (B \cap A')' = A \cap (B' \cup A) = (A \cap B') \cup A = A$.
2. $A - (A - B) = A \cap (A \cap B')' = A \cap (A' \cup B) = (A \cap A') \cup (A \cap B) = A \cap B$. But $A \cap B = B \cap A$, so the result follows from symmetry.
3. $(A - B) - C = A \cap B' \cap C' = A \cap C' \cap B' = (A - C) - B$.
4. Exercise.

We note as a corollary that intersection is expressible in terms of subtraction by $A \cap B = A - (A - B)$. But $A' = U - A$, so that if we are given U and the subtraction operation, then we can derive both intersection and complement, and hence all the other operations. Furthermore, we shall show in Chapter 7 how all the other properties of the operations can be derived from those of theorem 2-9. Theorem 2-9 can therefore be taken as a basis for all of the algebra of sets in terms of the binary operation of subtraction and the nullary operation U. From this point of view, the algebra of sets therefore becomes an algebra of type $\langle 2, 0\rangle$.

2-12. SET INCLUSION

So far we have treated the algebra of sets as an algebraic system in the sense of universal algebra. It consists of a carrier $\mathfrak{P}(U)$ and a family of operations which have certain properties. The particular type of algebra depends on which operations are taken as fundamental. For example, if we consider union and complement along with the nullary operations U and $\emptyset$ as basic, then it has type $\langle 2, 1, 0, 0\rangle$. There may therefore be distinct types of algebras modeled on the algebras of sets, and we will study many of these throughout the remainder of this book. However, set theory also involves relations as well as operations, and these cannot be treated under universal algebra as defined above. We therefore extend the subject to include relational algebraic systems as well as operational systems.

We have already defined the partial order relation of set inclusion in Chapter 1, and we here complete the discussion by relating it to the various operations. The first results are contained in the following theorem.

Theorem 2-11. 1. $A \subseteq A$ (*reflexive*),
2. $A \subseteq B \wedge B \subseteq A \Rightarrow A = B$ (*anti-symmetric*),
3. $A \subseteq B \wedge B \subseteq C \Rightarrow A \subseteq C$ (*transitive*),
4. $A \subseteq B \Rightarrow B' \subseteq A'$,
5. $A \subseteq B \Rightarrow A \cup C \subseteq B \cup C$,
$A \subseteq B \Rightarrow A \cap C \subseteq B \cap C$ (*isotone*),
6. $A \cap B \subseteq A, B$, (*lower bound*),
$C \subseteq A, B \Rightarrow C \subseteq A \cap B$, (*greatest lower bound*),
7. $A, B \subseteq A \cup B$ (*upper bound*),
$A, B \subseteq C \Rightarrow A \cup B \subseteq C$ (*least upper bound*),
8. $\emptyset \subseteq A \subseteq U$ (*universal bounds*).

As usual, we leave the proofs to the reader. Numbers 6 and 7 enable us to characterize the operations of intersection and union in terms of the inclusion relation. Thus 7 states that both A and B are contained in $A \cup B$, so that $A \cup B$ is an upper bound for A and B, while the second half states that $A \cup B$ is contained in any other common upper bound. Hence it is called a least upper bound. In the next chapter, we study systems with relations which generalize these notions in an abstract setting.

The final theorem is a sort of converse in that it characterizes the inclusion relation in terms of either intersection, union or subtraction.

Theorem 2-12. 1. $A \subseteq B \Leftrightarrow A \cap B = A$,
2. $A \subseteq B \Leftrightarrow A \cup B = B$,
3. $A \subseteq B \Leftrightarrow A - B = \emptyset$.

EXERCISES

1. Prove Theorem 5.

2. Prove Theorem 6.

3. Prove Theorem 7.

4. Prove Theorem 8.

5. Complete the proof of Theorem 10.

6. Prove Theorem 11.

7. Prove that: $A - B = B \Leftrightarrow A = B = \emptyset$.

8. Prove that: $A - (A \cap B) = A - B$.

9. Prove that: $A \cup B = \emptyset \Leftrightarrow A = B = \emptyset$.

10. Prove that: $A - B = A \Leftrightarrow B - A = B$.

11. Prove that: $A - B = B - A \Leftrightarrow A = B$.

12. Show by counterexamples that set subtraction is neither commutative nor associative.

13. Prove that the sets $A - B$, $A \cap B$, $B - A$ and $A' \cap B'$ form a partition of U.

14. Prove that $A \cap X = \emptyset$ and $A \cup X = U \Rightarrow X = A'$ (uniqueness of complements).

15. If U and V are two sets and f is a mapping from U to V, show that:
(*i*) $f_*(A \cup B) = f_*(A) \cup f_*(B)$ for any $A, B \subseteq U$,
(*ii*) $f^*(A \cup B) = f^*(A) \cup f^*(B)$ for any $A, B \subseteq V$.

16. If U and V are two sets, and f is a mapping from U to V, show that:
(*i*) $f_*(A \cap B) \subseteq f_*(A) \cap f_*(B)$, for $A, B \subseteq U$,
(*ii*) $f^*(A \cap B) = f^*(A) \cap f^*(B)$ for $A, B \subseteq V$.
Show by counterexample that the inequality of (*i*) cannot be improved.

17. If U and V are two sets and f is a mapping from U to V, show that:
(*i*) $f_*(A) - f_*(B) \subseteq f_*(A - B)$ for $A, B \subseteq U$,
(*ii*) $f^*(A - B) = f^*(A) - f^*(B)$ for $A, B \subseteq V$.
Show that equality does not hold in general in (*i*).

18. Show that if f in exercise 17 is one-to-one, the equality of (*i*) holds.

19. If U and V are two sets and f is a mapping from U to V, show that:
(*i*) if f is one-to-one, then $f_*(A') \subseteq (f_*(A))'$ for all $A \subseteq U$,
(*ii*) if f is onto, then $(f_*(A))' \subseteq f_*(A')$ for $A \subseteq B$;
(*iii*) if f is one-to-one and onto, then $f_*(A') = (f_*(A))'$ for $A \subseteq U$.
(*iv*) $f^*(A') = (f^*(A))'$.

20. If U and V are two sets and f is a mapping from U to V, show that: $A \subseteq B \subseteq U \Rightarrow f_*(A) \subseteq f_*(B)$ (isotone).

21. Prove: (*i*) $(A \cup B) \times C = (A \times C) \cup (B \times C)$,
(*ii*) $(A \cap B) \times C = (A \times C) \cap (B \times C)$,
(*iii*) $(A - B) \times C = (A \times C) - (B \times C)$.

22. Prove: $A \subseteq B \Rightarrow A \times C \subseteq B \times C$. (*Hint*: use $A \subseteq B \Leftrightarrow A \cup B = B$.)

23. Verify that the two place union function: $u = \{\langle\langle A, B\rangle, A \cup B\rangle | A, B \in \mathfrak{P}(U)\}$ satisfies:

$$u = \langle p_1, p_2\rangle \circ st = \langle\langle s_1, s_1\rangle \circ st, \langle s_2, s_2\rangle \circ st\rangle \circ st.$$

24. Show that the first difference function $d = \{\langle\langle A, B\rangle, A - B\rangle | A, B \in \mathfrak{P}(U)\}$ can be expressed in terms of the selector functions and stroke by:

$$d = \langle\langle s_1, \langle s_2, s_2\rangle \circ st\rangle \circ st, \langle s_1, \langle s_2, s_2\rangle \circ st\rangle \circ st\rangle \circ st.$$

25. If f is a function defined on a set A and $B \subseteq A$, then we define the restriction of f to B by:

$$f|_B = \{\langle x, y\rangle | \langle x, y\rangle \in f \wedge x \in B\}.$$

Show that the unary operation of complementation given by: $p = \{\langle A, A'\rangle | A \in \mathfrak{P}(U)\}$ can be obtained by restriction of stroke to the diagonal on U; *i.e.*,

$$p = st|_\Delta.$$

26. We define the composition of two unary functions g and h with a two place f by:

$$\langle g, h\rangle \circ f = \{\langle x, z\rangle | \exists u, v \wedge \langle x, u\rangle \in g \wedge \langle x, v\rangle \in h \wedge \langle\langle u, v\rangle, z\rangle \in f\}.$$

Show that $\langle g, h\rangle \circ f$ is a unary function.

27. If f is a binary function and g is a unary function, we define the composition of f and g by:

$$f \circ g = \{\langle\langle x, y\rangle, z\rangle | \exists u \wedge \langle\langle x, y\rangle, u\rangle \in f \wedge \langle u, z\rangle \in g\}.$$

Show that $f \circ g$ is a binary or two place function. Using this result, show that $u = \langle s_1 \circ p, s_2 \circ p\rangle \circ st$ is an expression of union in terms of the selector functions, unary complementation and stroke.

2-13. DUALITY

As the reader has undoubtedly noticed, there is a striking similarity between the concepts of intersection and union. In fact, the definition of union was stated in Chapter 1 by replacing the logical connective $\wedge$ with $\vee$ in the defininition of intersection. But in the underlying logic the laws governing "both. . . and" and "either. . . or" are the same, so that it is natural to find the laws for $\cup$ and $\cap$ similar. Furthermore, any properties and secondary concepts that arise in terms of $\cap$ will give similar properties and concepts in terms of $\cup$. We thus have a general principle that any law that holds in set theory will remain valid if $\cap$ and $\cup$ are interchanged. This is not strictly a theorem of set theory, but a theorem within the underlying logic. As such, it is known as a theorem of meta-mathematics. It is called the principle of duality and states:

Principle of Duality. *Any statement valid for the subsets of a fixed set U remains valid if $\cup$ and $\cap$ are interchanged throughout.*

Any two theorems related by this principle are called **duals**, and any theorem which is unchanged is called **self-dual**. The "throughout" in the statement of the principle implies that any secondary concept defined in terms of $\cup$ and $\cap$ must also be replaced by the dual concept; *i.e.*, the concept defined by replacing $\cup$ by $\cap$ and $\cap$ by $\cup$. For example, the null set can be characterized by the neutral property with respect to $\cup$; *i.e.*, $A \cup \emptyset = A \ \forall \ A \in \mathfrak{P}(U)$. The dual is the identity for $\cap$. But this is the universal set which satisfies: $A \cap U = A \ \forall \ A \in \mathfrak{P}(U)$. Hence $\emptyset$ and U are dual concepts and must be interchanged in using the principle of duality. Similarly, if a statement involves set inclusion, then $A \subseteq B$ must be replaced by $B \subseteq A$. For if we characterize inclusion in terms of union, we have $A \subseteq B \leftrightarrow A \cup B = B$. But the dual of this statement is $B \subseteq A \leftrightarrow A \cap B = B$. Otherwise, we could replace the relation of inclusion $\subseteq$ by its converse, $\supseteq$, "contains."

Notice that we have stated the principle of duality for the subsets of some universal set U. In general it does not apply without such a restriction since there is, for example, no dual of $\emptyset$ in general set theory. The importance of the principle of duality is that it reduces the number of proofs almost in half, since, for each theorem in set theory, we can obtain a dual theorem by dualization, and its proof will follow by the principle of duality. For example, the proof of the associative law for intersection follows by dualization from the corresponding associative law for union. We give further examples in the next section.

2-14. INFINITE UNIONS AND INTERSECTIONS

In Chapter 1 we defined the operations of union and intersection for pairs of sets. Clearly these can be extended to arbitrary finite collections of sets by ordinary induction, using the technique of exercise 13 of section 2-7. Thus we define:

$\bigcup_{i=1}^{n} A_i = A_1 \cup A_2 \cup \cdots \cup A_n = (\bigcup_{i=1}^{n-1} A_i) \cup A_n$, and similarly for $\bigcap_{i=1}^{n} A_i$. On the other hand, we can give a direct definition in terms of elements simply by generalizing the definitions of Chapter 1 to arbitrary families of sets, finite or infinite. Thus if $\mathfrak{F} = \{A_\alpha\}_{\alpha \in I}$ is an arbitrary family of sets indexed by some set I, then we define:

$$\bigcup_\alpha A_\alpha = \{x | x \in A_\alpha \text{ for some } \alpha \in I\}$$

and

$$\bigcap_\alpha A_\alpha = \{x | x \in A_\alpha \text{ for all } \alpha \in I\}.$$

If no confusion is likely, we may also write $\bigcup \mathfrak{F}$ and $\bigcap \mathfrak{F}$ for the union and intersection of all members of $\mathfrak{F}$. The special case where I (or $\mathfrak{F}$) is the empty set bears some comment. In this case, the intersection is the set of all elements x which satisfy $x \in A$ for all $A \in \mathfrak{F}$. But since $\mathfrak{F}$ is empty, every element of the universal set U satisfies this condition. Hence we write $\bigcap_{A \in \mathfrak{F}} A = \bigcap \mathfrak{F} = \bigcap \emptyset = U$. Similarly, there are no elements which satisfy $x \in A$ for some $A \in \emptyset$, so that we also write $\bigcup_{A \in \mathfrak{F}} A = \bigcup \emptyset = \emptyset$.

We note that in dealing with arbitrary unions and intersections, we cannot consider them as operations in the sense of universal algebra, since universal algebra is limited to finitary operations. Some of the results extend to infinitary operations, but in general, the theory of universal algebras has not been completely developed for such operations.

We can now extend the associative, commutative and distributive laws to arbitrary families of sets. Thus let the family $\mathfrak{F}$ be partitioned in subfamilies $\mathfrak{F}_i$ and denote a generic element of $\mathfrak{F}_i$ by A_{ij}. Then the general associative law states:

$$\bigcap_{A_\alpha \in \mathfrak{F}} A_\alpha = \bigcap_i \bigcap_j A_{ij}.$$

This law includes commutativity, since the order of elements does not enter into an indexing.

The simplest form of the infinite distributive law is the case when a single set is distributed over a family as given in the two following formulas:

(*i*) $A \cap \bigcup_\alpha A_\alpha = \bigcup_\alpha (A \cap A_\alpha)$,
(*ii*) $A \cup \bigcap_\alpha A_\alpha = \bigcap_\alpha (A \cup A_\alpha)$.

Similarly, the de Morgan laws extend to arbitrary families of sets as given by:

(*iii*) $\bigcup(_\alpha A_\alpha)' = \bigcap_\alpha A'_\alpha$,
(*iv*) $(\bigcap_\alpha A_\alpha)' = \bigcup_\alpha A'_\alpha$.

2-15. RINGS OF SETS

We conclude this chapter with a discussion of the algebra of sets and its relation to the theory of rings. We recall that a ring is an algebra with two binary, one nullary and one unary operation such that it is a group with respect to one of the binary operations, the nullary operation and the unary operation. Thus it is a system $\langle R, +, \cdot, 0, - \rangle$ where $+$ and $\cdot$ are the binary operations, 0 is the identity for $+$, and $-$ is the inverse operation for $+$. It then satisfies the following laws:

Definion 2-7. *A ring is an algebra* $\langle R, +, \cdot, 0, - \rangle$ *which satisfies:*

R1: $x + y = y + x$,

R2: $x + (y + z) = (x + y) + z$,

R3: $x + 0 = 0 + x = x$,

R4: $(-x) + x = x + (-x) = 0$,

R5: $x \cdot (y \cdot z) = (x \cdot y) \cdot z$,

R6: $x \cdot (y + z) = (x \cdot y) + (x \cdot z)$.

Conditions *R2–R4* state that $\langle R, +, 0, - \rangle$ is a group while *R1* states that this group is commutative. *R5* is the associative law of multiplication and *R6* is the distributive law. The ring is itself called **commutative** if its multiplication is commutative; *i.e.*:

$$R7: \; x \cdot y = y \cdot x.$$

A ring is called **idempotent** if it satisfies:

$$R8: \; x \cdot x = x \; \forall \; x \in R.$$

Finally a ring is called a **ring with identity** if it has a multiplicative identity; *i.e.*, an element e such that:

$$R9: \; x \cdot e = e \cdot x = x \; \forall \; x \in R.$$

For our purposes, the most important rings are those which are idempotent; *i.e.*, satisfy *R1–R8*. Such rings are called **Boolean rings**. A Boolean ring need not have an identity, as we shall see shortly. However, in a Boolean ring the commutative law is redundant, so that *R7* may be eliminated. The proof is left to the exercises. Finally in a Boolean ring each element is its own additive inverse; *i.e.*, $a + a = 0 \; \forall \; a$, so that we may write $-a = a$. Hence the additive inverse operation $a \to -a$ is the identity mapping on R. Using $2a$ for $a + a$, we also say that every element of R has characteristic 2, or that R has characteristic 2. The proof is left to the exercises.

Our principal result now states:

Theorem 2-13. *If U is any set, then the power set of U, $\mathfrak{P}(U)$, is a Boolean ring with respect to the operations of symmetric difference and intersection; i.e.,* $\langle \mathfrak{P}(U), \Delta, \cap, \emptyset, - \rangle$ *where* $-A = A$.

Proof. *R1:* $A \,\Delta\, B = B \,\Delta\, A$ follows from the symmetry of $A \,\Delta\, B$ in A and B.

$$\begin{aligned} R2: \; (A \,\Delta\, B) \,\Delta\, C &= \{[(A \cap B') \cup (A' \cap B)] \cap C'\} \\ &\quad \cup \{[(A \cap B') \cup (A' \cap B)]' \cap C\} \\ &= (A \cap B' \cap C') \cup (A' \cap B \cap C') \cup [(A \cap B')' \\ &\quad \cap (A' \cap B)' \cap C] \\ &= (A \cap B' \cap C') \cup (A' \cap B \cap C') \cup [(A' \cup B) \\ &\quad \cap (A \cup B') \cap C] \\ &= (A \cap B' \cap C') \cup (A' \cap B \cap C') \cup (A' \cap A \cap C) \\ &\quad \cup (A' \cap B' \cap C) \cup (A \cap B \cap C) \cup (B' \cap B \cap C) \\ &= (A \cap B' \cap C') \cup (A' \cap B \cap C') \cup (A' \cap B' \cap C) \\ &\quad \cup (A \cap B \cap C). \end{aligned}$$

But the latter is symmetric in A, B and C, so that the associative law follows.

$$R3:\ A \,\Delta\, \emptyset = (A \cap \emptyset') \cup (A' \cap \emptyset) = A.$$

$$R4:\ A \,\Delta\, A = (A \cap A') \cup (A' \cap A) = \emptyset.$$

Hence the additive inverse of A is A itself.

R5: is simply the associative law for $\cap$.

$$R6: \quad A \cap (B \,\Delta\, C) = A \cap [(B \cap C') \cup (B' \cap C)]$$
$$= (A \cap B \cap C') \cup (A \cap B' \cap C).$$

Similarly:

$$\begin{aligned}(A \cap B) \,\Delta\, (A \cap C) &= [(A \cap B) \cap (A \cap C)'] \cup [(A \cap B)' \cap (A \cap C)] \\ &= [A \cap B \cap (A' \cup C')] \cup [(A' \cup B') \cap A \cap C] \\ &= (A \cap B \cap A') \cup (A \cap B \cap C') \cup (A' \cap A \cap C) \\ &\quad \cup (B' \cup A \cap C), \\ &= (A \cap B \cap C') \cup (A \cap B' \cap C).\end{aligned}$$

Hence

$$(A \cap B) \,\Delta\, (A \cap C) = A \cap (B \,\Delta\, C).$$

R7: is the commutative law for $\cap$.
R8: is the idempotent law for $\cap$.

Corollary 1. $\langle \mathfrak{P}(U), \Delta, \cap, \emptyset, -, U \rangle$ *is a ring with identity.*

Proof. $A \cap U = A$. Hence U is an identity with respect to $\cap$ as multiplication.

Corollary 2. $\langle \mathfrak{P}(U), \leftrightarrow, \cup, U, -, \emptyset \rangle$ *is a ring with identity under equivalence and union.*

Proof. Use duality.

Corollary 3. $\langle \mathfrak{P}(U), \Delta, \emptyset, - \rangle$ *is a commutative group.*

In general we have studied the set of all subsets of a fixed set U as the carrier of our algebraic structure. On the other hand, we can also obtain a ring by taking subrings of the ring of theorem 11. Thus a subring is a subset closed under Δ and $\cap$ and containing $\emptyset$. However, it is sufficient to consider closure under Δ and $\cap$, since $\emptyset = A \,\Delta\, A$. Therefore if U is any set, then we call a family $\mathfrak{F}$ of subsets a **ring of sets** of U if it contains the symmetric difference and intersection of any two of its members. However, we also note that a subring will also be closed under union, since $A \cup B = (A \cap B) \,\Delta\, (A \,\Delta\, B)$, (exercise). Hence a ring of sets is also closed under union. The converse is not true, and a family of sets closed under union and intersection alone is not a subring of the Boolean ring of all subsets of U. In general, a family of sets closed under union and intersection is called a lattice of sets (see: Chapter 4). It should also be noted that a ring of subsets of U need not contain U itself. Thus, for example, if U is an infinite set, then the family of finite subsets if closed under symmetric difference and intersection, but does not contain U. It is therefore a ring of sets, but not closed under the multiplicative identity. It is therefore not a "subring with identity." Finally a family of subsets of U which contains U and is closed under complements as well as unions and intersections is called a **field of sets**. It is clearly a subalgebra of the complete algebra of sets, and is, as we shall see later, a subboolean algebra.

EXERCISES

1. Prove that: $A \cup B = (A \cap B) \Delta (A \Delta B)$.
2. Prove that in an idempotent ring every element is its own additive inverse. (Hint: apply the idempotent law to $x + x$.)
3. Prove that an idempotent ring is commutative (*Hint*: apply the idempotent law to $x + y$.)
4. Show that if $\mathfrak{F}$ and $\mathfrak{S}$ are two indexed families of sets indexed with the same index set I and $A_i \subseteq B_i$ for $A_i \in \mathfrak{F}$ and $B_i \in \mathfrak{S}$, $i \in I$, then:
   (*i*) $\bigcup_i A_i \subseteq \bigcup_i B_i$;
   (*ii*) $\bigcap_i A_i \subseteq \bigcap_i B_i$.
5. If $\mathfrak{F}$ is a family of sets and $\mathfrak{S}$ is a subfamily, show that:
   (*i*) $\bigcup_{\mathfrak{S}} A \subseteq \bigcup_{\mathfrak{F}} A$;
   (*ii*) $\bigcap_{\mathfrak{F}} A \subseteq \bigcap_{\mathfrak{S}} A$.
6. Prove the distributive laws (*i*) and (*ii*) of section 14.
7. Prove the de Morgan laws (*iii*) and (*iv*).
8. Prove the general distributive law: $(\bigcup_i A_i) \cap (\bigcup_j B_j) = \bigcup_{\langle i,j \rangle} (A_i \cap B_j)$ where the right hand side is indexed over $I \times J$ where $i \in I$ and $j \in J$.
9. Prove the two following distributive laws for subtraction onto union and intersection:
   (*i*) $(A \cup B) - C = (A - C) \cup (B - C)$;
   (*ii*) $(A \cap B) - C = (A - C) \cap (B - C)$.
10. Prove the general de Morgan laws for subtraction onto union and intersection:
   (*i*) $A - (B \cup C) = (A - B) \cap (A - C)$;
   (*ii*) $A - (B \cap C) = (A - B) \cup (A - C)$.
11. Extend exercises 9 and 10 to arbitrary unions and intersections.
12. State the duals of exercises 9 and 10.
13. Given two sets A and B in $\mathfrak{P}(U)$, show that using the operation of union alone, it is possible to construct four distinct sets, but no more. Hence subtraction cannot be defined in terms of union and intersection alone.
14. Given two sets A and B, show that it is possible to generate six different sets

from them by using the subtraction operation alone, but that all sixteen sets of Table 2-1 can be constructed if A, B and U are given.

15. Prove that the implication operation $A \to B$ satisfies:

(*i*) $(A \to B) \to A = A$;
(*ii*) $(A \to B) \to B = (B \to A) \to A$;
(*iii*) $A \to (B \to C) = B \to (A \to C)$.

16. Prove that:

(*i*) $U \to A = A$;
(*ii*) $A \to U = U$;
(*iii*) $\varnothing \to A = U$;
(*iv*) $A \to \varnothing = A'$;
(*v*) $A \subseteq B \Leftrightarrow A \to B = U$.

17. Prove that:

(*i*) $(A \to B) \cup (B \to A) = U$;
(*ii*) $A \subseteq A \to B$;
(*iii*) $B \cup (A \to B) = U$;
(*iv*) $B \cap (A \to B) = A$;
(*v*) $A' \subseteq (A \to B)$.

18. Show that A' may be characterized as the greatest lower bound of all sets such that $A \cup X = U$, *i.e.*, $A' = \bigcap \{X | (X \subseteq U) \wedge (A \cup X = U)\}$. State the dual.

19. Show that $A - B = B'_A = \bigcup \{X | (X \subseteq A) \wedge (X \cap B = \varnothing)\}$.

20. Give a characterization of $A \to B$ dual to that of subtraction in exercise 19.

21. Prove that:

(*i*) $A \leftrightarrow B = (A \to B) \cap (B \to A)$;
(*ii*) $(A - B) \cup (B - A) = A \Delta B$;
(*iii*) $A \Delta B = (A \cup B) \cap (A|B)$;
(*iv*) $A \leftrightarrow B = (A \cap B) \cup (A||B)$;
(*v*) $(A \leftrightarrow B)' = A \Delta B$;
(*vi*) $A \to B = (B - A)'$.

22. Reduce each of the following to one of the fundamental sets of Table 2-1:

(*a*) $(A - B)|(A \to B)$;
(*b*) $A \cap (B - A')$;
(*c*) $A \to A$;
(*d*) $(A \cup B) \Delta (A \cap B)$.

3

TRANSFINITE NUMBERS

3-1. CARDINAL NUMBERS

In this chapter we combine some of the theory of universal algebra with set theory. Specifically, we first consider abstract sets without operations and apply the concept of isomorphism to the resulting algebras. This leads to the concept of the cardinality of a set. We introduce an ordering relation between cardinals, and an arithmetic for combining them which is an extension of the arithmetic of the natural numbers. Then, later, we consider sets which are relational systems with a linear order relation. Again we study isomorphisms between such ordered sets, which gives us a theory of order types in the general case, and the theory of ordinal numbers in a special case. We again develop an arithmetic and an ordering for ordinals and order types in general. Finally, we relate the theories of cardinal and ordinal numbers to each other, and show how cardinals may be treated as special types of ordinals.

We begin by treating a set A as an algebra $\langle A, \emptyset \rangle$ with the empty set of operations. Thus we are dealing with pure sets without regard to any structure or relations placed on them. A subalgebra, for example, is simply a subset. The most important concept is that of an isomorphism, which in this case reduces to a one-to-one correspondence from one set A onto a second set B. In this case we say that ***A* and *B* have the same number of elements.** We write $A \sim B$, and say either that *A and B have **the same cardinality*** or are **equivalent.** This concept of equivalence is then a relation between sets defined over the class of all sets, using the term *class* in the von Neumann-Bernays sense. It is therefore not a relation in the strict sense of set theory, but a class relation. Nevertheless, it is reflexive, symmetric and transitive, and is therefore an equivalence relation. As such, it partitions the class of all sets into mutually disjoint equivalence classes of sets such that all sets in a given equivalence class "have the same number of elements." We therefore associate with every set an equivalence class which is called its **cardinality, cardinal number** or **power.** Hence the cardinality of a set is not defined directly, but is defined in terms of the relation "having the same cardinality." Following the lead of Cantor, we denote the cardinality of a set A by $\bar{\bar{A}}$, although some authors use $c(A)$. We also use lower case German $\mathfrak{a}$, $\mathfrak{b}$, $\mathfrak{c}$, for arbitrary cardinals with certain exceptions. Therefore, *two sets* will *have the same cardinality if and only if there exists a one-to-one mapping from one set onto the other; i.e.*, $A \sim B$ has the some meaning as $\bar{\bar{A}} = \bar{\bar{B}}$.

The simplest case is that of the set $\mathbf{P}_n$ of the *first n positive integers*, $\mathbf{P}_n = \{1, 2, \ldots, n\}$. In this case we denote the cardinality by n itself, so that $\bar{\bar{\mathbf{P}}}_n = n$. Another set A will have cardinality n if and only if there is a one-to-one correspondence between A and $\mathbf{P}_n$; *i.e.*, if and only if A can be indexed by $\mathbf{P}_n$. Hence its elements can be designated by $a_1, a_2, \ldots, a_n$. We also say that A is *finite* (*inductively finite*) if and only if it is equivalent to a set $\mathbf{P}_n$ for some natural number n. Later we give an alternate characterization of "finiteness."

The next simplest case is that of the set of all positive integers, $\mathbf{P} = \{1, 2, 3, \ldots\}$. Its cardinality is denoted by the Hebrew letter $\aleph_0$; *i.e.*, $\bar{\bar{\mathbf{P}}} = \aleph_0$. Any other set A will have cardinality $\aleph_0$ if and only if there exists a one-to-one correspondence between $\mathbf{P}$ and A; *i.e.*, there exists an indexing of A by the positive integers. The elements of A can therefore be written $a_1, a_2, a_3, \ldots$ We also say that A is denumerable (or denumerably infinite) in this case. More generally, the process of establishing a one-to-one correspondence between either $\mathbf{P}_n$ or $\mathbf{P}$ and a set A is called a counting process by members of A, and A is called **countable.**

As examples of denumerable sets, we first consider the set of natural numbers $\mathbf{N} = \{0, 1, 2, \ldots\}$. This set has $\aleph_0$ elements since the function $f(i) = i + 1$ establishes a one-to-one correspondence between $\mathbf{N}$ and $\mathbf{P}$. We note, however, that $\mathbf{P}$ is itself a proper subset of $\mathbf{N}$, so that we have an example of a proper subset of a set which has the same cardinality as the set itself. In a sense the cardinality is a measure of the size of a set, but this measure is not fine enough to distinguish between sets and proper subsets, so that it is not necessarily true that $A \subset B$ implies A has fewer elements than B.

Next the set $\mathbf{E} = \{2, 4, 6, \ldots\}$ of even positive integers has cardinality $\aleph_0$, since the indexing $f(2i) = i$ *counts* $\mathbf{E}$. Similarly, the set of odd integers, $\mathbf{O} = \{1, 3, 5, \ldots\}$ also has $\aleph_0$ elements. We therefore see that the set $\mathbf{P}$ has two disjoint subsets, both of which have cardinality $\aleph_0$, while their union is $\mathbf{P}$ itself.

An even "larger set" is the set of all positive rational numbers, $\mathbf{Q}^+$. This set also has cardinality $\aleph_0$. To establish a counting of $\mathbf{Q}^+$ we form an array of the form:

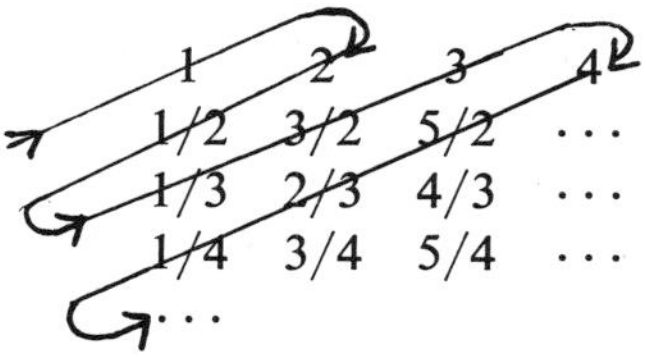

We then index this array by following the arrows obtaining the linear ordering: 1, 2, 1/2, 1/3, 3/2, 3, 4, 5/2, . . .

A similar argument applies to the set of all pairs of positive integers, $\mathbf{P} \times \mathbf{P}$. We leave it to the reader to show that the set, $\mathbf{Z}^2$, of pairs of integers, positive, negative or zero, also has cardinality $\aleph_o$. Hence that set of lattice points of the plane is denumerable.

The next cardinality of importance is the cardinality of the set of all real numbers which we denote by $\mathfrak{c}$; *i.e.*, $\bar{\bar{\mathbf{R}}} = \mathfrak{c}$. The first significant result is to show that $\mathfrak{c}$ is not the same as $\aleph_o$; *i.e.*, that the set of real numbers is not denumerably infinite. The proof goes back to Cantor and is known as Cantor's diagonal process. The method of contradiction is used. We assume that there is an enumeration of the real numbers between 0 and 1 by means of the positive integers. We assume that each real number is written in decimal expansion as a non-ending decimal, so that distinct real numbers have distinct expansions. For example, we write the ending decimal, $0.\, x_1 x_2 \cdots x_n$ as $0.\, x_1 x_2 \cdots (x_n - 1) \cdots (x_n \neq 0)$. The real numbers are then listed according to their indexing by $\mathbf{P}$ as:

$$x_1 = 0.\, x_{11} x_{12} x_{13} \cdots$$

$$x_2 = 0.\, x_{21} x_{22} x_{23} \cdots$$

$$x_3 = 0.\, x_{31} x_{32} x_{33} \cdots$$

$$\vdots$$

We now let $y = 0.\, y_1 y_2 y_3 \cdots$ where y_i is any digit different from x_{ii}, say $y_i = x_{ii} + 1$. It is clear that y is a real number between 0 and 1 and distinct from every x_i in the listing. We conclude that the listing did not contain every real number between 0 and 1 as assumed. Therefore the set of real numbers between 0 and 1 cannot be denumerable. Finally, we show that the set of all real numbers has the same cardinality as the set $\mathbf{X}$ of real numbers between 0 and 1. To establish this fact we need to find a one-to-one correspondence between $\mathbf{R}$ and $\mathbf{X}$. But this is accomplished by the mapping $\{\langle x, \tan \frac{1}{2}\pi(2x - 1)\rangle | x \in \mathbf{X}\}$; therefore we have shown that $\bar{\bar{\mathbf{R}}} = \bar{\bar{\mathbf{X}}} = \mathfrak{c}$.

We next note that the cardinality of the set of points in the unit square is also $\mathfrak{c}$. This is the set of pairs of real numbers between 0 and 1; *i.e.*, $\{\langle x, y\rangle | x, y \in \mathbf{X}\}$. We can write x and y in decimal form as

$$x = 0.\, x_1 x_2 x_3 \cdots$$

$$y = 0.\, y_1 y_2 y_3 \cdots$$

We then establish the mapping:

$$\langle x, y\rangle \longleftrightarrow z = 0.\, x_1 y_1 x_2 y_2 x_3 y_3 \cdots$$

between number pairs and single numbers. Hence if $\mathbf{X} = \{x \in \mathbf{R} | 0 < x < 1\}$, then $\mathbf{X}^2 \sim \mathbf{X}$; *i.e.*, the cardinality of the set of points on the real interval $\mathbf{X}$ is the same as that of the set of points in the unit square. We leave it to the reader to show that the cardinality of the set of all points of the real plane, or of $\mathbf{R}^n$, is still $\mathfrak{c}$. Our next step is to establish the existence of cardinals greater than $\mathfrak{c}$. For this purpose, we first define a relative size for cardinals.

3-2. MAGNITUDE OF CARDINALS

In order to establish a relative magnitude among cardinals, we say that *one cardinal* $\mathfrak{a}$ *is less than or equal to a second* $\mathfrak{b}$, *if there exist sets* A *and* B *with* $\bar{\bar{A}} = \mathfrak{a}$ *and* $\bar{\bar{B}} = \mathfrak{b}$ *such that* A *is equivalent to a subset of* B; *i.e., there exists* $B_1 \subseteq B$ *such that* $A \sim B_1$. We then write $\mathfrak{a} \leq \mathfrak{b}$. If $\mathfrak{a} \leq \mathfrak{b}$ *but* $\mathfrak{a} \neq \mathfrak{b}$, *then we say* $\mathfrak{a} < \mathfrak{b}$. We note that this definition of order is compatible with the definition of order for natural numbers given by: $m \leq n \Longleftrightarrow$ there exists $k \in \mathbf{N}$ such that $n = m + k$, (exercise).

Our first major problem is to show that this definition of order is in fact an order relation. First, the identity map on any set A shows that $\bar{\bar{A}} = \bar{\bar{A}}$, which is the reflexive law. We leave it is an exercise to show that $\leq$ is transitive. It therefore remains to establish antisymmetry: $\mathfrak{a} \leq \mathfrak{b}$ and $\mathfrak{b} \leq \mathfrak{a}$ imply $\mathfrak{a} = \mathfrak{b}$. These results will show that $\leq$ is a partial order relation for cardinals. We leave until later the problem of showing that any two cardinal numbers are comparable. The antisymmetry law for inequality of cardinals was first established by Bernstein during the latter part of the nineteenth century and is known as the Bernstein Theorem.

Theorem 3-1. *If* A *and* B *are two sets such that there exist subsets* $A_1 \subseteq A$ *and* $B_1 \subseteq B$, *such that* $A \sim B_1$ *and* $B \sim A_1$, *then* A *and* B *are equivalent.*

Proof. By hypothesis $A \sim B_1$ and $B \sim A_1$ so that there exist one-to-one mappings f and g from A onto B_1 and from B onto A_1 respectively. Let $x \in X$. Then either $x \in A - A_1$ or $x \in A_1$. In the first case x has no inverse under the mapping g, while in the second case it has an inverse image $g^{-1}(x)$ in B. In the second case, either $g^{-1}(x) \in B - B_1$ in which case $g^{-1}(x)$ has no inverse image under f^{-1}, or $g^{-1}(x) \in B_1$. Again, in the latter case there exists a unique inverse image $f^{-1}(g^{-1}(x))$ of $g^{-1}(x)$ under f^{-1}. Again either $f^{-1}(g^{-1}(x))$ is in $A - A_1$ or A_1, and hence has no inverse image under g^{-1}, or there exists a unique inverse $g^{-1}(f^{-1}(g^{-1}(x)))$. We call the elements $g^{-1}(x), f^{-1}(g^{-1}(x))$, $g^{-1}(f^{-1}(g^{-1}(x))), \ldots$ the ancestors of x. There are then three mutually exclusive cases possible:

(*a*) either x has an even number of ancestors, (*b*) x has an odd number of ancestors, or (*c*) x has an infinite number of ancestors.

These three cases form a partition of A into three subsets which we designate as A_a, A_b, and A_c. Similarly, we may partition B into three mutually exclusive and exhaustive sets B_a, B_b and B_c consisting of those elements of B having (*a*) an even number of ancestors, (*b*) an odd number of ancestors, and (*c*) having an infinite number of ancestors. (Hence the ancestry of $y \in B$ consists of $f^{-1}(y), g^{-1}(f^{-1}(y), \ldots)$ If now $x \in A_a$; *i.e.*, x has an even number of ancestors, then $f(x)$ will have an odd number of ancestors; *i.e.*, $f(x) \in B_b$. Hence f is a one-to-one mapping from all of A_a onto all of B_b. Next, if $x \in A_b$, then x has an odd number of ancestors and $g^{-1}(x) \in B_a$. Then g^{-1} is a one-to-one mapping from A_b onto B_a. In the final case, $x \in A_c$ and x has an infinite ancestry. In this case, $f(x)$ also has infinite ancestry and is therefore in B_c. Thus f is a one-to-one mapping from A_c onto B_c. We therefore define the single mapping h by:

$$h(x) = \begin{cases} g^{-1}(x) & \text{if } x \in A_b, \\ f(x) & \text{if } x \in A_a \cup A_c. \end{cases}$$

h will then be defined from all of A onto all of B and will be one-to-one. Hence it defines an equivalence between A and B. Therefore $A \sim B$.

Using this concept of order among cardinals, we can now arrange the cardinals according to magnitude. We begin with the cardinal 0, which is the cardinality of the empty set; *i.e.*, $0 = \bar{\bar{\emptyset}}$. We then have the sequence of finite cardinals $1, 2, 3, \ldots, n, \ldots$ corresponding to the sets $\mathbf{P}_n$ for any positive integer n. The same symbol, n, is therefore used interchangeably for the positive integer n and for the finite cardinal n. (We also note that $\mathbf{P}_n \sim \{0, 1, 2, \ldots, (n - 1)\}$ so that we could just as well have used the first n natural numbers to represent the finite cardinal number n.) Following the sequence of finite cardinals, we have $\aleph_o$. Clearly $n \leq \aleph_o$ for any finite n, since the identity map maps $\mathbf{P}_n$ into $\mathbf{P}$. On the other hand, there does not exist a one-to-one map from $\mathbf{P}$ into $\mathbf{P}_n$ for any finite n, so that $n < \aleph_o$. It therefore remains to show that there is no other cardinal greater than all finite n and $< \aleph_o$; *i.e.*, that $\aleph_o$ is the smallest infinite cardinal. Thus we wish to show that if a set A is infinite, then it must contain some denumerably infinite subset A_1, so that $\aleph_o \leq \bar{\bar{A}}$. Heretofore the word "finite" has meant "inductively finite" in the sense that a set is finite if and only if it is equivalent to $\mathbf{P}_n$ for some n. "Infinite" then means "not finite." We now give an alternative definition of finiteness due to Dedekind and known as Dedekind's finiteness condition. A set A is called **reflexively finite** (Dedekind finite), *if and only if there does not exist an equivalence between A and a proper subset of A*. We then have the following theorem.

Theorem 3-2. *A set A is infinite if and only if there exists a proper subset $A_1 \subset A$ such that $A \sim A_1$.*

Proof. (*i*) Let A be inductively infinite; *i.e*,, there does not exist a one-to-one mapping from A onto $\mathbf{P}_n$ for any n. Let $a_1 \in A$ be any element of A, and let $A_1 = \{a_1\}$. Since A is infinite, A_1 does not exhaust A; *i.e.*, $A - A_1 \neq$

$\emptyset$. Hence there exists $a_2 \in A - A_1$. Let $A_2 = \{a_1, a_2\}$ where a_1 and a_2 are distinct. Proceeding by induction we assume A_n is defined and consists of n distinct elements. Furthermore, by hypothesis A_n does not exhaust A, so that $A - A_n \neq \emptyset$. Hence there exists $a_{n+1} \in A - A_n$. We then define $A_{n+1} = A_n \cup \{a_{n+1}\}$. Note that the choice of an a_{n+1} in $A - A_n$ for the infinite sequence of A_n's requires the axiom of choice. We now let $B = \{a_1, a_2, a_3, \ldots\}$ be the union of the sets A_n. B is now a denumerably infinite set of distinct elements contained in A. The mapping $a_n \to a_{n+1}$ is now a mapping from B into its proper subset $B_1 = B - \{a_1\}$. If $A = B$, then this mapping is a reflexive mapping from A into a proper subset of itself. Otherwise, we extend this mapping to all of A by mapping every element of A not in B onto itself, so that we again obtain a mapping of A onto $A - \{a_1\}$. In any case, we have established an equivalence between A and a proper subset of A, so that A is infinite in the sense of Dedekind.

(*ii*) Now let A be reflexively infinite. Then there exists $A_1 \subset A$ such that $A \sim A_1$. Let f be a one-to-one mapping from A onto A_1. Since $A_1 \subset A$, there exists $a_0 \in A - A_1$. Let $a_1 = f(a_0)$, $a_2 = f(a_1), \ldots, a_n = f(a_{n-1}), \ldots$, and let $B = \{a_1, a_2, a_3, \ldots\}$. We now assert that B is equivalent to $\mathbf{N}$. We therefore need to prove that $a_k \neq a_n$ for $k \neq n$. Assume, on the contrary, that $a_k = a_n$ for $k \neq n$ and we may as well assume $k < n$. We now let k and n be the least k and n such that $k < n$ and $a_k = a_n$. First we note that $k \neq 0$; *i.e.*, $a_0 \neq a_n$, for $a_0 \in A - A_1$, whereas each $a_n = f(a_{n-1}) \in A_1$ for $n \neq 0$. But since $k \neq 0$, $a_k = f(a_{k-1})$ while $a_n = f(a_{n-1})$. But the one-to-oneness of f now implies that $a_{k-1} = a_{n-1}$, contrary to the fact that k and n were the least k and n such that $a_k = a_n$ for $k < n$. Hence we conclude that A contains the denumerably infinite subset B. It therefore cannot be equivalent to $\mathbf{P}_n$ for any n.

Corollary 1. *Every infinite set contains a denumerably infinite subset.*

Corollary 2. $\aleph_0 \leq \mathfrak{a}$ *for any infinite cardinal* $\mathfrak{a}$; *i.e.*, $\aleph_0$ *is the smallest infinite cardinal.*

Our next result now establishes the existence of cardinals greater than $\aleph_0$. In fact, it establishes the existence of a denumerably infinite collection of infinite cardinals.

Theorem 3-3. *If* $\mathfrak{a}$ *is any cardinal, and if A is any set with cardinality* $\mathfrak{a}$, *then the power set of A has cardinality greater than* $\mathfrak{a}$; *i.e.*, $\overline{\overline{A}} < \overline{\overline{\mathfrak{P}(A)}}$ *for any set A.*

Proof. We know that $\overline{\overline{A}} \leq \overline{\overline{\mathfrak{P}(A)}}$ since the identity mapping $a \to \{a\} \in \mathfrak{P}(A)$ is a one-to-one mapping from A into $\mathfrak{P}(A)$. It therefore remains to show that $\overline{\overline{A}} \neq \overline{\overline{\mathfrak{P}(A)}}$ by showing that there cannot exist a one-to-one mapping from

A onto $\mathfrak{P}(A)$, Assuming that such a mapping f exists, we let $N = \{x \in A | x \notin f(x)\}$ where $f(x)$ is the subset of A associated with x. Let $n = f^{-1}(N)$. n exists since we assumed that f was one-to-one and onto. Furthermore, N exists by the axiom of abstraction. If now $n \in N$, then $n \notin f(n) = N$ which is a contradiction. On the other hand, $n \in N$ implies $n \notin N$ which is also a contradiction. Hence we conclude that no one-to-one mapping f can exist from A onto all of $\mathfrak{P}(A)$. Therefore $\bar{\bar{A}} < \overline{\overline{\mathfrak{P}(A)}}$.

Using this theorem, we can now generate cardinals greater than any given cardinal by simply taking the cardinal of the power set of a set with the given cardinal. Starting with the infinite cardinal $\aleph_0$ which is the cardinality of the set $\mathbf{N}$ of natural numbers, we can form the denumerably infinite sequence of distinct cardinals, $\bar{\bar{\mathbf{N}}}$, $\overline{\overline{\mathfrak{P}(\mathbf{N})}}$, $\overline{\overline{\mathfrak{P}(\mathfrak{P}(\mathbf{N}))}}$, $\overline{\overline{\mathfrak{P}(\mathfrak{P}(\mathfrak{P}(\mathbf{N})))}}$, . . . We now give a lemma which gives an alternate characterization of $\mathfrak{P}(A)$ in terms of functions. For this purpose we let $\mathbf{2} = \{0, 1\}$. $\mathbf{2}^A$ then stands for the set of all mapping defined over A into $\mathbf{2}$. We then have:

Lemma. $\mathfrak{P}(A) \sim \mathbf{2}^A$.

Proof. Let S be any subset of A, and let f_S be defined by:

$$f(x) = \begin{cases} 1 \text{ if } x \in A. \\ 0 \text{ if } x \notin A. \end{cases}$$

Then f is a function defined over A into $\mathbf{2} = \{0, 1\}$. It is called the **characteristic function** of the set S and is a member of $\mathbf{2}^A$. Conversely, given any $f \in \mathbf{2}^A$, we can determine a subset S_f of A defined by:

$$S_f = \{x | f(x) = 1\}.$$

The correspondences $S \rightarrow f_s$ and $f \rightarrow S_f$ then form a bijection from $\mathfrak{P}(A)$ onto $\mathbf{2}^A$ as required.

We apply this lemma to show that the second member of our list of cardinals above is the cardinality $\mathfrak{c}$ of the set of real numbers.

Theorem 3-4. $\overline{\overline{\mathfrak{P}(\mathbf{N})}} = \overline{\overline{\mathbf{2}^N}} = \mathfrak{c}$.

Proof. We let $\mathbf{X} = \{x \in \mathbf{R} | 0 < x < 1\}$ be the set of real numbers between 0 and 1. We have already seen that $\bar{\bar{\mathbf{X}}} = \mathfrak{c}$. We now let each x in $\mathbf{X}$ be expanded into a non-ending binary expansion of the form:

$$x = 0.\, x_1 x_2 x_3 \cdots \qquad \text{where}$$

$x_i \in \mathbf{2}$. We have used non-ending expansions to avoid the possibility of two distinct expansions for the same real number. Thus an ending binary decimal would be written $0.\, x_1 x_2 \cdots x_n = 0.\, x_1 x_2 \cdots (x_n - 1)\, 111 \cdots (x_n \neq 0)$.

But now each binary decimal determines a function over the set of positive integers into the set $\mathbf{2} = \{0, 1\}$, given by $f(n) = x_n$. Conversely, every characteristic function on the set of positive integers determines a unique binary decimal between 0 and 1. Hence $\mathbf{X} \sim \mathbf{2}^{\mathbf{N}}$.

Thus $\mathfrak{c}$ is the cardinality of the power set of the set of natural numbers (or positive integers). The next cardinal $\mathfrak{f}$ in the list, $\overline{\overline{\mathfrak{P}(\mathfrak{P}(\mathbf{N}))}}$, is therefore the same as the cardinality of the power set of $\mathbf{R}$; *i.e.*, $\mathfrak{f} = \overline{\overline{\mathfrak{P}(\mathbf{R})}}$. $\mathfrak{P}(\mathbf{R})$ is the set of all subsets of real numbers. It is equivalent to the set of all functions defined on the real numbers with values in $\mathbf{2}$. We shall also see that it is equivalent to the set of all real functions of a real variable. Therefore we know that there are more real functions than real numbers.

Three main questions now remain regarding our sequence of cardinal numbers. First, do there exist cardinals between the elements of our sequence? Second, are there cardinals greater than any of these? And third, are there cardinals incomparable to these? The second question is perhaps the easiest to answer, and we shall see in the next section that such cardinals do exist. The third question is answered by use of the axiom of choice and we leave it until later. The most intriguing and difficult is the first question. The first case is the existence of a cardinal strictly between $\aleph_0$ and $\mathfrak{c}$. We call the real line the **continuum**, so that this question can be formulated in the form: *do there exist subsets of the real continuum with cardinality greater than* $\aleph_0$ *and smaller than* $\mathfrak{c}$? The assertion that there are none is known as **the continuum hypothesis** and has bothered mathematicians since it was first proposed by Cantor. The more general denial of the existence of other cardinals between the other members of our infinite sequence is known as the **generalized continuum hypothesis**. Cantor's opinion was that the continuum hypothesis was true, but he was unable to prove it. The situation remained essentially unchanged until 1938 when Gödel proved his now-famous theorem on the consistency of the continuum hypothesis (*cf:* Gödel or Nagel and Newman). This states briefly that if the axioms of Zermelo-Fraenkel set theory without the axiom of choice are consistent, then they will remain consistent under the addition of the continuum hypothesis. More recently, in the 1960's, Cohen and others have shown that the question is essentially unanswerable within the confines of Zermelo-Fraenkel set theory. Specifically, Cohen has shown that the continuum hypothesis and the generalized continuum hypothesis are independent of the axioms I–X of Chapter 1 (*cf:* Cohen). They have thus established models for set theory satisfying axioms I–IX in which the axiom of choice and the continuum hypothesis are true and other models in which they are false. Therefore, whether to adopt the axiom of choice and the continuum hypothesis as further axioms of set theory depends on the needs of the mathematics to be developed. Both assumptions are consistent and independent (*cf also:* Scott).

EXERCISES

1. Show that the set of lattice points in the plane is denumerable; *i.e.*, $\overline{\overline{\mathbf{Z}^2}} = \aleph_o$.
2. Show that the set of points in the plane with both coordinates rational is denumerable; *i.e.*, $\overline{\overline{\mathbf{Q}^2}} = \aleph_o$.
3. Show that the set of points on any open interval, $a < x < b$, of the real line has cardinality $\mathfrak{c}$.
4. Show that the set of points on the real plane has cardinality $\mathfrak{c}$; *i.e.*, $\overline{\overline{\mathbf{R}^2}} = \mathfrak{c}$. Extend this result to $\overline{\overline{\mathbf{R}^n}} = \mathfrak{c}$.
5. Use the Bernstein Theorem to prove that the set of points in the interior of the unit circle has cardinality $\mathfrak{c}$.
6. Show that the cardinality of the set of points on the closed interval $\{x | 0 \leq x \leq 1\}$ is $\mathfrak{c}$.
7. Show that the definition of order for cardinal numbers is compatible with that of the natural numbers.
8. Prove that the relation $\leq$ for cardinals is transitive.
9. Show that **N** can be expressed as a denumerable union of denumerable disjoint sets.
10. Prove that $\overline{\overline{\mathbf{C}}} = \mathfrak{c}$, where **C** is the set of complex numbers.
11. If A is a denumerably infinite set, show that A contains a subset A_1 such that both A_1 and $A - A_1$ are infinite.
12. Show that a denumerable union of denumerable sets is denumerable.
13. Use Bernstein's Theorem to show that the denumerable union of disjoint finite sets is denumerable.
14. Use the preceding exercise to show that the number of polynomials in a single variable x with integral coeffecients is denumerable.

3-3. THE ARITHMETIC OF CARDINALS

Having defined an order relation for cardinals, we next introduce operations of addition, multiplication and exponentiation. To define the sum of two arbitrary cardinal numbers $\mathfrak{a}$ and $\mathfrak{b}$, we consider two disjoint sets A and B with cardinalities $\mathfrak{a}$ and $\mathfrak{b}$ respectively; *i.e.*, $\overline{\overline{A}} = \mathfrak{a}$ and $\overline{\overline{B}} = \mathfrak{b}$. Note that we can always assume A and B disjoint, since if they are not, we form two news sets $A_1 \sim A$ and $B_1 \sim B$ by subscripting the members with different subscripts. We now form the union $A \cup B$ and call its cardinality the **sum** $\mathfrak{a} + \mathfrak{b}$ of $\mathfrak{a}$ and $\mathfrak{b}$; *i.e.*,

$$\mathfrak{a} + \mathfrak{b} = \overline{\overline{A \cup B}} \textit{ where } \mathfrak{a} = \overline{\overline{A}} \textit{ and } \mathfrak{b} = \overline{\overline{B}}.$$

The existence follows from the existence of the union of A and B. To establish the uniqueness, let $A_1 \sim A$ and $B_1 \sim B$ where $A_1 \cap B_1 = A \cap B = \emptyset$. Then there exist one-to-one mappings g and h from A_1 and B_1 onto A and B, respectively. We now define the map f by:

$$f(x) = \begin{cases} g(x) \text{ for } x \in A_1 \\ h(x) \text{ for } x \in B_1. \end{cases}$$

It is then an exercise to show that f is a one-to-one map from $A_1 \cup B_1$ onto $A \cup B$. Thus $\overline{\overline{A_1 \cup B_1}} = \overline{\overline{A \cup B}}$. The arithmetic properties of addition follow from the properties of the union operation for sets. Thus addition is both commutative and associative; *i.e.*:

$$\mathfrak{a} + \mathfrak{b} = \mathfrak{b} + \mathfrak{a},$$

$$\mathfrak{a} + (\mathfrak{b} + \mathfrak{c}) = (\mathfrak{a} + \mathfrak{b}) + \mathfrak{c}.$$

We remark next that the definition of addition for cardinals is compatible with that of addition of the natural numbers. For example, if n and m are two finite cardinals, then they correspond to (finite) natural numbers, while their sum corresponds to the sum defined *inductively* for these same natural numbers. We leave the details to the exercises. However, all the arithmetic laws for addition of natural numbers do not carry over to arbitrary infinite cardinals. For example, we saw that the set $\mathbf{P}$ of positive integers and the set $\mathbf{N}$ of natural numbers have the same cardinality, while $\mathbf{N}$ is formed from $\mathbf{P}$ by adjoining 0. Therefore we have $\aleph_o = \overline{\overline{\mathbf{N}}} = \overline{\overline{\mathbf{P} \cup \{0\}}} = \overline{\overline{\mathbf{P}}} + \overline{\overline{\{0\}}} = \aleph_o + 1$; *i.e.*, $\aleph_o = \aleph_o + 1$ which cannot happen for finite cardinals. A second example is obtained by writing $\mathbf{N}$ as the union of the sets $\mathbf{E} = \{0, 2, 4, \ldots\}$ and $\mathbf{O} = \{1, 3, 5, \ldots\}$. Then we have: $\aleph_o = \overline{\overline{\mathbf{N}}} = \overline{\overline{\mathbf{E} \cup \mathbf{O}}} = \overline{\overline{\mathbf{E}}} + \overline{\overline{\mathbf{O}}} = \aleph_o + \aleph_o$. Both of these examples are special cases of the following more general result:

If $\mathfrak{a}$ and $\mathfrak{b}$ are two cardinals of which at least one is infinite, then $\mathfrak{a} + \mathfrak{b} = \max\{\mathfrak{a}, \mathfrak{b}\}$.

The proof requires the axiom of choice and we defer it until later. We note as a corollary that the cancellation law for arbitrary cardinals fails. Hence the equation $\mathfrak{a} + \mathfrak{X} = \mathfrak{b}$ does not in general have a unique solution, so that cardinals under addition form a semigroup but not a group.

Addition can be extended to arbitrary families of cardinals. Thus if $\{\mathfrak{a}_i\}$ is an indexed family of cardinals, then we consider a family of sets $\{A_i\}$ with cardinals $\overline{\overline{A}}_i = \mathfrak{a}_i$ where we may assume the A_i's disjoint (by adding an indexing to the elements of the A_i to distinguish between them, if necessary). The sum of the cardinals $\mathfrak{a}_i$ is then given by:

$$\textstyle\sum_i \mathfrak{a}_i = \overline{\overline{\bigcup_i A_i}}.$$

This definition is an extension of that for two cardinals and the existence and uniqueness follow along similar arguments as for two cardinals. Furthermore, the general associative law extends to arbitrary families of cardinals. We note that the definition is quite different from the sum of a series of real numbers. For example, as an infinite series, the sum $1 + 1 + 1 + \cdots$ fails to converge, and therefore does not define a real number. However, the cardinal sum is now $1 + 1 + 1 + \cdots = \aleph_0$.

We can now apply the concept of an infinite sum of infinite cardinals to our sequence of increasing cardinals $\overline{\overline{\mathbf{N}}}$, $\overline{\overline{\mathfrak{P}(\mathbf{N})}}$, $\overline{\overline{\mathfrak{P}(\mathfrak{P}(\mathbf{N}))}}, \ldots$ We form the sum of these cardinals by first forming the union, A, of the sets $\mathbf{N}$, $\mathfrak{P}(\mathbf{N})$, $\mathfrak{P}(\mathfrak{P}(\mathbf{N})), \ldots$ This union exists as we saw in Chapter 1. Furthermore, its cardinal, $\overline{\overline{A}}$, will be greater than any of the cardinals in our sequence. For A contains each of the sets of the sequence, so that its cardinal $\overline{\overline{A}}$ is greater than or equal to each of the individual cardinals in the sequence. But $\overline{\overline{A}}$ cannot equal any cardinal $\overline{\overline{\mathfrak{P}(\mathfrak{P}(\mathfrak{P}(\mathbf{N})\cdots)}}$, since the next one in the sequence is still greater. Hence $\overline{\overline{A}}$ is a new cardinal greater than any of those previously generated. We form the cardinal $\overline{\overline{\mathfrak{P}(A)}}$ and proceed via Theorem 3-3 to generate a new sequence of increasing cardinals. We then apply the technique just developed for $\mathbf{N}$ to the set A and obtain a still greater cardinal. We thereby have a sequence of sequences of increasing cardinals.

The process used to obtain a cardinal greater than the members of a given sequence of cardinals can be generalized as in the following theorem.

Theorem 3-5. *If* $\{\mathfrak{a}_i\}$ *is any indexed set of cardinals, then there exists a cardinal* $\mathfrak{a}$ *such that* $\mathfrak{a}_i < \mathfrak{a} \ \forall\, i$.

Proof. By our previous discussion $\mathfrak{a}_i \leq \sum_i \mathfrak{a}_i = \mathfrak{b}$. But by Theorem 3-3, there exists a cardinal $\mathfrak{c}$ greater than $\mathfrak{b}$. $\mathfrak{c}$ is therefore greater than $\mathfrak{a}_i \ \forall\, i$.

We note as a corollary that there cannot exist a greatest cardinal nor a set of all cardinals. This simply means that the property of "being a cardinal number" does not define a set within the limits of Zermelo-Fraenkel set theory. The "set of all cardinals" leads to an antinomy comparable to that of the Russell paradox.

We next define the product of two cardinals. If $\mathfrak{a}$ and $\mathfrak{b}$ are two arbitrary cardinals, let $\overline{\overline{A}} = \mathfrak{b}$ and $\overline{\overline{B}} = \mathfrak{b}$. Then the **product** of $\mathfrak{a}$ and $\mathfrak{b}$ is defined as:

$$\mathfrak{a}\mathfrak{b} = \overline{\overline{A \times B}}.$$

The existence and uniqueness follow from the similar properties of $A \times B$. The commutative law for multiplication follows from the equivalence of $A \times B$ and $B \times A$ established by the correspondence $\langle a, b\rangle \leftrightarrow \langle b, a\rangle$, for $a \in A$ and $b \in B$. Note that $A \times B \neq B \times A$, but we merely have $A \times B \sim B \times A$. The associative law follows similarly. Furthermore, multiplication is distributive with respect to addition, since $A \times (B \cup C) \sim (A \times B) \cup (A \times C)$, if $B \cap C = \emptyset$. Thus the arithmetic of cardinals follows the laws:

$$\mathfrak{a} + \mathfrak{b} = \mathfrak{b} + \mathfrak{a},\ \mathfrak{a}\mathfrak{b} = \mathfrak{b}\mathfrak{a};$$

$$\mathfrak{a} + (\mathfrak{b} + \mathfrak{c}) = (\mathfrak{a} + \mathfrak{b}) + \mathfrak{c}, \mathfrak{a}(\mathfrak{b}\mathfrak{c}) = (\mathfrak{a}\mathfrak{b})\mathfrak{c};$$
$$\mathfrak{a}(\mathfrak{b} + \mathfrak{c}) = \mathfrak{a}\mathfrak{b} + \mathfrak{a}\mathfrak{c}.$$

We note that, as for addition, multiplication of finite cardinals is compatible with multiplication of the natural numbers. The product of two natural numbers was defined by induction by the recursive formula: $n(m + 1) = nm + n$. We therefore must show that $A \times (B \cup \{x\}) \sim (A \times B) \cup A$ where A and B have cardinality n and m respectively and x is any element not in B. We leave this to the exercises.

As an example, consider the product $2\aleph_o$. This can be represented by a denumerable set of pairs $\langle x, y\rangle$ where $x = 0$ or 1 and $y \in \mathbf{N}$. It is also the set of lattice points on the lines $x = 0$ and $x = 1$ and is denumerable. Hence $2\aleph_o = \aleph_o$. A similar result holds for $n\aleph_o$ as well as $\aleph_o\aleph_o$, so that $2\aleph_o = n\aleph_o = \aleph_o\aleph_o$. The latter is represented by the set of all lattice points in the first quadrant of the plane. Again, as for addition of infinite cardinals, this last example is an illustration of the more general result that $\mathfrak{a} + \mathfrak{b} = \mathfrak{a}\mathfrak{b} = \max\{\mathfrak{a}, \mathfrak{b}\}$ for any pair of infinite cardinals (*cf*: Tarski). Again we omit the proof, but remark that this theorem is equivalent to the axiom of choice. The arithmetic of infinite cardinals is therefore much simpler than that of the finite cardinals.

As was the case with addition, we can extend multiplication to an arbitrary family of cardinal numbers $\{\mathfrak{a}_i\}$. We first consider a family of sets $\{A_i\}$ with $\bar{\bar{A}}_i \leq \mathfrak{a}_i$, and then form the cartesian product $\Pi_i A_i$. Its cardinal is taken as the product of the $\mathfrak{a}_i$; *i.e.*, $\Pi_i\mathfrak{a}_i = \overline{\overline{\Pi_i A_i}}$. The associative law for multiplication then extends to arbitrary products. If $I = \mathbf{U}_j I_j$ is a partition of the index set into disjoint subsets, then $\Pi_I \mathfrak{a}_i = \Pi_j \Pi_{I_j} \mathfrak{a}_{ij}$ where the $\mathfrak{a}_{ij}$ are the members corresponding to the partition I_j. The infinite distributive law also holds in the form:

$$\mathfrak{a}\textstyle\sum_i \mathfrak{a}_i = \sum_i \mathfrak{a}\mathfrak{a}_i.$$

We can define exponentiation for cardinals by simply taking all $\mathfrak{a}_i$'s equal in an arbitrary product. For example, if $\mathfrak{a}$ is any cardinal, we define $\mathfrak{a}^2 = \overline{\overline{A \times A}}$ where $\bar{\bar{A}} = \mathfrak{a}$. More generally $\mathfrak{a}^n$ is the cardinality of the cartesian product A^n which is the set of all n-tuples from A. But as we have already seen, the cartesian product A^n is also the set of functions defined on the index set $\mathbf{N}_n$ into A, and this definition extends to arbitrary index sets. Therefore if A and B are arbitrary sets with cardinals $\mathfrak{a}$ and $\mathfrak{b}$, then A^B is the set of functions from B into A. Its cardinality is then an extension of $\mathfrak{a}^n$ to $\mathfrak{a}^\mathfrak{b}$. We therefore define:

$$\mathfrak{a}^\mathfrak{b} = \overline{\overline{A^B}}.$$

The definition will also agree with the infinite product of $\mathfrak{a}$'s taken over an index set with cardinality $\mathfrak{a}$; *i.e.*, $\mathfrak{a}^\mathfrak{b} = \prod_I \mathfrak{a}_i$ where $\mathfrak{a}_i = \mathfrak{a}\ \forall\ i$ and $\bar{\bar{I}} = \mathfrak{a}$.

The laws for exponentiation for cardinals now follow from the general associative law for multiplication. We therefore have:

$$\mathfrak{a}^{\mathfrak{b}}\mathfrak{a}^{\mathfrak{c}} = \mathfrak{a}^{\mathfrak{b}+\mathfrak{c}},$$

$$(\mathfrak{a}^{\mathfrak{b}})^{\mathfrak{c}} = (\mathfrak{a})^{\mathfrak{b}\mathfrak{c}},$$

$$(\mathfrak{a}\mathfrak{b})^{\mathfrak{c}} = \mathfrak{a}^{\mathfrak{c}}\mathfrak{b}^{\mathfrak{c}}.$$

Using the notation of exponentiation, we can now write $\mathbf{2}^{\mathfrak{a}}$ for $\mathbf{2}^{\overline{\overline{A}}}$ where $\mathfrak{a} = \overline{\overline{A}}$, so that theorem 4 now reads:

$$\overline{\overline{\mathfrak{P}(A)}} = 2^{\mathfrak{a}}.$$

Thus $\mathfrak{c} = \overline{\overline{\mathfrak{P}(\mathbf{N})}} = 2^{\aleph_0}$. Similarly, the infinite sequence of cardinals becomes:

$$0, 1, 2, \ldots, \aleph_0, 2^{\aleph_0}, 2^{2^{\aleph_0}}, \ldots, (\aleph_0 + 2^{\aleph_0} + 2^{2^{\aleph_0}} + \ldots), \ldots$$

This sequence continues by alternate applications of Theorems 3-4 and 3-5 and has no maximum. However, it does not define a *set* of cardinals by itself.

EXERCISES

1. Show that if $A \sim A_1$, $B \sim B_1$, and $A \cap B = A_1 \cap B_1 = \emptyset$, then $A \cup B \sim A_1 \cup B_1$.
2. Prove that $A \sim A_1$ and $B \sim B_1$ imply $A \times B \sim A_1 \times B_1$.
3. Prove that $A \times (B \times C) \sim (A \times B) \times C$.
4. Prove by induction that the cardinal sum of two finite cardinal numbers n and m is the same as their inductive sum as defined for natural numbers. (*cf*: Maclane and Birkhoff for the definition of the sum of finite cardinals.)
5. Repeat exercise 4 for the product of two finite cardinals.
6. Prove that $\mathfrak{a} \leq \mathfrak{b}$ implies $\mathfrak{a} + \mathfrak{c} \leq \mathfrak{b} + \mathfrak{c}$ where $\mathfrak{a}$, $\mathfrak{b}$ and $\mathfrak{c}$ are three arbitrary cardinals. Is the corresponding result for $<$ true? Explain.
7. Prove that $\aleph_0 + n = \aleph_0 n = \aleph_0$ for any finite n.
8. Prove that $\aleph_0 + \mathfrak{c} = \mathfrak{c} = \aleph_0\mathfrak{c}$ where $\mathfrak{c}$ is the power of the continuum.
9. If $\mathfrak{f}$ is the cardinal number of the set of all real functions of a real variable; *i.e.*, $\mathfrak{f} = \overline{\overline{\mathbf{R}^{\mathbf{R}}}}$, prove that $\mathfrak{f} + \mathfrak{c} = \mathfrak{f}\mathfrak{c} = \mathfrak{c}$.
10. If IR is the set of irrational numbers, show that $\overline{\overline{IR}} = \mathfrak{c}$.
11. Prove that the cardinality of the set of algebraic numbers (roots of real equations with integral coefficients) is $\aleph_0$.
12. Prove that the set of transcendental numbers (real numbers not algebraic) has cardinality of the continuum.
13. Prove that the cancellation law for multiplication fails for infinite cardinals.
14. Prove that; $1 + 2 + 3 + \cdots = \aleph_0$.
15. Prove that for any cardinal $\mathfrak{a}$, $\mathfrak{a} = 1 + 1 + 1 + \cdots (\mathfrak{a}$ summands).
16. Complete the proof of the distributive law for arbitrary cardinals.

17. Prove that if $\mathfrak{a}$ is an infinite cardinal satisfying $\mathfrak{a} + \mathfrak{a} = 2\mathfrak{a} = \mathfrak{a}$, then $\mathfrak{a} + \mathfrak{b} = \max\{\mathfrak{a}, \mathfrak{b}\}$.

18. Prove that $n^{\aleph_0} = 2^{\aleph_0}$.

19. If $\mathfrak{a}$ and $\mathfrak{b}$ are two infinite cardinals such that $\mathfrak{a} = \mathfrak{b}^{\aleph_0}$, then $\mathfrak{a}^{\aleph_0} = \mathfrak{a}$. Hence conclude that there exist arbitrarily large cardinals for which $\mathfrak{a}^{\aleph_0} = \mathfrak{a}$. ($\mathfrak{c}$ is such a cardinal.)

20. Prove that if $\mathfrak{a}_1 < \mathfrak{a}_2 < \cdots$ is a strictly increasing sequence of cardinals, and $\mathfrak{a} = \sum_i \mathfrak{a}_i$, then $\mathfrak{a} < \mathfrak{a}^{\aleph_0}$. Hence there exist arbitrarily large cardinals satisfying $\mathfrak{a} \neq \mathfrak{a}^{\aleph_0}$.

21. Prove that the cardinality of the set of lattice points of $\mathbf{R}^\infty$ ($\mathbf{E}^{\mathbf{N}}$) is $\mathfrak{c}$. Compare with $\mathbf{E}^n$.

3-4. ORDER TYPES

In defining the concept of cardinality for sets, we considered a set without any structure imposed on it and defined an equivalence relation between such sets which reduced to a one-to-one correspondence. In this section, we consider sets with an order structure on them, and again define an equivalence relation which leads to the concept of an order type for ordered sets. We are therefore dealing with relational systems $\langle A, \leq \rangle$ in which the relation is a linear ordering. By this we mean a relation $\leq$ with satisfies the four following conditions:

(*i*) $x \leq x$ (*reflexive*),
(*ii*) $x \leq y$ *and* $y \leq x \Rightarrow x = y$ (*anti-symmetric*),
(*iii*) $x \leq y$ *and* $y \leq z \Rightarrow x \leq z$ (*transitive*), *and*
(*iv*) *for any* x, y *either* $x \leq y$ *or* $y \leq x$. (*dichotomous*).

We call such a system a ***linear*** or ***totally ordered system*** or a ***chain*** (in contrast to partially ordered systems which we shall study in the next chapter).

The concept of a subsystem for linear ordered sets is now a subset with the same order defined on it; *i.e.*, *$\langle B, \leq \rangle$ is a subsystem of $\langle A, \leq \rangle$ if B is a subset of A and the order in B agrees with that in A.* The next concept is that of an isomorphism which is a bijection ϕ that preserves the order; *i.e.*, such that $a \leq b \Rightarrow \phi(a) \leq \phi(b)$. We say that *$\langle A, \leq \rangle$ and $\langle B, \leq \rangle$* ***have the same order type*** or ***are similar***. We write $A \simeq B$. This concept is an equivalence relation that partitions the class of sets into order types in a way similar to the classification of sets into cardinality classes, except that similar sets have the same order. An order type is therefore a similarity class under $\simeq$. Clearly $A \simeq B \Rightarrow A \sim B$, so that an order class is a subclass of a cardinality class. Following Cantor, we designate the order type of an ordered set $\langle A, \leq \rangle$ by $\bar{A}$. $\bar{A}$ is therefore an abstraction from a set in which all features are ignored except the order of the elements. Cantor therefore thought of it as a first abstraction, while the cardinality of a set is a second abstraction which ignores the order as well. In general we use Greek lower case type for order types, so that if $\langle A, \leq \rangle$ is any ordered set, we write $\alpha = \bar{A}$ for its order type and $\mathfrak{a} = \bar{\bar{A}}$ for its cardinality or power. In line with this notation we write $\bar{\alpha}$ for the cardinality associated with an order type α; *i.e.*, $\bar{\alpha}$ is the cardinality class containing the order class α.

Finally, if α designates the order type of the ordered system, $\langle A, \leq \rangle$ then we write $*\alpha$ for the order type of the system $\langle A, \leq' \rangle$ where $x \leq' y$ if and only if $y \leq x$. Thus $*\alpha$ is the order type which is the inverse of α.

The simplest example is the set of the first n natural numbers ordered according to their natural order given by $n \leq m \leftrightarrow \exists k$ such that $n + k = m$. We designate this ordered set by $\langle \mathbf{N}_n, \leq \rangle$. If now $\langle F, \leq \rangle$ is any other ordered set with the same cardinality as $\mathbf{N}_n$, then we can designate the elements of F by $a_0, a_1, a_2, \ldots, a_{n-1}$ where $a_i \leq a_j \leftrightarrow i \leq j$ (use a renumbering if necessary). Hence two finite sets have the same order type if and only if they have the same cardinal number. We therefore can again use the notation, n, for the order type of the finite ordered set, $\langle \mathbf{N}_n, \leq \rangle$. For the sake of completeness, we designate the order type of the empty set $\emptyset$ by 0. Note that for finite sets $*n = n$; *i.e.*, a rearrangement of the order within a finite set does not change the order type.

For infinite sets the situation is much less simple. The first example, the set of all natural numbers arranged in their natural order is $\langle \mathbf{N}, \leq \rangle = \langle 0, 1, 2, 3, \ldots \rangle$. We designate the order type of this set by ω. Its associated cardinality is $\aleph_o$, so that we have $\bar{\omega} = \aleph_o$. Any other set will then have order type ω if it has a first element, a second, a third, etc.; *i.e.*, if there is a one-to-one mapping from $\langle \mathbf{N}, \leq \rangle$ into the given set *which preserves order*. On the other hand, not every set with cardinality $\aleph_o$ has order type ω. For example, the natural numbers in reverse order has type $*\omega$. This is the set ... 3, 2, 1, 0. This set has a last element, 0, but no first, so that there cannot exist an order-preserving map from ω into $*\omega$. Yet $\bar{\omega} = *\bar{\omega} = \aleph_o$. Still further distinct order types with the cardinality $\aleph_o$ can be formed by further rearrangements of the natural numbers. For example, we may write $1, 2, 3, \ldots, 0$ in which 0 is a last element while 1 is a first element. Also, every element except 0 has an immediate successor while all elements but 0 and 1 have immediate predecessors. Another distinct type with cardinality $\aleph_o$ is obtained by the arrangement $0, 2, 4, \ldots 1, 3, 5, \ldots$. Note however, that $1, 0, 2, 3, \ldots$ has the same order type as $\langle \mathbf{N}, \leq \rangle$. In general, if A is any denumerably infinite set, then A has at least one ordering of type ω, for the one-to-one mapping ϕ between A and $\mathbf{N}$ which defines the enumeration of A also induces an ordering on A according to $a \leq b \leftrightarrow \phi(a) \leq \phi(b)$; *i.e.*, the counting process in effect determines an order on A.

The next order type of interest with associated cardinal $\aleph_o$ is the order type of the rationals $\langle \mathbf{Q}, \leq \rangle$ in their natural order. This type is designated by η. It has neither a first nor last element. Furthermore, given any two rational numbers a and b, there always exists a third c which is strictly between a and b; *i.e.*, $a < c < b$. Such an order type is called *everywhere dense*. No element can have an immediate successor; *i.e.*, there is no least element greater than a given rational. There are, of course, other distinct orderings of the set of rationals. Thus the enumeration given by Cantor defines an order of type ω. Moreover, the order type of the set of rationals between 0 and 1, $\{x \in \mathbf{Q} | 0 < x < 1\}$, has the same order type η as $\mathbf{Q}$, while the set of rationals in the corresponding closed interval, $\{x \in \mathbf{Q} | 0 \leq x \leq 1\}$, is again a distinct order. In general, the order type η can be characterized by the three following conditions:

(*1*) η is denumerable; *i.e.*, $\bar{\eta} = \aleph_0$,
(*2*) η is everywhere dense,
(*3*) η has neither a first nor last element.

We omit the proof here (*cf:* Fraenkel).

The order type of the real numbers in their natural order is again a different order type from any of the order types with cardinals $\aleph_0$. We designate it by λ. It satisfies the conditions (2) and (3) but not (1) for order type η. In general, a characterization of the order type λ requires a complete study of the notion of a real number in terms of Dedekind cuts and is also omitted here (*cf:* Fraenkel).

In general, we have seen that there may be many distinct order types associated with a given cardinal number $\mathfrak{a}$. We can establish an upper bound for the number $\tau(\mathfrak{a})$ of order types with cardinal $\mathfrak{a}$, for every order relation defined on a set A is a relation on A; *i.e.*, a subset of $A \times A$. But the cardinality of the set of subsets of $A \times A$ is $\overline{\overline{\mathfrak{P}(A \times A)}}$, while the cardinality of $A \times A$ is $\mathfrak{a}\mathfrak{a} = \mathfrak{a}^2$. Hence $\tau(\mathfrak{a}) \leq 2^{\mathfrak{a}^2}$. On the other hand, we have not yet established the fact that $0 < \tau(\mathfrak{a})$; *i.e.*, we do not yet know whether or not a given set A can be ordered by a linear order relation. We return to this question in section 3-6.

3-5. THE ARITHMETIC OF ORDER TYPES

We can now define an arithmetic for order types in a fashion somewhat similar to the arithmetic of cardinals. If α and β are two order types with representative set $\langle A, \leq_1 \rangle$ and $\langle B, \leq_2 \rangle$, then we first define an ordered set on $A \cup B$ by:

$$x \leq y \leftrightarrow x \leq_1 y \text{ for } x, y \in A,$$

$$x \leq y \leftrightarrow x \leq_2 y \text{ for } x, y \in B, \text{ and}$$

$$x \leq y \leftrightarrow \text{ for } x \in A \text{ and } y \in B.$$

Thus the order in $A \cup B$ is defined by putting all elements of A before those of B and otherwise preserving the orders within A and B separately. The *order type of the system* $\langle A \cup B, \leq\rangle$ *is then called the* **ordered sum** $\alpha + \beta$ *of the order types* α *and* β. We leave it as an exercise to show that the relation $\leq$ so defined is an order within $A \cup B$, and that the definition of $\alpha + \beta$ is independent of the particular sets A and B chosen to represent α and β.

Again we first note that addition of order types agrees for finite order types with the definition of addition of the natural numbers. Hence the arithmetics of finite cardinals, finite ordinals and the natural numbers are identical. However, the situation is quite different for infinite order types. Thus the order type $1 + \omega$ is represented by the set $\langle\{0\} \cup \{1, 2, 3, \}, \leq\rangle$ where $0 \leq n$ for all $n \in \{1, 2, 3, \ldots\}$, and otherwise the order is the same as that of the natural numbers. But this is exactly the order type of the full set of natural numbers which has order type ω. Hence $1 + \omega = \omega$. On the other hand, the ordered sum $\langle\{1, 2, 3, \ldots\} \cup \{0\}, \leq\rangle = \langle 1, 2, 3, \ldots, 0\rangle$ where $n \leq 0 \ \forall \ n \neq 0$ has a distinct order type, so that $\omega + 1 \neq \omega$. Therefore the commutative law for infinite order types fails. The associative law, however, holds. We leave it to the reader. More generally, not only is $\omega + 1 \neq \omega$, but the order types ω, $\omega + 1$, $\omega + 2$, $\omega + 3, \ldots$ are all distinct although all have the same associated cardinal, $\aleph_o$.

Our next operation for order types is that of multiplication. Here there are two possible approaches, and we begin by defining multiplication in terms of repeated additions. First, if we have an ordered family $\langle A_i, \leq_i\rangle$ of ordered sets indexed by an ordered set $\langle I, \leq\rangle$, then we define their ordered union as the union of the A_i's ordered by:

(1) $x \leq y \leftrightarrow x \leq_i y$ *for* $x, y \in A_i$ *for some* i,
(2) $x \leq y$ *if* $x \in A_i$ *and* $y \in A_j$ where $i < j$ *in* I.

If α_i is the order type of $\langle A_i, \leq_i\rangle$, and β is the order type of I, then we write: $\sum_{i \in I}^{\beta} \alpha_i$ for the order type of the ordered union of the A_i's. In particular, if $\alpha_i = \alpha$, a fixed order type, then we call $\sum_{i \in I} \alpha_i = \alpha\beta$ the product of α and β; *i.e.*, $\alpha\beta$ is the order type of β summands each of type α*.

As an example, $\omega 2 = \omega + \omega$ is ω added to itself. This is the order type of $\{0, 2, 4, \ldots \ 1, 3, 5, \ldots\}$. It is distinct from ω itself. On the other hand, $2\omega = 2 + 2 + 2 + \cdots$ is the order type of $\langle 0, 1; 2, 3; 4, 5; \ldots\rangle$. But this is ω, so that $2\omega = \omega \neq \omega 2$. Multiplication is therefore not commutative. However, the associative law is simply a special case of the general associative law for addition. Moreover, the distributive law for multiplication from the left is also a direct consequence of the associative law of addition. Thus we have as laws

*This notation is that of Cantor. Other authors, however, use $\beta\alpha$ when we have used $\alpha\beta$. *Cf.* Birkhoff, for example.

of arithmetic:

$$\alpha + (\beta + \gamma) = (\alpha + \beta) + \gamma,$$
$$\alpha(\beta\gamma) = (\alpha\beta)\gamma, \qquad \text{and}$$
$$\alpha(\beta + \gamma) = \alpha\beta + \alpha\gamma.$$

Note, however, that the distributive law for multiplication from the right onto addition fails, as the following example shows. $(\omega + 1)2 = (\omega + 1) + (\omega + 1) = \omega + (1 + \omega) + 1 = \omega + \omega + 1$. On the other hand, $\omega 2 + 2 = \omega + \omega + 2$, so that $(\omega + 1)\,2 \neq \omega 2 + 2$. We see that the arithmetic of order types has some, but by no means all, of the characteristics of the arithmetic of the natural numbers.

The final operation for order types to be considered is that of exponentiation. We first give an alternative characterization of multiplication in terms of cartesian product. If $\langle A, \leq_1\rangle$ and $\langle B, \leq_2\rangle$ are two ordered sets with order types α and β, then we can define an order on the cartesian product $A \times B$ by:

$$\langle x, y\rangle \leq \langle u, v\rangle \leftrightarrow \textit{either } (1)\ y <_2 v \textit{ or}$$
$$(2)\ y = v \textit{ and } x \leq_1 u.$$

Such an ordering is called an **anti-lexicographic ordering** *or ordering by last differences*. We leave it to the exercises to show that it orders $A \times B$ linearly. It remains to show that the order type of $\langle A \times B, \leq\rangle$ is $\alpha\beta$ as defined above. For this purpose, let $\langle A_y, \leq_1\rangle$ be defined on the family of sets order-isomorphic to $\langle A, \leq_1\rangle$ indexed by the elements y of B. Then this family of sets will all have the order type α, while the index set has order type β. Furthermore, the members of this family are pairwise disjoint, while their union $\bigcup_{y \in \beta} A_y$ is equivalent to $A \times B$ under the bijection $\phi(x_y) \leftrightarrow \langle x, y\rangle$ for $x_y \in A_y$ and $y \in B$ where $A_y \sim A\ \forall\ y \in B$. Moreover, ϕ carries the ordering defined on $\bigcup_y A_y$ as a union of ordered sets into the order by last differences in the product $A \times B$. Therefore, the product $\alpha\beta$ defined as the order type of $\langle \bigcup_y A_y, \leq\rangle$ is the same as that of $\langle A \times B, \leq\rangle$. As a corollary we note that the cardinality of the product $\alpha\beta$ is the same as the product of the cardinalities of α and β; *i.e.*, $\overline{\alpha\beta} = \bar{\alpha}\bar{\beta}$.

The concept of product of order types can be extended to any finite family of order types. This purpose is accomplished by extending the notion of anti-lexicographic order to the cartesian product of a finite family of sets. Let $\langle A_i, \leq_i\rangle$ $i = 1, 2, \ldots, n$ be n ordered sets of types α_i. The cartesian product is then ordered by:

$$\langle x_1, x_2, \ldots, x_n\rangle \leq \langle y_1, y_2, \ldots, y_n\rangle \Longleftrightarrow \text{either}$$

(1) $x_n < y_n$ or
(2) $x_n = y_n$ and $x_{n-1} < y_{n-1}$ or
(3) $x_n = y_n$ and $x_{n-1} = y_{n-1}$ and $x_{n-2} < y_{n-2}$, or$\cdots$.

This ordering so defined is then a linear order on $\Pi_i A_i$. We call its order type the product of the α_i's; *i.e.*, $\Pi_i \alpha_i = \overline{\langle \Pi_i A_i, \leq \rangle}$.

Now by letting $\alpha_i = \alpha$ for $i = 1, 2, \ldots, n$, we define the exponentiation of α by n to be: $\alpha^n = \overset{n}{\Pi}\alpha$; *i.e.*, the repeated product of α taken n times. The rules for exponentiation now follow and are left to the exercises.

Finally, we note that this definition of exponentiation does not extend to arbitrary families of order types, as was the case for families of cardinals. The reason is that we defined the elements of an arbitrary cartesian product of sets as functions on the indexing set, but in general there is no way of extending the notion of anti-lexicographic order to such elements; *i.e.*, there will in general be no last difference on which to order two functions. Consequently, there is no reasonable way to define order types such as ω^ω, for example.

The last topic of interest in the arithmetic of order types is that of the magnitude of an order type; *i.e.*, the question of comparing order types as to size. Here again there is no satisfactory solution. In the case of cardinals we defined an order between $\mathfrak{a} = \bar{\bar{A}}$ and $\mathfrak{b} = \bar{\bar{B}}$ by writing $\mathfrak{a} \leq \mathfrak{b}$ if A is equivalent to a subset of B. We would like to use this same technique for order types by replacing equivalence by similarity. However, this may not be possible, as may be seen from the example of ω and $^*\omega$. Here ω is represented by $\langle 0, 1, 2, 3, \ldots \rangle$ while $^*\omega$ is the type of $\langle \ldots, 3, 2, 1, 0 \rangle$. But neither of these ordered sets is similar to a subsystem of the other. Hence ω and $^*\omega$ are essentially incomparable as order types. We are therefore led in the next section to a special kind of ordered set in which the order types can be compared.

3-6. WELL-ORDERED SETS AND ORDINAL NUMBERS

Of all the ordered sets, $\langle A, \leq \rangle$, the most important are those which satisfy the fifth condition:

(*v*) *if B is a non-empty subset of A, then B has a first element; i.e., an element $b \in B$ such that $b \leq x \; \forall \; x \in B$.*

Such sets are called **well-ordered**, while their order types are called **ordinal numbers**. The arithmetic of ordinal numbers is therefore obtained as a special case of that of ordered types.

The simplest examples are the finite order types represented by $\langle \mathbf{P}_n, \leq \rangle$, and designated by n. Therefore, n now means either a natural number, a finite cardinal or a finite ordinal. The next ordinal number is the order type ω of the set of all natural numbers. In fact, the statement that $\langle \mathbf{N}, \leq \rangle$ is well-ordered is equivalent to the principle of induction contained in the very definition of the natural numbers. Its existence is assured by the axiom of infinity. We state this result as a theorem.

Theorem 3-6. *The ordered set* $\langle \mathbf{N}, \leq \rangle$ *is well-ordered.*

Proof. The principle of mathematical induction states that if A is a subset of $\mathbf{N}$ such that (*i*) $0 \in A$ and (*ii*) $n \in A \Rightarrow n + 1 \in A$, then $A = \mathbf{N}$. Now let $B \subseteq \mathbf{N}$ be any non-empty subset of $\mathbf{N}$ and assume that B has no first element. Let $A = \{x \in \mathbf{N} | x < b \ \forall \ b \in B\}$. Then $A \subseteq \mathbf{N} - B$. Furthermore $0 \in A$, for otherwise $0 \in B$ is a first element of B. A therefore satisfies condition (*i*) for induction. Now let $n \in A$. Then $n < b \ \forall \ b \in B$, whence $n + 1 \leq b$. If for some particular b_0, $b_0 = n + 1$, then $b_0 \leq b \ \forall \ b \in B$ so that b_0 is a first element of B. Otherwise, $n + 1 < b \ \forall \ b \in B$, whence condition (*ii*) is fulfilled. In this case we can apply the principle of induction and conclude that $A = \mathbf{N}$, whence $B = \emptyset$ contrary to the hypothesis.

Conversely, we can derive the principle of induction from the well-ordering principle. For if A is any set satisfying (*i*) and (*ii*) where $A \neq \mathbf{N}$, then $B = \mathbf{N} - A \neq \emptyset$. By the well-ordering, B will have a first element b_0. By (*i*) $b_0 \neq 0$. Hence $b_0 = n + 1$ for some n. But then $n \in A$, whence condition (*ii*) implies $n + 1 = b_0 \in A$ contrary to $b_0 \in B$.

Other examples of ordinals are the order types $\omega + 1, \omega + 2, \ldots, \omega + \omega, \ldots$ On the other hand, the order type $^*\omega$ is not an ordinal number. More generally, a well-ordered set can be characterized by the fact that it fails to contain a subset of type $^*\omega$, as given in the following theorem.

Theorem 3-7. *A set* $\langle A, \leq \rangle$ *is well-ordered if and only if it does not contain a subsystem* $\langle B, \leq \rangle$ *of type* $^*\omega$.

Proof. (*i*) Clearly, if A contains a system of type $^*\omega$, then A is not well-ordered.

(*ii*) Conversely, let $\langle A, \leq \rangle$ be an ordered set which is not well-ordered. Then A contains a subset B which has no first element. Let $b_0 \in B$ be any element of B. Then b_0 is not the first element of B, so that there exists $b_1 \in B$ where $b_1 < b_0$. Continuing by induction, let $b_n < \cdots < b_1 < b_0 \in B$. Then since b_n is not a first element of B, there exists $b_{n+1} \in B$ where $b_{n+1} < b_n$. The sequence so generated consisting of $\cdots b_n < \cdots < b_1 < b_0$ is then a subsystem of A of type $^*\omega$.

Theorem 3-7 characterizes ordinal numbers as order types of ordered sets which fail to contain a subset of type $^*\omega$. On the other hand, we can characterize infinite ordinals as those whose associated ordered sets contain subsets of type ω.

Theorem 3-8. *A well-ordered set is infinite if and only if it contains a subset of type* ω.

Proof. Let $\langle A, \leq \rangle$ be a well-ordered set such that A is infinite. Then A contains a first element a_0. Since A is infinite, $A - \{a_0\}$ is non-empty and contains a first, a_1. Continuing by induction, A will contain a sequence S: $a_0 < a_1 < a_2 < \cdots$ indexed by $\mathbf{N}$. Hence $\langle S, \leq \rangle$ is a subset of type ω.

As a corollary, we note that every element of S precedes all elements of A not in S. Hence $\langle A, \leq \rangle$ can be written as an ordered union of two sets of which the first is of type ω. Therefore if α is the type of $\langle A, \leq \rangle$, then we have:

Corollary 1. *If α is an infinite ordinal number, then $\alpha = \omega + \beta$ for some β.*

As a second corollary we give the alternative characterization of finiteness for ordinals.

Corollary 2. *An ordinal number α is finite if and only if both α and $^*\alpha$ are well-ordered.*

This result is an immediate consequence of Theorems 3-7 and 3-8.

Another important consequence of Theorem 3-8 is the following theorem.

Theorem 3-9. *If f is a similarity mapping from a well-ordered set $\langle A, \leq \rangle$ onto itself, then f is the identity, $f = \Delta_A$.*

Proof. If f is not the identity, there exists $x \in A$ such that $f(x) \neq x$. Therefore the set $B = \{x | f\{x\} \neq x\}$ is non-empty. By the well-ordering, it has a first, b_0. We may assume $b_1 = f(b_0) < b_0$, since otherwise we could use the similarity mapping f^{-1}. But the similarity property of f implies $f(b_1) < f(b_0) = b_1$ where $b_1 < b_0$, contrary to the fact that b_0 was a least element of B.

Corollary. *If $\langle A, \leq \rangle$ and $\langle B, \leq \rangle$ are two similar well-ordered sets, then there is one and only one similarity mapping f from A onto B.*

Proof. The existence follows from the fact that A and B are similar. If f and g are two similarity maps from A onto B, then the composite $g^{-1} \circ f$ is a similarity of A onto itself. By the theorem it is the identity on A; *i.e.*, $g^{-1} \circ f = \Delta_A$. Thus $f = g$.

EXERCISES

1. Give the order types of the following sets:
   (*a*) $\langle \mathbf{Z}, \leq \rangle$;
   (*b*) $\{x \in \mathbf{R} | 0 < x \leq 1\}$;
   (*c*) $\{x \in \mathbf{R} | x < 0\}$;
   (*d*) $\{x \in \mathbf{Q} | 0 \leq x \leq 1\}$.

2. Give examples of sets with the following order types: (*a*) $\omega + 3$; (*b*) $\omega + 1 + \omega$, (*c*) $\eta + 1$, (*d*) ω^2.
3. Show that the definition of order in an ordered sum satisfies the conditions for a linear order relation.
4. If $\langle A, \leq\rangle \simeq \langle A_1, \leq\rangle$ and $\langle B, \leq\rangle \simeq \langle B_1, \leq\rangle$ prove that $\langle A \cup B, \leq\rangle \simeq \langle A_1 \cup B_1, \leq\rangle$.
5. Prove the associative law for ordered sums of sets.
6. Show that the associative law for products of order types follows from the general associative law for sums.
7. Prove the distributive law for arbitrary order types in the form:

$$\alpha(\textstyle\sum_i \beta_i) = \sum_i \alpha\beta_i.$$

8. Show that the ordered union of two well-ordered sets is well-ordered.
9. Show that the product of two ordinals is an ordinal.
10. Prove: $\alpha 0 = 0\alpha = 0$ and $\alpha 1 = 1\alpha = \alpha$ for any order type α.
11. Prove that a subset of a well-ordered set is well-ordered.
12. Prove that a set similar to a well-ordered set is well-ordered.
13. Prove that if f is a similarity mapping of an orderd set $\langle A, \leq\rangle$ onto an ordered set $\langle B, \leq\rangle$; *i.e.*, a bijection, then f^{-1} is also.
14. Prove the alternative form of Theorem 9; *if f is a similarity mapping of an ordered set into itself (an injection), then $x \leq f(x)\ \forall\ x$.*
15. Show that the left cancellation law for addition of ordinals holds; *i.e.*, $\gamma + \alpha = \gamma + \beta \Rightarrow \alpha = \beta$.
16. Give an example to show that the right cancellation for addition does not hold in general.
17. Use exercise 14 to show how left subtraction of ordinals can be defined by: $(-\alpha + \beta)$ is the unique solution of the equation $\chi + \alpha = \beta$ if $\alpha \leq \beta$.
18. Show that the left cancellation for multiplication holds for ordinals. Hence, outline a definition of left division. Is it reasonable to define right division?
19. Prove the laws of exponentiation:

$$\alpha^n \alpha^m = \alpha^{n+m},$$

$$(\alpha^n)^m = \alpha^{nm}.$$

Does the law $(\alpha\beta)^n = \alpha^n \beta^n$ hold for order types? Explain.

20. Prove that if $\langle A, \leq\rangle$ is an ordered set such that every subset B has either a first or last element, then A can be written as the ordered union of a well-ordered set and an anti-well-ordered set.

3-7. TRANSFINITE INDUCTION

One of the most important applications of the theory of well-ordered sets is to an extension of the principle of mathematical induction to sets of arbitrary size. We have already given one form of the principle of ordinary induction in the preceding section. An alternative formulation is given by the following: *if* B *is a non-empty subset of the natural numbers such that* $a \in B$ *whenever* $x \in B \; \forall \; x < a$, *then* $B = \mathbf{N}$. The equivalence of this form with that previously given is left to the reader. Note, however, that it implies that $0 \in B$, since "$x \in B \; \forall \; x < 0$" is false and a false statement p implies the truth of "p implies q". The advantage of this alternative form is that it will still hold if we replace $\mathbf{N}$ by any well-ordered set.

Theorem 3-10. (*Principle of Transfinite Induction*) *If* $\langle A, \leq \rangle$ *is any well-ordered set and* B *is a subset of* A *such that* $a \in B$ *whenever* $x \in B \; \forall \; x < a$, *then* $B = A$.

Proof. If $B \neq A$, then $A - B \neq \emptyset$. By the well-ordering, $A - B$ has a first element x_0. But then $x \in B \; \forall \; x < x_0$. By the inductive hypothesis, this implies $x_0 \in B$, which is a contradiction. Therefore $B = A$.

Alternatively, the principle of transfinite induction can be stated in terms of properties as given in the following corollary.

Corollary. *If* $\langle A, \leq \rangle$ *is a well-ordered set and* $\{p(a) | a \in A\}$ *is a set of statements indexed by* A *such that the truth of* $p(x) \; \forall \; x < a$ *implies the truth of* $p(a)$, *then* $p(a)$ *is true for all* $a \in A$.

We have already seen numerous applications of the ordinary principle of mathematical induction, mostly in the exercises. The general principle for transfinite sets was used extensively in analysis up until the early 1940's, but since then it has been gradually replaced by maximality principles developed by Zorn and others, so that today it is less in vogue as a direct method of proof. We shall discuss these other techniques in the next chapter, after we discuss partially ordered sets.

Mathematical induction is also used extensively in defining functions by defining a value for 0 and then defining the value for $n + 1$ in terms of the value for n. Functions defined by such techniques are called *recursive functions* and form a branch of mathematical logic. Here we shall indicate briefly how the method can be extended to the transfinite case.

We first introduce a few auxiliary terms for well-ordered sets. A subset I of an ordered set $\langle A, \leq \rangle$ is called an *ideal of* A *if* $a \in I$ *and* $x \leq a \Rightarrow x \in I$. In particular, the set $[a]\downarrow \; = \{x | x \leq a\}$ is an ideal called **the principal ideal generated by *a***. In contrast, the set $I_a = \{x | x < a\}$ is also an ideal. It is called the **initial segment of *A* determined by *a***. For example, in the well-ordered set $A = \langle 0, 1, 2, \ldots \omega \rangle$ the principal ideal generated by ω is all of A, while the initial segment is the set of natural numbers and is not a principal ideal.

Next, if $a, b \in A$ where $a < b$, but there do not exist elements x strictly between a and b, then b *is called the* **immediate successor** *of* a and a *the* **immediate predecessor** *of* b. In well-ordered sets every element a has an immediate successor, namely, the first element of the set $\{x|a < x\}$, but not every element need have an immediate predecessor. Thus in the well-ordered set $0, 1, 2, \ldots, \omega$, the element ω has no immediate predecessor. More generally, every ideal $I \neq A$ also determines an immediate successor which is the first element of $A - I$. If a is the immediate successor of I, then we can also write $I = I_a$, so that every proper ideal ($\neq A$) is an initial segment. Therefore, in the theory of well-ordered sets, initial segments are more significant than principal ideals.

We also note that the family $\mathfrak{I}$ of all ideals of A is itself a well-ordered set under set inclusion. For every proper ideal corresponds to an element of a, and this correspondence preserves order since $a \leq b \Rightarrow I_a \subseteq I_b$, while A is a greatest element of $\mathfrak{I}$.

Our final concept is a generalization of the notion of a sequence as defined above for the natural numbers, in which we replace **N** by an arbitrary well-ordered set $\langle A, \leq \rangle$. If X is any set and I is an ideal of A, then a function s_I defined on I with values in X is called a **sequence of type *I*.** It is therefore a subset of X indexed by elements of I; *i.e.*, $s_I = \{\langle x, s_I(x)\rangle | x \in I\}$. If $I = I_a$, we also write s_a and call s_a a **sequence of type *a*.** For example, if $I = \mathbf{N}_n$, then a sequence of type n is simply an n-tuple in X; $s_n = \langle a_0, a_1, \ldots, a_{n-1}\rangle$. On the other hand, a sequence of type ω is an infinite sequence as ordinarily defined in analysis; *i.e.*, $s_\omega = \langle a_0, a_1, \ldots \rangle$.

We now return our attention to the process of defining functions by transfinite induction. We first examine the case of ordinary induction, using the second form discussed at the beginning of this section. We are given the natural numbers **N**, a set X and a fixed element c_0 of X. We then define a function on **N** into X by letting $f(0) = x_0$ and then define $f(n)$ in terms of the set of preceding values of f; *i.e.*, $f(0), f(1), \ldots, f(n-1)$. The phrase "in terms of" means that we have a rule which assigns to the sequence $\langle f(0), f(1), \ldots, f(n-1)\rangle$ a particular value in X. If we denote this sequence of type n by s_n, then the "rule" is simply a function ϕ which assigns to each sequence in X of type n a value $\phi(s_n)$ in X. Such a function ϕ is called a **recursive rule**. The general problem is to show that every recursive rule determines a unique function f on N. This function must satisfy the general law:

$$(*)\ f(x) = \phi(\langle f(0), f(1), \ldots, f(n-1)\rangle).$$

But the sequence $\langle f(0), f(1), \ldots, f(n-1)\rangle$ is nothing more than the function f restricted to the ideal $I_n = \{0, 1, \ldots, (n-1)\}$ of $\mathbf{N}_n$; *i.e.*, $f|_{I_n}$. Thus condition (*) becomes:

$$(*)\ f(x) = \phi(f|_{I_n}).$$

A function satisfying this condition is said to be **recursively defined by ϕ**.

To generalize this process we replace **N** by an arbitrary well-ordered set

$\langle A, \leq \rangle$ with first element a_0. We are also given a recursive rule ϕ which is defined for all sequences of type a with values in X; *i.e.*, $\phi = \{\langle s_a, \phi(s_a)\rangle | a \in A\}$. We now say that a function f is **recursively determined by** ϕ if it satisfies:

$$(*)\ f(x) = \phi(f|_{I_x}) \qquad \text{where}$$

$f|_{Ix}$ is the restriction of f to $I_x = \{t | t < x\}$; *i.e.*, $f|_{I_x} = s_x = \{\langle t, f(t)\rangle | t < x\}$ is the sequence of values of f on the initial segment I_x. The recursive rule (*) therefore says that f at any point is determined from the values at all preceding points by the rule ϕ. Our problem is to establish the existence and uniqueness of f.

We first prove the uniqueness; *i.e.*, if f_1 and f_2 are two functions defined on the same well-ordered set A satisfying (*) for a given ϕ, then $f_1 = f_2$. The proof is a fairly simple application of transfinite induction and is left to the reader.

To establish the existence we first examine a few specific cases to gain insight into the process. We consider the set $\mathfrak{J}$ of all ideals of A and show that for each $I \in \mathfrak{J}$ there exists a function f_I defined on I which satisfies (*). We begin with $I_0 = I_{a_0} = \{x | x < a_o\}$. But I_0 is the empty set, so that $f_0 = f_{I_0}$ is the empty function. The next case is that of the ideal $I_1 = I_{a_1} = \{a_0\}$ where a_1 is the second element of A. According to the rule (*), the associated function $f_1 = f_{I_1}$ must be defined on $I_1 = \{a_0\}$ and satisfy:

$$f_1(a_0) = \phi(f_1|_{I_0}).$$

But I_o is empty, so that the sequence $s_0 = f_1|_{I_0}$ is the empty sequence. However, the rule ϕ assigns values to every sequence, so that it assigns a value $c_0 \in X$ to the empty sequence. Hence $f_1(a_0) = c_o$; *i.e.*, the function f_1 is simply the single ordered pair $f_1 = \{\langle a_0, c_0\rangle\}$. It clearly satisfies the rule (*). Next consider the third element a_2 and its associated ideal $I_2 = I_{a_2} = \{a_0, a_1\}$. The associated function $f_2 = f_{I_2}$ must be defined on I_2 and satisfy (*). We define:

$$f_2(a_0) = f_1(a_0) \text{ and}$$

$$f_2(a_1) = \phi(f_2|_{I_2}) = \phi(\langle c_o\rangle), \text{ where } c_o = f_1(a_o).$$

We note that f_2 is then an extension of f_1 from I_1 to I_2.

We now assume as inductive hypothesis that functions f_J are defined for all subideals of an ideal I which satisfy the recursive rule (*). We further assume that if $K, J, K \subseteq J$ are two ideals of I, then the function f_J is an extension of f_K. Hence the set of functions is itself a well-ordered set ordered by extension. We now show that ϕ determines a unique extension to f_I defined on I and satisfying (*). We consider two cases according as to whether I is principal, $I = [a]\downarrow$, or not; *i.e.*, has a last element or not. In the first case f_I is defined by:

$f_I(x) = f_{I_a}(x)$ for $x < a$ where $I_a = \{x | x < a\}$ is a proper ideal of I,

$$f_I(a) = \phi(f_{I_a}) = \phi(f_I|_{I_a}).$$

f_I is then defined on I, satisfies rule (*) and is a common extension of all f_J for $J \subset I$.

In the second case we define:

$$f_I(x) = f_J(x)$$

where J is any proper subideal of I containing x. The fact that all the ideals I_J are extensions of one another means that it doesn't make any difference which one we choose. Again f_I is an extension of the f_J for $J \subset I$ and satisfies (*). Therefore in either case we have extended the set of functions $\{f_J\}$ to f_I as required. But since A is itself an ideal, there is a function f_A defined on A uniquely satisfying (*). This is the required function.

3-8. THE SEQUENCE OF ORDINALS

Using the technique of transfinite induction introduced in the last section, we can now define an order for ordinals such that the class of all ordinals is well-orderd with a specific canonical form for each well-ordered set. To compare ordinals, we use the same method used in comparing cardinals except that equivalence is replaced by similarity. If α and β are two ordinal numbers represented by the well-ordered sets $\langle A, \leq \rangle$ and $\langle B, \leq \rangle$ respectively, then we write $\alpha \leq \beta$ if $\langle A, \leq \rangle$ is similar to an ideal $\langle I, \leq \rangle$ of $\langle B, \leq \rangle$. The first problem is to show that $\leq$ is a linear ordering for ordinals. For this purpose we first prove the following lemma.

Lemma. *If $\langle A, \leq \rangle$ is similar to an ideal I of itself, then $A = I$.*

Proof. If $A \neq I$, then I has an immediate successor a, $a \notin I$. If f is the similarity mapping between A and I, then f maps a into $f(a) \in I$. But then $f(a) < a$ contrary to Theorem 3-9 (see exercise 13 of section 3-6). Thus $A = I$.

Theorem 3-11. *The ordering of ordinals is reflexive, antisymmetric and transitive.*

Proof. We leave the reflexivity and transitivity to the reader. To prove antisymmetry, let $\alpha \leq \beta$ and $\beta \leq \alpha$. Then $\langle A, \leq \rangle \simeq \langle J, \leq \rangle$ where J is an ideal of B. Let this similarity be defined by a function f: $A \to J$. Similarly, $\langle B, \leq \rangle$ is similar to an ideal I of A under a similarity mapping g: $B \to I$. The mapping $g|_I$ (g restricted to I) composed with f is then a similarity mapping of A into itself. Furthermore, the range of $f \circ g|_I$ is an ideal in A (exercise). Hence by the lemma, $f \circ g|_I$ must be the identity on A. Therefore g maps I onto all of A; *i.e.*, is surjective. But $I \subseteq B \Rightarrow g(I) \subseteq g(B)$ whence $J = g(B) = A$. Thus g is a surjective similarity map of B onto A, so that $A \simeq B$. Therefore $\alpha = \beta$.

To prove the dichotomy of the order relation for ordinals, we first prove the following theorem.

Theorem 3-12. *If $\langle A, \leq\rangle$ and $\langle B, \leq\rangle$ are two well-ordered sets, then either A is similar to an ideal of B or B is similar to an ideal of A.*

Proof. Assume that B is not similar to any ideal of A. Then we shall use the method of definition by induction to construct a similarity function on A onto a proper ideal of B. We begin with a recursive rule ϕ defined for all sequences s_a of type $a (a \in A)$ in B. By the successor b of s_a in B we mean the first element of the set $\{t | y \leq t \ \forall \ y \in s_a\}$, provided this set is non-empty. We now define ϕ by:

$$\phi(s_a) = \begin{cases} b \text{ if } s_a \text{ has a successor,} \\ b_o \text{ if } s_a \text{ has no successor } (b_0 \text{ is the first element of } B). \end{cases}$$

Then ϕ is defined for all sequences in B of type a. It therefore determines a unique function f on A which satisfies the recursive law:

$$f(x) = \phi(f|_{I_x}).$$

Note, for example, that this implies that $f(a_0) = \phi(f|_{I_0})$ where I_0 is the empty sequence and the successor of I_0 is therefore b_0, the first element of B. Hence $f(a_0) = b_0$. We now prove by transfinite induction that f is a similarity function of A into a proper ideal of B. The induction is on the set of ideals of A, and the inductive hypothesis is that f is a similarity map for every subideal J of a given ideal I. We must then prove that f is a similarity map of I onto a proper ideal of B.

In the first case we assume that I is a principal ideal, $I = [a]\downarrow$, so that $J = I_a$ is a proper ideal of I. By inductive hypothesis, the function $f|_J$ is then a similarity map of J into a proper ideal of B. As such it is a sequence of type J_a and has a successor b in B. Hence $\phi(f|_J) = b = f(a)$. Therefore, in this case, f maps I onto the ideal $[b]\downarrow$ of B. Furthermore, if $[b]\downarrow$ exhausts B, then B would be similar to an ideal of A, contrary to assumption.

In the case that I is not a principal ideal; *i.e.*, has no last element, $f(x)$ is given by:

$$f(x) = \phi(f|_{I_x})$$

where I_x is a proper ideal contained in I. Hence we again apply the inductive hypothesis under which $f|_{I_x}$ is a similarity map. It follows (exercise) that $f|_I$ is a similarity map of all of I onto a proper ideal of B. Finally, by taking $I = A$ we see that f is a similarity map of A onto a proper ideal of B.

Finally, it remains to show that the ordering $\leq$ for ordinals is a well-ordering. We first consider a well-ordered set $\langle A, \leq\rangle$ with ordinal α. If β is any other ordinal such that $\beta \leq \alpha$, then β is represented by a well-ordered set $\langle B, \leq\rangle$ such that B is similar to a proper ideal of A. Conversely, every proper ideal of A has an ordinal $\beta < \alpha$. Therefore the family $\mathfrak{I}^-$ of proper ideals of A is a set of representatives for all ordinals β less than α. But as we have already seen, every proper ideal is an initial segment I_a determined by some a in A and the mapping $x \longleftrightarrow I_x$ is a similarity between A and $\mathfrak{I}^-$. By composition of these two correspondences, every ordinal $\beta < \alpha$ is represented by an element of A. Hence the set $S(\alpha)$ of all ordinals less than α is itself a well-ordered set with order type α. These well-ordered sets $\langle S(\alpha), \leq \rangle$ thus serve as canonical representatives of the corresponding ordinals α. We may therefore dispense with arbitrary well-ordered sets and simply consider well-ordered sets of ordinals of the form $\langle S(\alpha), \leq \rangle$. Von Neumann, for example, defines an ordinal as a specific set of this form, and thereby avoids the difficulties inherent in defining an order type as a class of similar sets.

Theorem 3-12 now shows that two ordinals are always comparable under $\alpha \leq \beta \leftrightarrow S(\alpha) \subseteq S(\beta)$. Moreover, since each $S(\alpha)$ is well-ordered, the class of all ordinals is also well-ordered. The ordinals themselves form a transfinite sequence, the first few terms of which are given by:

$$0, 1, 2, \ldots, \omega, \omega + 1, \omega + 2, \ldots, \omega + \omega = \omega 2, \omega 2 + 1, \ldots, \omega 3, \ldots, \omega\omega = \omega^2, \ldots, \omega^3, \ldots$$

If α is any ordinal in this sequence, then the initial segment I_α is exactly the set $S(\alpha)$ of ordinals which precede α, and its order type is α itself. In general there are two types of ideals in this sequence, those which are principal and those which are not. If $I = [\alpha]\downarrow$ is principal, then $I = I_{\alpha+1}$ is the initial segment determined by the successor of α. The ordinal $\alpha + 1$ has an immediate predecessor α and is called an **ordinal of the first kind.** On the other hand, if an ordinal α has no immediate predecessor, then initial segment I has no last element and is therefore not a principal ideal. Such elements are called **ordinals of the second kind (limit ordinals**). We also write $\alpha = \lim \{\beta | \beta < \alpha\}$.

We note finally that although $\leq$ is a well-ordering for ordinals, there is no last ordinal. Furthermore, there is no set of all ordinals. For if S is a set of all ordinals, then its ordinal would be greater than all its elements and hence not in S. This is known as Cantor's paradox. It simply means that the property of "being an ordinal" does not define a set in Zermelo-Fraenkel set theory. We may speak of the class of all ordinals in the von Neumann sense, but it is not a set.

3-9. THE WELL-ORDERING THEOREM AND COMPARABILITY OF CARDINALS

The final point to be cleared up in the theory of transfinite numbers is that of the comparability of cardinals. This is solved by showing that every set can be well-ordered so that every cardinal may be represented by an ordinal. The comparability of cardinals then follows from the comparability of ordinals. The key point is therefore to show that every set can be used as the carrier for some well-ordered set. This is done by the use of the axiom of choice, and, in fact, we show that the axiom of choice is exactly equivalent to the statement that every set can be well-ordered. This result is due to Zermelo and was first proved in 1904. The proof given here is taken from Hausdorff (*cf:* Hausdorff). Later a much simpler proof will be given, using the more powerful techniques of partially-ordered set theory.

Theorem 3-13. *For any set A there exists a well-ordered system $\langle A, \leq \rangle$ with carrier A.*

Proof. The idea of the proof is first to construct a well-ordered family $\mathfrak{F}$ of subsets X of A such that:

(*i*) the empty set is in $\mathfrak{F}$,
(*ii*) $\mathfrak{F}$ is closed under a successor operation, $X \to X^*$,
(*iii*) $\mathfrak{F}$ is closed under arbitrary unions.

This family will have $\emptyset$ as its first element and culminate in A itself. We then introduce a well-ordering $\leq_X$ into each member X of $\mathfrak{F}$, so that the eventual set $\langle A, \leq_A \rangle$ will be the required well-ordered set.

We begin with the definition of that successor operation involved in (*ii*). Basically, the successor X^* of X is formed from X by adjoining an element not in X to X, and is defined only for proper subsets of A. The construction of X^* therefore involves the choosing of an element from subsets of A. We assume the existence of a choice function f which picks a representative $f(X) = x$ out of each set X; *i.e.*, such that $f(X) \in X$. The existence of f is guaranteed by the axiom of choice, so that the particular successor operation is dependent on the choice function given. We now define X^* for all $X \neq A$, $X \in \mathfrak{P}(A)$ by:

$$X^* = X \cup \{f(A - X)\}.$$

We apply the choice function to $A - X$, so that X^* will differ from X by the adjunction of a single element. For example, the successor of $\emptyset$ is $\{f(A)\}$.

We now consider families of sets satisfying (*i*)-(*iii*). In general, such a family is not well-ordered, in fact, not even linearly ordered. For example, the family of all proper subsets of A is a family of this type. However, if we consider the smallest family of sets satisfying (*i*)-(*iii*), then we shall show that this family is well-ordered and contains A. The members of such a family will serve as the carriers for our well-orderd sets. To obtain the smallest family of our required type, we note that intersection of any collection of such families is again of the desired type. Hence this intersection will be the required family, $\mathfrak{F}$. For example, $\mathfrak{F}$ will contain $\emptyset$, $\{f(A)\}$, $\{f(A)\}^*$, etc.

The next step is to show that $\mathfrak{F}$ is linearly ordered under set inclusion. For this purpose we call a set N normal if it is comparable to every other set X of $\mathfrak{F}$; *i.e.*, N is normal if for any $X \in \mathfrak{F}$ either $X \subseteq N$ or $N \subseteq X$. Our desire is to prove that every set in $\mathfrak{F}$ is normal. For a fixed normal N we consider the family $\mathfrak{S}_N$ of sets $X \in \mathfrak{F}$ which satisfies either (*a*) $X \subseteq N$ or (*b*) $N^* \subseteq X$. We shall show that $\mathfrak{S}_N$ is a family of sets satisfying (*i*)–(*iii*), so that $\mathfrak{F} \subseteq \mathfrak{S}_N \subseteq \mathfrak{F}$; *i.e.*, $\mathfrak{S}_N = \mathfrak{F}$. It will then follow that every $X \in \mathfrak{F}$ satisfies (*a*) or (*b*). (*i*) $\emptyset$ is clearly in $\mathfrak{S}_N$. (*ii*) Let $X \in \mathfrak{S}_N$. Then either (*a*) $X \subset N$, (*b*) $X = N$, or (*c*) $N^* \subseteq X$. In case (*a*) either $X^* \subseteq N$ or $N \subset X^*$, since N was normal. If $X^* \subseteq N$, then $X^* \in \mathfrak{S}_N$, and (*i*) holds. If $N \subset X^*$, then $X^* - X = (X^* - N) \cup (N - X)$ where $X^* - N \neq \emptyset$ and $N - X \neq \emptyset$, so that $X^* - X$ contains two distinct elements, contrary to $X^* - X = \{f(X)\}$. In case (*b*), $X = N \Rightarrow X^* = N^*$ and $X^* \in \mathfrak{S}_N$. In case (*c*) $N^* \subseteq X \subseteq X^* \Rightarrow N^* \subseteq X^*$, so that $X^* \in \mathfrak{S}_N$. Thus, in all three cases $\mathfrak{S}_N$ satisfies (*ii*). Finally, if $X_i \in \mathfrak{S}_N$ for some collection of X_i, then either $X_i \subseteq N \ \forall\ i$, in which case $\mathbf{U}_i X_i \subseteq N$ or $N^* \subseteq X_{i_0}$ for some i_0, in which case $N^* \subseteq \mathbf{U}_i X_i$. Therefore $\mathfrak{S}_N$ satisfies (*iii*). But since $\mathfrak{S}_N$ now satisfies (*i*)–(*iii*), it follows that $\mathfrak{S}_N = \mathfrak{F}$.

It remains to show next that every X in $\mathfrak{F}$ is normal. Again, let $\mathfrak{N}$ be the family of normal sets. Then (*i*) $\emptyset \in \mathfrak{N}$. Furthermore, we have just shown that if N is normal, then so is N^*. Hence $\mathfrak{N}$ satisfies (*ii*). Finally, let $\{N_i\}$ be a family of normal sets with union $N = \mathbf{U}_i N_i$. For a given X either $N_i \subseteq X \ \forall\ i$, in with case $N \subseteq X$, or there exists i_0 such that $X \subseteq N_{i_0}$, in which case $X \subset \mathbf{U}_i N_i = N$. $\mathfrak{N}$ therefore satisfies (*iii*), whence $\mathfrak{N} = \mathfrak{F}$; *i.e.*, every $X \in \mathfrak{F}$ is normal.

Our next step is to show that $\langle \mathfrak{F}, \subseteq \rangle$ is well-ordered. Let $\mathfrak{S}$ be a subfamily of $\mathfrak{F}$ and let $\mathfrak{H} = \{X \in \mathfrak{F} | X \subseteq Y \ \forall\ Y \in \mathfrak{S}\}$; *i.e.*, $\mathfrak{H}$ is the family of all sets X in $\mathfrak{F}$ which precede every $Y \in \mathfrak{S}$. Then $H = \mathbf{U}\{X | X \in \mathfrak{H}\}$ is also in $\mathfrak{F}$, and $H \subseteq Y \ \forall\ Y \in \mathfrak{S}$. If $H \in \mathfrak{S}$, then it is the first element of $\mathfrak{S}$. Otherwise, H^* is the first element of $\mathfrak{S}$. In any case $\mathfrak{S}$ has a first element.

Finally, A itself is in $\mathfrak{F}$. For if not, let $F = \mathbf{U}\{X | X \in \mathfrak{F}\}$. Then $F \neq A$, since $F \in \mathfrak{F}$. But then F^* is defined and in $\mathfrak{F}$, contrary to the fact that $X \subseteq F \ \forall\ X \in \mathfrak{F}$.

Our final step is to define a well-ordering for each X in $\mathfrak{F}$. We let $\mathfrak{W}$ be the family of sets on which a well-ordering can be defined. Then clearly $\emptyset \in \mathfrak{W}$. Next let $\langle X, \leq_X \rangle$ be a well-ordered set defined on X. Define $\leq_{X^*}$ on X^* by: $x \leq_{X^*} y \Leftrightarrow x \leq_{X^*} y$ for $x, y \in X$ and $x \leq_{X^*} f(A - X)$; *i.e.*, let $\leq_{X^*}$ be defined by extension from $\leq_X$ by letting $f(A - X)$ follow every $x \in X$. Finally, if $\langle X_i, \leq_i \rangle$ is a family of well-ordered sets defined on X_i, we define a well-ordering on $X = \mathbf{U}_i X_i$ as follows: Let $x, y \in X$. Then $x \in X_i$ and $y \in X_j$ for some i, j. By the well-ordering of $\mathfrak{F}$, either $X_i \subseteq X_j$ or $X_j \subseteq X_i$, say $X_i \subseteq X_j$. Then $x, y \in X_j$. Let $x \leq_X y$ in $X \Leftrightarrow x \leq_{X_j} y$. We leave it to the reader to show that the ordering so defined in X is independent of the X_i and X_j chosen. We have therefore shown that the class $\mathfrak{W}$ satisfies (*i*)–(*iii*), so that $\mathfrak{W} = \mathfrak{F}$.;

i.e., every $X \in \mathfrak{F}$ can be well-ordered. As a specific case $A \in \mathfrak{W}$ implies that A can be well-ordered.

Our final result now follows as a corollary.

Theorem 3-14. *If* $\mathfrak{a}$ *and* $\mathfrak{b}$ *are two cardinal numbers, then either* $\mathfrak{a} \leq \mathfrak{b}$ *or* $\mathfrak{b} \leq \mathfrak{a}$.

Proof. Let A and B be two sets such that $\bar{\bar{A}} = \mathfrak{a}$ and $\bar{\bar{B}} = \mathfrak{b}$. Then there exist relations $\leq_A$ on A and $\leq_B$ on B such that $\langle A, \leq_A \rangle$ and $\langle B, \leq_B \rangle$ are well-ordered sets. By Theorem 12, either A is similar to an ideal J of B, or B is similar to an ideal I of A. But $A \simeq J$ implies $A \sim J$, so that $\bar{\bar{A}} = \bar{\bar{J}} \leq \bar{\bar{B}}$; *i.e.*, $\mathfrak{a} \leq \mathfrak{b}$. Similarly, in the second case, $\mathfrak{b} \leq \mathfrak{a}$.

Our final remark is that if $\mathfrak{a}$ is any cardinal number, then $\mathfrak{a}$ can be represented by a set A, which in turn admits a well-ordering relation $\leq$, such that $\langle A, \leq \rangle$ is of order type α where $\bar{\alpha} = \mathfrak{a}$. If we consider the family of all ordinals α with the same cardinal, $\mathfrak{a}$, then by the well-ordering of the ordinals, there is a least α_0. This least ordinal associated with a given cardinal then acts as a canonical form for $\mathfrak{a}$. We could therefore have started with the theory of ordinal numbers and obtained the cardinals as a special subcase. In this approach, a cardinal number is defined as a special kind of ordinal. This is the method developed by von Neumann. The class of cardinals is then a well-ordered class indexed by the ordinals themselves. We designate them by: 0, 1, 2, . . . $\aleph_0, \aleph_1, \ldots, \aleph_\omega, \aleph_{\omega+1}, \ldots, \aleph_{\omega 2}, \ldots$ The problem of the continuum then asks where the power of the continuum $\mathfrak{c}$ fits in this series.

EXERCISES

1. Prove the equivalence of the two forms of ordinary induction given in section 3-7.
2. Prove the reflexive and transitive properties for order for ordinal numbers.
3. Prove that if b is the immediate predecessor of a, then $I_a = [b]\downarrow$.
4. Extend the division algorithm to arbitrary ordinal numbers; *i.e.*, if α and β are two given ordinal numbers, then there exist γ and δ such that $\alpha = \beta\gamma + \delta$ with $\delta < \beta$.
5. Show by example that the unique factorization theorem does not hold for arbitrary ordinal numbers.
6. Prove the following laws for inequalities for ordinal numbers:

   (*a*) $\alpha < \beta \Rightarrow \gamma + \alpha < \gamma + \beta$,
   (*b*) $\alpha < \beta \Rightarrow \alpha + \gamma \leq \beta + \gamma$
   (*c*) $\alpha < \beta \Rightarrow \gamma\alpha < \gamma\beta$; $\quad \gamma \neq 0$
   (*d*) $\alpha < b \Rightarrow \alpha\gamma \leq \beta\gamma$, $\quad \gamma \neq 0$.
7. If f_1 and f_2 are two functions defined on a well-ordered set $\langle A, \leq \rangle$ in terms of a recursive rule ϕ, show that $f_1 = f_2$.

8. Show that if $\langle A, \leq \rangle$ and $\langle B, \leq \rangle$ are two well-ordered sets and f is a mapping from A onto an ideal I in B, and g is a mapping from B onto an ideal J of A, then the range of the composite $f \circ g|_I$ is an ideal of A.

9. Prove that the order defined on $\bigcup_i X_i$ described in the text in section 3-9 is independent of the particular X_i and X_j containing x and y.

10. Prove the following form of the principle of transfinite induction: If $\{p_\alpha\}$ is a set of statements indexed by a set of ordinals $\alpha < \gamma$ for some fixed γ such that

(i) the truth of p_α implies the truth of $p_{\alpha+1}$,
(ii) the truth of p_α for any limit ordinal follows from the truth of all p_β for all $\beta < \alpha$,

then p_α is true for all $\alpha < \gamma$.

4

PARTIALLY ORDERED SETS AND LATTICE THEORY

4-1. INTRODUCTION

In the first three chapters we developed, first the axioms of set theory and second, the algebra of sets. Set theory turned out to be extremely rich in relations, operations, and properties of these relations and operations. In this chapter we turn to the study of abstract algebraic systems modeled on various aspects of the algebra of sets, and we can expect to find a similar variety within the systems which we shall develop. We begin with a set of elements, A, and introduce binary relations within A by specifying various subsets of $A \times A$ and binary operations by specifying mappings from $A \times A$ into A. We list certain properties of these relations and operations as postulates. A convenient way of specifying these relations and operations is by means of tables. We list the elements of A both as row and column headings, so that each position in the table corresponds to an element of $A \times A$. Thus the ordered pair $\langle x, y \rangle$, $x, y \in A$, determines the position in the x-row and y-column. If ρ is a relation on A, then ρ specifies certain positions in the table which we indicate by a check or some other suitable device. The resulting table is essentially the graph of ρ. On the other hand, if $\circ$ is a binary operation, then $\circ$ specifies a value from A for each position in the table; *i.e.*, $\circ$ fills out a value $x \circ y$ for the position designated by the ordered pair $\langle x, y \rangle$. The resulting table is called the **operation table** of $\circ$. We have already encountered examples in Chapter 2. As a further example, let A be the set of integers $\{1, 2, 3, 4, 6, 12\}$ and let $|$ be the relation "divides"; *i.e.*, $m \mid n \Longleftrightarrow n = km$ for some integer k. The table for this example is given as Table 4-1. On the other hand, Table 4-2 is a table for the operation of multiplication of the integers $\{0, 1, 2, 3, 4\}$ taken modulo 5.

Since an operation is a mapping defined on $A \times A$; *i.e.*, with domain the set of all ordered pairs $\langle x, y \rangle$ $x, y \in A$, every position in the table must be filled in with values in A, but it is not necessary that $\circ$ be either one-to-one or onto. For example, the constant operation $\phi(X, Y) = \emptyset$, $\forall X, Y \in \mathfrak{P}(U)$, assigns the fixed value $\emptyset$ to every position in the table. If on the other hand,

1	1	2	3	4	6	12
1	×	×	×	×	×	×
2		×		×	×	×
3			×		×	×
4				×		×
6					×	×
12						×

TABLE 4-1

·	0	1	2	3	4
0	0	0	0	0	0
1	0	1	2	3	4
2	0	2	4	1	3
3	0	3	1	4	2
4	0	4	3	2	1

TABLE 4-2

it happens that a mapping is defined in $A \times A$, (the domain is a subset of $A \times A$) with values in A, then it is called a *partial operation*. However, convention dictates that the word "operation" means a mapping *on* $A \times A$.

The properties that we choose as postulates for our system are the governing laws of the system. From them we derive theorems by applications of the rules of the underlying logic. Applications of the system then occur whenever we can find a model which satisfies the postulates, and all other theorems must then be true laws for the model. Theoretically, there are no bounds on the selection of the basic postulates outside of a certain psychological dispensation toward efficiency, practicality and aesthetics. The only real requirement is that they be *consistent*. By this we mean that it shall not be possible to deduce from the postulates both the truth and falsity of the same theorem. An inconsistent theory is rather useless, since every theorem is both true and false within it. Methods of testing for consistency generally consist of setting up an example in some other part of mathematics which we are willing to believe is consistent. Thus if $\langle A, \circ \rangle$ is a given system and if $\langle M, * \rangle$ is a model which is consistent, then we deduce that $\langle A, \circ \rangle$ is consistent. Here by a model we mean a specific set M within some other theory and a specific operation $*$ such that $*$ satisfies the postulates for $\langle A, \circ \rangle$ amongst possible others. Then if it is possible to derive a contradiction from the postulates of $\langle A, \circ \rangle$, the same contradiction would also appear in the system containing $\langle M, * \rangle$ contrary to its assumed consistency. This is, of course, not an absolute proof of consistency but merely a "*relative consistency proof*." We merely relay the absolute proof to the study of the system which contained the model. The importance of set theory here is that it serves as a rich source of models for many other systems. The absolute consistency of set theory relies on the contradictory free axiomatization which we have assumed rather than proved. We leave any further discussion of the matter to the meta-mathematicians.

The next general question concerning postulate systems is that of *redun-*

dancy within the postulates. This matter is considerably less significant and is perhaps more a question of aesthetics than anything else. We wish to list a set of postulates which is to a certain degree minimum; *i.e.*, such that none can be eliminated without changing the nature of the system. Otherwise, we have redundancies built into the system. If one of the postulates can be derived as a theorem from the others, then it is called *dependent*, and otherwise, *independent*. An irredundant system is one in which each postulate is independent. The way independency is proven is again by means of models. If we wish to prove a given postulate is independent from a set of others, then we construct a model in which the others are all true theorems, while the given statement is false. Clearly if the given statement were derivable from the others, it would have to hold in the model. If we do this for each of the postulates in turn, then we have established the independence of all the postulates and we have no redunancies. This means that we must construct a number of, perhaps artificial, models which would otherwise have no practical value. Redundancy is not in itself harmful, and, in fact, most of the commonly used postulate systems for Boolean algebra, for example, have some redundancy in them. Redundancy simply means that we have postulated more than we really needed to. Of course, the extreme would be to postulate all the known theorems of a theory, in which case there would be very little to prove except the consistency of the system. Perhaps the most desirable feature of an independent set of postulates is that it is simpler to test a proposed example; the fewer postulates, the less the work.

The third general property of a postulate system is that of *categoricalness*. A system is said to be *categorical* if it determines a single system; *i.e.*, if two proposed candidates satisfy the postulates, then they are isomorphic in the sense of Chapter 2. Thus, for example, the postulates for the real number system are categorical, and there is essentially only one set of real numbers. On the other hand, the postulates for groups are certainly not categorical, and there are many nonisomorphic examples of groups.

Our final consideration in choosing a set of postulates is mainly one of practicality. As pointed out above, any set of consistent postulates defines an algebraic structure. However we do not, in general, pick postulates at random, but have some eye out as to usefulness of the system. In fact, we generally have some specific example in mind before choosing our postulates. Thus we have some guarantee that the theory they generate will have some appeal to others and not be a waste of time. In this text most of the initial appeal comes from the algebra of sets, which supplies both models on which the postulates are based as well as examples of their usefulness. In fact, most of our postulates will be taken from the theorems of Chapter 2. Thus we guarantee a model of the system which automatically assures its relative consistency. On the other hand, many other applications will arise elsewhere in mathematics so that the systems which arise are of general interest.

4-2. PARTIALLY ORDERED SETS

Our first example of an abstract system is a set P with a relation $\leq$ which is reflexive, anti-symmetric and transitive. Such a system is called a partially ordered set. The system is modeled on 1–3 of Theorem 2-10, so that our first example is the power set $\mathfrak{P}(U)$ of a fixed set U where $\leq$ is to be interpreted as set inclusion. The formal definition is:

Definition 4-1. *A* **partially ordered set,** $\langle P, \leq \rangle$ *is a set P with a relation* $\leq$ *such that for all* $x, y, z \in P$:

$PO1$: $x \leq x$ (*reflexive*),
$PO2$: $(x \leq y) \wedge (y \leq x) \Rightarrow (x = y)$ (*anti-symmetric*),
$PO3$: $(x \leq y) \wedge (y \leq z) \Rightarrow (x \leq z)$ (*transitive*).

It is emphasized that, although the algebra of sets served as a model for the definition, $\leq$ is not necessarily set inclusion. $\langle P, \leq \rangle$ is simply any set with any relation that is reflexive, anti-symmetric and transitive. For example, the set of real numbers under the usual order is a partially ordered set, $\langle \mathbf{R}, \leq \rangle$. It is this example that inspired the notation $\leq$. In fact, we also frequently read $\leq$ as "precedes" or "is less than." The proof is left to the exercises. For another example, let W be the set of words in the dictionary and let $\leq$ mean lexicographic ordering. Then $\langle W, \leq \rangle$ is a partially ordered set. If $\mathbf{Z}$ is the set of integers and $|$ means divisibility, then $\langle \mathbf{Z}, | \rangle$ is a partially ordered set. Similarly, $\langle \mathbf{Z}, \leq \rangle$, where $\leq$ is the usual order, is a partially ordered set. Note that in these last two examples, the base set is the same but the partial orders are quite different. For example $2 \leq 3$, but $2 \nmid 3$. Therefore it is important to specify the relation as well as the set in defining a partially ordered set.

A useful device in the study of partially ordered sets and lattices is the partially ordered set diagram. If $\langle P, \leq \rangle$ is a partially ordered set, we say that y **covers** x if $x \leq y$, $x \neq y$ and there are no intervening elements between x and y. We write $x \prec y$; *i.e.*,

$$x \prec y \Leftrightarrow x \leq z \leq y \Rightarrow x = z \quad \text{or} \quad y = z$$

The covering relation is a subrelation of the partial order relation: $x \prec y \Rightarrow x \leq y$. We represent the elements of P by points in the plane such that if $x \leq y$, then y occurs above x, and we connect x to y by a line segment if and only if x covers y or y covers x. The resulting diagram is called the **partially ordered set diagram** of $\langle P, \leq \rangle$. We leave it to the exercises to show that if P is finite, then a partially ordered set diagram can always be constructed.* However, the notion of a partially ordered set diagram is also useful even when P is infinite. See, for example, figure 4-1(c), as well as the

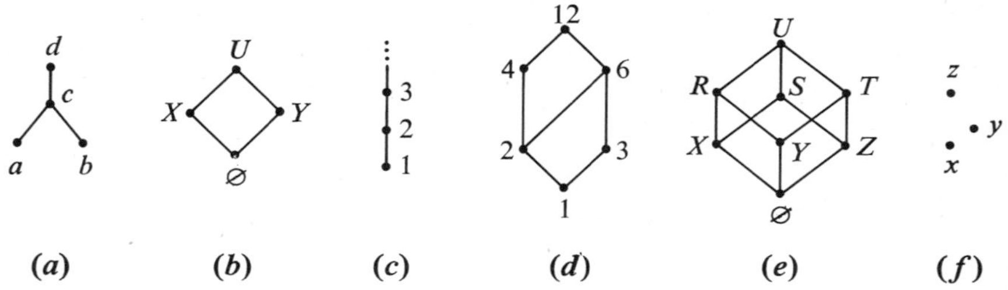

FIGURE 4-1

exercises. Examples of diagrams are given in figure 4-1.(a) is the set $P = \{a, b, c, d\}$ with the partial order given by the pairs $\langle a, c\rangle, \langle a, d\rangle, \langle b, c\rangle, \langle b, d\rangle, \langle c, d\rangle, \langle a, a\rangle, \langle b, b\rangle, \langle c, c\rangle$ and $\langle d, d\rangle$. (b) is the diagram of the set of subsets of $U = \{0, 1\}$ where $X = \{0\}$ and $Y = \{1\}$. (c) is the set $\mathbf{N}$ under $\leq$. Note that this set is infinite. (d) is the set of integral divisors of 12 under $|$. (e) is the power set of $U = \{x, y, z\}$ where $X = \{x\}$, $Y = \{y\}$, $Z = \{z\}$, $R = \{x, y\}$, $S = \{x, z\}$, and $T = \{y, z\}$. Finally (f) is the set $P = \{x, y, z\}$ under the equality relation. Other examples are given in the exercises.

EXERCISES

1. Show that the relation ρ on a set P is reflexive if and only if $\Delta_P \subseteq \rho$ where Δ_P is the identity relation on P.
2. Show that ρ is transitive on P if and only if $\rho \circ \rho \subseteq \rho$.
3. Show that ρ is symmetric if and only if $\rho = \rho^{-1}$.
4. A relation on a set P is called a *pre-ordering* if it is reflexive and transitive; *i.e.*, (i) $a\rho a \ \forall \ a \in P$ and (ii) $a\rho b$ and $b\rho c$ imply $a\rho c$. If $\langle P, \rho\rangle$ is a pre-ordered set, define $a \equiv b$ if and only if $a\rho b$ *and* $b\rho a$. Show that $\equiv$ is an equivalence relation.

*A partially ordered set diagram is a directed graph in the sense of the theory of graphs. The vertices of the graph are the elements of P, and the edges are the pairs $\langle x, y\rangle$ such that y covers x.

In the quotient set $\bar{P} = P/\equiv$, define $\bar{\rho}$ by $\bar{a}\bar{\rho}\bar{b}$ if and only if $a\rho b$ where $\bar{a}$ is the coset containing a. Show that $\bar{\rho}$ is well defined; *i.e.*, is independent of the representative chosen from a. Show that $\langle \bar{P}, \bar{\rho} \rangle$ is a partially ordered set.

5. Prove that if $\langle P_n, \leq \rangle$ is a partially ordered set defined on a finite carrier set P_n with n elements, then $\langle P_n, \leq \rangle$ always has a partially ordered set diagram. (*Hint*: Use induction on n, assuming that $\langle P_n, \leq \rangle$ has a diagram and constructing the extension from $\langle P_n, \leq \rangle$ to $\langle P_{n+1}, \leq \rangle$.)
6. In what sense is the partially ordered set diagram of $\langle P_n, \leq \rangle$ unique?
7. Show how the graph of a partially ordered set determines the partially ordered set; *i.e.*, show how the cover relation $\prec$ determines the partial ordering $\leq$.
8. Construct the partially ordered set diagram for the set $\langle \mathbf{N}, | \rangle$.

4-3. TOTALLY ORDERED SETS, MAXIMAL AND MINIMAL ELEMENTS, ATOMS

In the two examples $\langle \mathbf{N}, \leq \rangle$ and $\langle \mathbf{N}, | \rangle$ we note an essential difference, in that in the second there are elements which are not related by the partial order, whereas this does not occur in the first. If both of the statements $x \leq y$ and $y \leq x$ are false, then we say that x and y are **incomparable**. In terms of the diagram, neither x nor y can be arrived at by a strictly upward (or downward) sequence of line segments. For example, a and b are incomparable in (a) of figure 4-1 while in (f) all elements are incomparable. In this last case, wherein every element is incomparable to every other, $\langle P, \leq \rangle$ is called **totally disordered.** At the other extreme is the case when every pair of elements is comparable. This is the more important case and was already defined in Chapter 3. Such a partially ordered set $\langle P, \leq \rangle$ is called **totally ordered (linearly ordered, simply ordered)** and P is called a **chain**. The first case above, $\langle \mathbf{N}, \leq \rangle$, is an example. Thus, *a partially ordered set* $\langle P, \leq \rangle$ *is* **totally ordered** *if it satisfies:*

PO4: For all $x, y \in P$ *either* (*i*) $x \leq y$ *or* (*ii*) $y \leq x$.

This is known as the law of *dichotomy* (or connexity). The diagram of a chain can therefore always be represented as a set of points on a line, which clarifies the alternate terminology, linearly ordered set. Figure 4-1(c) is an example, whereas each of the other examples contains a pair of incomparable elements. A second example of a chain is the set of real numbers under their usual order, $\langle \mathbf{R}, \leq \rangle$.

In the system of real numbers considered as a totally ordered set, we speak of z being between x and y, of open and closed intervals, etc. Much of this terminology can be carried over into partially ordered sets in general, provided we take into consideration incomparable elements. Thus we say that z is **between** x and y if either $x \leq z \leq y$ or $y \leq z \leq x$. The set of all z between x and y is then called the **interval** $[x, y]$. If the further condition $z \neq x, y$ is met, then we say that z is **strictly between** x and y. In this case we call the set of elements strictly between x and y the **open interval**, (x, y). In contrast, the interval including the end points x and y is called a **closed interval**, $[x, y]$. Mixed situations where the interval contains one but not both end points are called **half-open** intervals and designated by either $(x, y]$ or $[x, y)$. Finally, corresponding to the infinite intervals $(-\infty, y]$ or $[x, +\infty)$ of the real number system, we have the sets $[x]\downarrow = \{t|x \leq t\}$ and $[x]\uparrow = \{t|t \leq x\}$. These sets are also called *upper* and *lower ideals* of $\langle P, \leq\rangle$ and considerable use will be made of them later. We have already used them in Chapter 3. An upper ideal is also called a **filter**.

If $\leq$ designates the partial order relation of a partially ordered set, then we also write $x < y$ to mean that $x \leq y$ and $x \neq y$. x is called strictly below y, and $<$ is called a **strict inequality**. Thus an open interval can also be defined as $(x, y) = \{t|x < t < y\}$, etc. In figure 4-1(e) the set of elements $\{R, T, Y, U\}$ is the interval $[Y, U]$. The interval $[Y, U]$ is also the set $Y\uparrow$, while $Y\downarrow = \{Y, \emptyset\}$. On the other hand, the chain $\{Y, R, U\}$ is not an interval. In figure 1(d), $\{2, 3, 6\}$ is the half-open interval $(1, 6]$.

We can also speak of the **converse relation** to a partial order as has already been defined in Chapter 1. Thus $y \geq x$ if and only if $x \leq y$. The partially ordered set $\{P, \geq\}$ is then called the **dual** of $\{P, \leq\}$. Its diagram is obtained by inverting that for $\{P, \leq\}$. In figure 4-1, (b), (d), (e) and (f) are all self-dual while (a) and (c) are not. For example, in (c) there is a first element at the bottom but none at the top.

In figure 4-1(a) the elements a and b are distinguished by the fact that there are no elements below them in the diagram. Such elements are called **minimal** elements of $\langle P, \leq\rangle$. Hence an element *m is minimal if* $x \leq m$ *implies* $x = m$. Similarly, an element is called **maximal** *if* $m \leq x$ *implies* $x = m$. Note that (a) and (c) have minimal elements, while (a) has a maximal element but (c) does not. Note also that a set may have more than one minimal or maximal element. For example, both a and b are minimal elements in 1(a). Distinct minimal elements will, however, always be incomparable. If, on the other hand, there exists an element m which is minimal and at the same time $m \leq x \; \forall \; x \in P$, then m is called a **least** element. Hence *m is a* **least** *if and only if* $m \leq x \; \forall \; x \in P$. Dually, *m is a* **greatest** *element if* $x \leq m \; \forall \; x \in P$. Clearly a partially ordered set can have only one least or one greatest element. In figure 4-1(a) there is no least element, but d is a greatest element. We also call a least element 0 a **lower unit** or **zero** of P, and a greatest element 1 an **upper unit** or **universal element**. Thus in the power set of U, $\emptyset$ and U are lower and upper units, respectively.

If $\langle P, \leq\rangle$ is a partially ordered set with a least element 0, then any element which covers 0 is called an **atom**. Hence *a is an atom if* $a \neq 0$ *and* $0 \leq x \leq a$ *implies either* $x = 0$ *or* $x = a$. If every element of a partially ordered set contains an atom, then $\langle P, \leq\rangle$ is called **atomic**. Similarly, if P has an upper unit, u, then we may define a **dual atom** as an *element* $d \neq 1$ *such that* $d \leq x \leq 1$ *implies either* $x = d$ *or* $x = 1$. The partially ordered set of figure 4-1(a) has no atoms since it has no zero, while 2 is an atom in 4-1(c). The element c is a dual atom in 4-1(a), while in 4-1(c) there are no dual atoms. In the power set $\mathfrak{P}(U)$ of a set U every singleton set is an atom, while a dual atom is any set whose complement is a singleton. We can extend the concept of an atomic partially ordered set to that of local atomicity by specifying that the ideals $[a]\uparrow$ and $[a]\downarrow$ should be atomic. Thus we say that $\langle P, \leq \rangle$ is *locally atomic* at a if every x such that $a \leq x$ contains an element y such that y covers a and similarly if $z \leq a$, then z is contained in some w such that w is covered by a. For example, every power set algebra is locally atomic at every element.

EXERCISES

1. Construct the operation table for set union for the power set of $U = \{0, 1\}$. Derive the table for the relation, set inclusion, from this table using the fact that $X \subseteq Y \Leftrightarrow X \cup Y = Y$. Compare this table with the diagram of figure 4-1(b).
2. Construct the table for addition for **N** mod 5.
3. Construct the tables for Δ and $\cap$ for the power set of $U = \{0\}$. Construct the tables for multiplication and addition for **N** mod 2. Construct tables for addition and multiplication on evens and odds; *i.e.*, $\{e, o\}$ where the tables show whether the sum or product of two elements is even or odd. Show that these three examples are isomorphic algebraic systems.
4. Construct a table for the operation, implication, for the six sets X, Y, XY, YX, $X \cup Y$ and U, where X and Y are subsets of U. Using the theorem $X \subseteq Y \Leftrightarrow XY = U$, use this table to construct the table for the relation $\subseteq$ for these sets. Construct the diagram. (Here XY is $X \rightarrow Y$).
5. Construct a diagram for the following sets:
   (a) The set of divisors of 24 under divisibility;
   (b) The set of negative integers in their natural order;
   (c) The set $P = \{a, b, c, d\}$ with $\leq$ defined by $\langle a, b\rangle, \langle c, d\rangle$ and $\langle x, x\rangle \ \forall\ x \in P$;
   (d) The living members of your family under "is a descendant of."
6. Prove that the set of postulates for a partially ordered set are independent.
7. Construct a diagram for the set $\langle \mathbf{R}, \leq \rangle$.
8. Show that the set of positive real numbers $\mathbf{R}^+$ is a partially ordered set without a least element. Show that the set of reals greater than or equal to zero is a partially ordered set with a least element but no atoms.
9. Prove that if every subset of a partially ordered set has a least element, then it is totally ordered.
10. Show that if the power set of a set U is totally ordered, then U is either a singleton or the null set.

11. Prove that a partially ordered set can have at most one least element.

12. Prove that a least element is minimal.

13. Prove that if x and y are distinct minimal elements, then they are incomparable.

14. Show that the diagram of a totally unordered set $\langle P, \phi \rangle$ is totally disconnected.

15. Prove that a set is totally unordered if every element is maximal.

16. An element is called *isolated* if it is not related to any element distinct from itself. Show that if x is isolated, then it is both minimal and maximal, and conversely.

17. If $<$ is a relation on a set P satisfying: (*i*) $x < y \Rightarrow y \not< x$, and (*ii*) $(x < y) \wedge (y < z) \Rightarrow (x < z)$ and $\leq$ is defined by $x \leq y \Leftrightarrow (x < y) \vee (x = y)$, then $\langle P, \leq \rangle$ is a partially ordered set.

18. Prove that $\{\mathbf{P}, |\}$ is a partially ordered set.

19. If $\mathbf{R}$ is the set of real numbers and $x \leq y$ if and only if either $x - y \in \mathbf{R}^+$ or $x = y$, prove that $\{\mathbf{R}, \leq\}$ is a partially ordered set.

20. Show that $[x, y] = [x]\uparrow \cap [y]\downarrow$.

21. Let $x \equiv y$ if and only if x is connected to y by a sequence of line segments (not necessarily ascending). Show that $\equiv$ is an equivalence relation and that $P/\equiv$ is totally unordered, where $\leq$ is defined in $P/\equiv$ by relating two cosets if and only if there exist related elements within them.

22. Let $\mathbf{C}$ be the set of complex numbers. Define $x + iy \leq u + iv \Leftrightarrow$ either $x < u$ or $x = u$ and $y \leq v$. Show that $\leq$ is a total order (lexicographic order). If $x + iy \leq u + iv \Leftrightarrow (x \leq u) \wedge (y \leq v)$, show that the order is partial but not total. Describe the set of positive elements in each case.

23. If $\langle \mathfrak{P}(U), \subseteq \rangle$ is the power set of U under inclusion and $X \in \mathfrak{P}(U)$, describe $[X]\uparrow$ and $[X]\downarrow$. If $X \subseteq Y$, describe the interval (X, Y). Show that $X \subseteq Y$ implies $[Y]\uparrow \subseteq [X]\uparrow$.

24. Prove that a chain can have at most one minimal and one maximal element.

25. A partial order $\leq$ on a set P is called a **well-ordering** if every subset of P contains a least element. Show that every well-ordering is a total ordering; *i.e.*, every well-ordered set is totally ordered. (*See* Chapter 3.)

4-4. UPPER AND LOWER BOUNDS

In our discussion of set intersection and union, we saw that these two operations could be characterized in terms of the set inclusion relation by making use of the auxiliary concepts of greatest lower bound and least upper bound. These concepts generalize to arbitrary partially ordered sets. We first define an **upper bound** for a pair of elements a and b of a partially ordered set $\langle P, \leq \rangle$ as *an element x such that $a \leq x$ and $b \leq x$*. Dually, a **lower bound** is *an element x such that $x \leq a$ and $x \leq b$*. In terms of the diagram an upper bound is above both a and b and connected to them by a sequence of ascending line segments. In figure 4-1(a), c and d are both upper bounds for a and b, but a and b have no lower bounds and therefore no common lower bound. Clearly the concepts of upper and lower bound can be extended to arbitrary collections of elements of P. If A is any subset of P, then x is an **upper bound of** A $\leftrightarrow a \leq x$ *for all* x *in* A. Dually, x is a lower bound $\leftrightarrow$ $x \leq a \; \forall \; x \in A$. For example, if A is the set of negative real numbers, then every real number greater than or equal to zero is an upper bound for A in the partially ordered set $\langle \mathbf{R}, \leq \rangle$. Also if $\langle P, \leq \rangle$ has upper and lower units, 1 and 0, then they are upper and lower bounds for every subset of P. If A is a singleton set $A = \{a\}$, then every element above a is an upper bound for A. Hence the set of all upper bounds is the set previously described as $[a]\uparrow = \{x | a \leq x\}$. This set is called the *principle filter generated by a*. More generally, we use the same notation for arbitrary subsets, A, of P and write:

$$A\uparrow = \{x \in P | a \leq x \; \forall \; a \in A\}$$

for the set of all upper bounds for A. (It is not to be confused with $\{x \in P | a \leq x$ for some $a \in P\}$. In figure 4-2, (a) is a partially ordered set in which

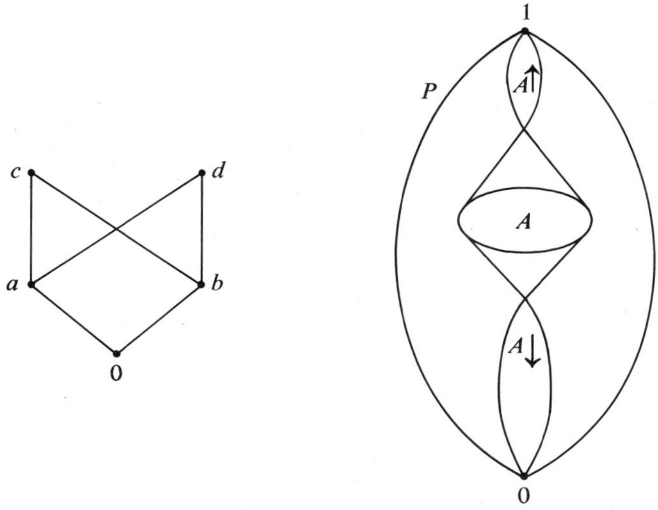

(a) (b)

FIGURE 4-2

$\{a, b\}\uparrow = \{c, d\}$; *i.e.*, c and d are both upper bounds for the set consisting of a and b. In figure 4-2(b) a more general situation is shown wherein A is any subset of P while $A\uparrow$ lies entirely above A while $A\downarrow$ is below A. In this case,

P has an upper unit 1 and lower unit 0. Either set $A\downarrow$ or $A\uparrow$ may, of course, be empty, as for example $\{c, d\}\uparrow = \emptyset$ in figure 4-2(a). If U is a fixed set and A is any subset, then within $\mathfrak{P}(U)$, $A\uparrow$ is the set of all subsets of U which contain A; *i.e.*, $A\uparrow = \{X \in \mathfrak{P}(U) | A \subseteq X\}$, while $A\downarrow$ is the set of all subsets of A. If on the other hand $\mathfrak{A}$ is any family of subsets of U, then $\mathfrak{A}\uparrow$ is the family of all subsets which contain *every* set A in $\mathfrak{A}$.

Returning to the special case of a set of two elements a and b, then the set $\{a, b\}\uparrow$ is the set $\{x \in P | (a \leq x) \wedge (b \leq x)\}$. But this is exactly the set intersection of the sets $\{x \in P | a \leq x\}$ and $\{x \in P | b \leq x\}$. Hence $\{a, b\}\uparrow = [a]\uparrow \cap [b]\uparrow$ where $\cap$ means set intersection. Generalizing to arbitrary subsets A of P, we have

$$A\uparrow = \bigcap_{a \in A} [a]\uparrow$$

and dually,

$$A\downarrow = \bigcap_{a \in A} [a]\downarrow .$$

For example, in figure 4-1(c), $\{1, 2\}\uparrow = \{2, 3, 4, \ldots\}$; *i.e.*, the set of integers 2, 3, 4, . . . is the set of upper bounds for the set $\{1, 2\}$.

We can now introduce the concepts of a *least* upper bound and *greatest* lower bound within partially ordered set theory. Again we first treat the case of a set of two elements a and b and say that *c is a* **least upper bound** *of a and b if c is itself an upper bound for a and b and at the same time is contained in every other upper bound. c* is called the **least upper bound** or **supremum** *of a and b and satisfies:*

$$(i)\ a, b \leq c$$

and

$$(ii)\ a, b \leq x \text{ implies } c \subseteq \leq x$$

Dually, d is called a **greatest lower bound** or **infimum** of a and b if:

$$(i)\ d \leq a, b$$

and

$$(ii)\ x \leq a, b \Rightarrow x \leq d$$

We also write $c = \boldsymbol{a \cup b}$ and call c the **join** or **union** of a and b, while the greatest lower bound is designated by $\boldsymbol{a \cap b}$ and called the **meet** or **intersection** of a and b. To avoid some confusion, we shall try to use meet and join in arbitrary partially ordered sets and intersection and union for the special case of set theory, although such usage is not universal. In figure 4-1(a), $c = a \cup b$ while in figure 4-2(a), there is no element $a \cup b$. In this second case c and d are both upper bounds for a and b, but there is no least such. Hence, in general, the concepts of meet and join do not define operations in the sense of Chapter 1, but only partial operations. On the other hand, even though a and b may not have any join or meet at all, if they do have one, then it is unique. Thus if c and c' are both candidates as joins for a and b, then by (*ii*) $c \leq c'$, while at the same time $c' \leq c$. Hence $c = c'$ and a and b can have at most one join. Dually, meets are also unique. We can now summarize the definitions so far and at the same time extend them to arbitrary sets within P by:

Definition 4-2. *If $\langle P, \leq \rangle$ is any partially ordered set and A is any subset, then the element c is a* **least upper bound**, (*supremum, join, union*) *of A if:*

$$(i)\ a \leq c \ \forall\ a \leq A,$$
$$(ii)\ a \leq x \ \forall\ a \in A \Rightarrow c \leq x.$$

c is designated by $c = l.u.b.A = sup\ A = \bigcup_{a \in A} a$.

Alternative notations are $a \cup b$ if $A = \{a, b\}$, $\bigcup_{i=1}^{n} a_i = a_1 \cup a_2 \cup \cdots \cup a_n$ if A is finite, $\bigcup_{i \in I} a_i$, if A is indexed by I, etc.

Dually, *d is a* **greatest lower bound** (*infimum, meet, intersection*) *of A if:*

$$(i)\ d \leq a \ \forall\ a \in A,$$
$$(ii)\ x \leq a \ \forall\ a \in A \Rightarrow a \leq d.$$

d is designated by $d = \text{g.l.b.}A = infA = \bigcap_{a \in A} a$, etc.

As for the special case of two elements, least upper bounds and greatest lower bounds are unique. As examples, in the partially ordered set $\langle \mathbf{R}, \leq \rangle$, $\sqrt{2} = \text{l.u.b. } \{x | x^2 < 2\}$. The terminology supremum and infimum are taken from common usage in real variable theory. In particular, if A is any finite subset of $\mathbf{R}$, then we can also write max A for sup A, since the least upper bound of A will be its maximum. We also write max $\{a_1, a_2, \ldots, a_n\} = a_1 \cup a_2 \cup \cdots \cup a_n$ in this case. However, a set A may not have a maximum element, in which case the terminology *supremum* becomes more appropriate. The fact that every subset A which is bounded above has a supremum within $\mathbf{R}$ is the very heart of the distinction between the rationals and the reals, and will be discussed more later on. In the case of $\langle \mathbf{P}, | \rangle$, the concept of union reduces to that of least common multiple. Thus an upper bound for two integers a and b is an integer m such that m is a multiple of both a and b; *i.e.* $a, b | m$. A least common multiple is then a common multiple which divides every other common multiple; *i.e.*, a least upper bound with respect to the partial order $|$. Dually, the concept of greatest lower bound becomes identical with that of greatest common division. Thus $8 \cap 10 = 2$ for example, while $8 \cup 10 = 40$. In this case, the more commonly used notation is parentheses; *i.e.*, $m \cap n$ is written $(m, n) = GCD\{m, n\}$, while $m \cup n$ is written $[m, n] = LCM\{m, n\}$.

As a further example, we may consider the set of linear subspaces of a fixed vector space V_n. If $n = 3$, this is the set of lines through the origin, the set of planes through the origin, the origin itself and the whole space V_3. This set $\mathfrak{V}$ of subspaces is a partially ordered set under the partial order "is a linear subspace of." If A and B are two linear subspaces, then the set of points common to them; *i.e.*, the point set intersection, is also a subspace and is therefore their meet within $\mathfrak{V}$. On the other hand, if l_1 and l_2 are two distinct lines (through the origin), then their point set union is not a linear subspace. However, if we consider the plane spanned by l_1 and l_2, then it will be a subspace, will contain both l_1 and l_2 and will be contained in any other subspace which contains l_1 and l_2. Hence, the join of l_1 and l_2 within $\mathfrak{V}$ is the plane spanned by l_1 and l_2. In general, if A and B are arbitrary subspaces, then the meet is their point set intersection, while their join is the space spanned by them; *i.e.*, their least upper bound according to definition 4-2. This example points out the need for care in distinguishing point set union from join as determined by definition 4-2. The real difficulty is that we frequently use the same notation, $\subseteq$, for two essentially different partial orders. Thus in defining point set intersection, $\subseteq$ is interpreted as point set inclusion, while within $\mathfrak{V}$ $\subseteq$ means "is a linear subspace of" and these two are not the same. The same difficulty occurs frequently in the theory of subalgebras in universal algebra. For example, in the theory of groups the partial orders "is a subgroup of" and "is a subset of" are different, but this fact is not usually brought out in the notation.

4-5. SEMI-LATTICES AND LATTICES

In the last section we defined the meet and join of any set of elements and showed that they were unique. However, we also noted that every pair of elements of a partially ordered set does not have to have a meet or join. For example, in a totally unordered set such as (f) of figure 4-1, no pair of distinct elements has a meet or join. Thus the mapping $a, b \to a \cup b$ does not define an operation but may be at best a partial operation. In this section we shall be concerned with the case when our system is closed under meets or joins; *i.e.*, when meets or joins exist for every pair of elements within the system. Such systems are called semi-lattices, or if *both* meet and join always exist for every pair of elements, the system is called a lattice as given by:

Definition 4-3. *If $\langle L, \leq \rangle$ is a partially ordered set such that $a, b \in L$ implies there exists $a \cap b$ in L, then $\langle L, \leq \rangle$ is called a* **meet semi-lattice (lower semi-lattice)**. *Dually, if there exists $a \cup b$ for every pair $a, b \in L$, then L is called a* **join semi-lattice** *(upper semi-lattice). If there exist both $a \cap b$ and $a \cup b \in L$, then L is called a* **lattice.**

To indicate that L is a system with operations, we also write $\langle L, \cap \rangle$ and $\langle L, \cup \rangle$ for semi-lattices and $\langle L, \cap, \cup \rangle$ for a lattice. Many of the examples given above are lattices or semi-lattices. For example, figure 4-1(a) is a join semi-lattice, while all the other examples of figure 4-1 except (f) are lattices. In general, any chain is a lattice, since in this case if $a \leq b$, then $a \cap b = a$ while $a \cup b = b$. Thus the real numbers form a lattice under $\leq$ in which $a \cap b = \min \{a, b\}$ and $a \cap b = \max \{a, b\}$. The power set of a fixed set U is always a lattice in which "meet" means set intersection while "join" means set union. The set of divisors of a fixed integer form a lattice under GCD and LCM for meet and join. Moreover, the set **P** of all positive integers is also such a lattice, but without an upper unit. The set of linear subspaces of a fixed linear vector space is a lattice. The set of subgroups of a group is a lattice, etc. Proofs are left to the exercises.

As might be expected, many of the properties of intersection and union in the algebra of sets carry over into general lattice theory and become theorems. Thus our first theorem of lattice theory is:

Theorem 4-1. *If $\langle L, \cup, \cap \rangle$ is any lattice, then:*

$L1$: $x \cup y = y \cup x$,
$x \cap y = y \cap x$ (*commutative laws*);
$L2$: $x \cup (y \cup z) = (x \cup y) \cup z$,
$x \cap (y \cap z) = (x \cap y) \cap z$ (*associative laws*);
$L3$: $x \cup x = x \cap x = x$ (*idempotent laws*);
$L4$: $x \cup (x \cap y) = x \cap (x \cup y) = x$ (*absorption laws*).

Proof. $L1$: $x \cap y = \text{g.l.b.}\, \{x, y\} = \text{g.l.b.}\, \{y, x\} = y \cap x$. Note that the proof here rests essentially on the fact that the set $\{x, y\}$ is the same as the set $\{y, x\}$. Thus once again, the commutative laws follow basically from the similar laws for the logical connectives and receive their basic justification from logic.

We leave the remainder of the proof to the exercises except for $L4$. By reflexivity, $x \leq x$, and by definition 4-2, $x \cap y \leq x$. Hence $x \cup (x \cap y) \leq x$ by definition of join. Conversely, $x \leq x \cup (x \cap y)$. Therefore, by antisymmetry $x = x \cup (x \cap y)$.

We note that $L1$–$L4$ also hold in a semi-lattice, provided the requisite elements exist. In fact, they also hold in any partially ordered set as in:

Corollary: *If $\langle P, \leq \rangle$ is any partially ordered set, then $L1$–$L4$ hold whenever the proper elements exist within P.*

The theorems relating meet and join to the partial order also carry over from the algebra of sets.

Theorem 4-2. *In any partially ordered set, the following three statements are equivalent:*

(*i*) $x \leq y$,
(*ii*) $x \cup y = y$,
(*iii*) $x \cap y = x$.

Proof. By hypothesis, (*i*) $x \leq y$, and by reflexivity $y \leq y$, so that $x \cup y \leq y$. But $y \leq x \cup y$ by definition. Hence by anti-symmetry $x \cup y = y$. Therefore (*i*) implies (*ii*).

Conversely, let $x \cup y = y$. Then by definition $x \leq x \cup y = y$ so that (*ii*) implies (*i*). Therefore (*i*) and (*ii*) are equivalent. Similarly, (*i*) and (*iii*) are equivalent, and therefore all three are equivalent.

In definition 4-3 we defined a join semi-lattice as a partially ordered set in which every pair of elements has a least upper bound; *i.e.*, a semi-lattice was defined basically as a relational system $\langle L, \leq \rangle$ with a relation, $\leq$. We then introduced the join operation as a secondary concept. We can, however, reverse the process and make the operation fundamental and the relation secondary as in the following theorem:

Theorem 4-3. *A join semi-lattice (meet semi-lattice) is a system $\langle L, \cup \rangle$ ($\langle L, \cap \rangle$) closed under a single binary operation which is idempotent, commutative and associative. Further, if $x \leq y$ is defined by $x \leq y \Leftrightarrow x \cup y = y$, then $x \cup y$ is the least upper bound of x and y under $\leq$.*

Proof. Define $x \leq y \Leftrightarrow x \cup y = y$. Then (*i*) $x \cup x = x$ implies $x \leq x$ by idempotence and the definition. (*ii*) Let $x \leq y$ and $y \leq x$. By definition $x \cup y = y$ and $y \cup x = x$. By commutativity $x = y \cup x = x \cup y = y$. (*iii*) Let $x \leq y$ and $y \leq x$. Then $x \cup y = y$ and $y \cup z = z$. Therefore $x \cup z = x \cup (y \cup z) = (x \cup y) \cup z = y \cup z = z$ by associativity. Thus $x \leq z$, and $\leq$ is therefore a partial order.

To show that $x \cup y = \text{l.u.b.}\,\{x, y\}$ first, $x \cup (x \cup y) = (x \cup x) \cup y = (y \cup y) \cup x = y \cup x$, so that $y \cup x \leq y$. Hence $x \cup y$ is an upper bound of x and y. Next let $x \leq z$ and $y \leq z$. Then by definition $x \cup z = z$ and $y \cup z = z$. Therefore $(x \cup y) \cup z = x \cup (y \cup z) = x \cup z = z$ so that $x \cup y \leq z$. Hence $x \cup y$ is a least upper bound for x and y.

Theorem 4-3 characterizes a semi-lattice as an idempotent, commutative semi-group. As such, the postulates for a meet semi-lattice are exactly the same as for a join semi-lattice, so that there is no distinction between these two concepts. It is only when we introduce a partial order into the semi-lattice that we have a choice of defining $x \leq y$ either by $x \cup y = y$ or by $x \cup y = x$. Hence, given any semi-lattice $\langle L, \cup \rangle$ with a single binary operation, we can always introduce a partial order; and then by means of this partial order, we can define a second partial operation by $x \cap y =$ g.l.b. $\{x, y\}$ in $\langle L, \cap, \leq\rangle$. But since every semi-lattice is not necessarily a lattice, as for example, in figure 4-1(*a*), it is clear that the closure of $\langle L, \cup, \leq\rangle$ under $\cap$ will not follow from the idempotent, commutative and associative laws of $\cup$ alone. To define a lattice as a special case of a semi-lattice, we therefore need a postulate to guarantee closure under $\cap$ where $x \cap y$ is characterized in terms of $\leq$, which is itself characterized in terms of $\cup$ as in Theorem 4-3. We leave the details to the reader in the exercises.

An alternative approach is to define a lattice as a system with two binary operations to start with. In this case, we would postulate closure under both operations at the beginning and then introduce a partial order. But there would be two partial orders, depending on which operation was chosen to define it; *i.e.*, we would define $x \leq_1 y \leftrightarrow x \cup y = y$ and $x \leq_2 y \leftrightarrow x \cap y = x$. It would then be necessary to show that these two partial orders are the same. An example, however, shows that this is not the case. Let $L = \{a, b, c\}$ and let $\cup$ and $\cap$ be defined by the tables of figure 4-3. Both tables are identical,

$\cup$	a	b	c
a	a	c	c
b	c	b	c
c	c	c	c

$\cap$	a	b	c
a	a	c	c
b	c	b	c
c	c	c	c

FIGURE 4-3

but generate dual partially ordered sets $\langle L, \leq_1\rangle$ and $\langle L, \leq_2\rangle$ as shown in the accompanying diagrams. Clearly $\langle L, \cup\rangle$ and $\langle L, \cap\rangle$ are join and meet semi-lattices respectively, so that both operations are idempotent, commutative, and associative. Thus *L1–L3* of Theorem 4-1 hold. However, $\langle L, \cup, \cap\rangle$ is not a lattice, and the two partial orders are distinct; *i.e.*, $\langle L, \leq_1\rangle$ is not the same as $\langle L, \leq_2\rangle$. Clearly, what is needed is some law interrelating the two operations. This is the absorption law, *L4*, of Theorem 4-1. Incidentally, our example shows that it is clearly independent of the other laws. In general, we may characterize a lattice by all four of the laws of Theorem 4-1 as in:

Theorem 4-4. *A lattice is a set L closed with respect to binary operations satisfying L1–L4.*

Proof. The only step remaining in our proof is to show that if $x \leq y$ is defined by $x \cup y = y$, then $x \cap y = x$ so that $\leq_1$ and $\leq_2$ are identical. But by *L4* $x \cap y = x \cap (x \cup y) = x$.

We only made use of one half of the absorption laws, so that the second half is not independent of the remaining postulates. In fact, the postulates may be made less redundant by the elimination of the idempotent laws entirely, but using both absorption laws. We leave the proof to the exercises. Thus a lattice can be characterized most simply as a set with two operations which are commutative and associative and satisfy both absorption laws. The proof of the independence of these laws is omitted here (*cf:* Fraenkel). However, as a corollary to this formulation, we may obtain the principle of duality for lattice theory. We call two statements of lattice theory *duals* if each can be obtained from the other by interchanging the two operations $\cup$ and $\cap$. But each of the laws *L1*, *L2*, and *L4* are self-dual; *i.e.*, each half may be obtained from the other half by interchanging $\cup$ and $\cap$. Hence any theorem that may be derived from these postulates can also be dualized within the theory, the proof being obtained from interchanging $\cup$ and $\cap$ at each step. Hence lattice theory as a whole is a self-dual theory, as stated in the following principle:

Principle of Duality: *Any valid statement of lattice theory remains valid if* $\cup$ *and* $\cap$ *are interchanged throughout.*

Again the significance of the "throughout" is that every secondary concept defined in terms of $\cup$ and $\cap$ must also be dualized. For example, we defined $x \leq y$ by $x \cup y = y$. The dual conccpt is $x \geq y \Leftrightarrow x \cap y = y$. Hence the two partial orders $\leq$ and its converse $\geq$ are duals, and, in applying the principle of duality, we must interchange $\leq$ and $\geq$ also. For example, we proved the statement $x \leq x \cup y$. The dual statement is $x \geq x \cap y$.

Note, however, that the principle of duality does not apply in semi-lattice theory, since the postulates are not self-dual; e.g. join semi-lattice theory is not self-dual. However, the two theories, join semi-lattice theory and meet semi-lattice theory are dual theories and one can be obtained from the other by interchanging $\cup$ and $\cap$, $\leq$ and $\geq$, 0 and 1, maximal and minimal, etc.

EXERCISES

1. Complete the proof of Theorem 4-1.
2. Derive the idempotent laws for $\cup$ and $\cap$ from *L1*, *L2*, *L4*.
3. Show that a lattice can be characterized as a set L with a single binary operation $\cup$ which is commutative, associative, and idempotent, and such that for all $x, y \in L$ there exists an element $z \in L$ satisfying:
   (*i*) $z \cup x = x$ and $z \cup y = y$ and
   (*ii*) $t \cup x = x$ and $t \cup y = y$ imply $t \cup z = z$.

4. If L is a set closed under two operations satisfying $L1$–$L4$ and $x \leq y$ is defined by $x \cup y = y$, prove that $x \cup y$ and $x \cap y$ are least upper and greatest lower bounds for x and y.

5. Prove that every finite subset of a lattice has a least upper bound and greatest lower bound.

6. Prove that every finite lattice has a least and a greatest element.

7. Prove that in any lattice the following distributive inequalities hold:
   (*i*) $x \cup (y \cap z) \leq (x \cup y) \cap (x \cup z)$,
   (*ii*) $(x \cap y) \cup (x \cap z) \leq x \cap (y \cup z)$.

8. Show that $[a]\uparrow \; = [a]\downarrow\,\uparrow$. Is this statement true for any set A?

9. Show that $a \leq b \Longleftrightarrow [b]\uparrow \; \subseteq [a]\uparrow$, where $\subseteq$ is point set inclusion.

10. Show that $A\uparrow \; = \bigcap_{a \leq A} [a]\uparrow$ where $\bigcap$ is set intersection. What is the dual statement?

11. Prove that the set of subgroups of a group is a lattice.

12. Prove that the set of linear subspaces of a linear vector space is a lattice.

13. Let $\mathfrak{K}$ be the set of circles in the plane. Let $K_1 \leq K_2$ mean that circle K_1 is contained within circle K_2. Show that $\langle \mathfrak{K}, \leq \rangle$ is a lattice and interpret $K_1 \cap K_2$. Compare with set intersection, inclusion and union.

14. Let $\mathfrak{C}$ be the set of convex regions in the plane and let $C_1 \leq C_2$ mean that C_1 is a subregion of C_2. Show that $\leq$ is set inclusion, $C_1 \cap C_2$ is set intersection, but that $C_1 \cup C_2$ is not set union. Describe $C_1 \cup C_2$. Show that $\langle \mathfrak{C}, \leq \rangle$ is a lattice.

15. Let $\mathfrak{F}$ be the family of real-valued functions defined on the real unit interval $[0, 1]$. Define $f \leq g$, $f, g \in \mathfrak{F} \Longleftrightarrow f(x) \leq g(x) \; \forall \; x \in [0, 1]$. Show that $\langle \mathfrak{F}, \leq \rangle$ is a lattice and interpret $f \cup g$ and $f \cap g$.

16. Let $\mathfrak{R}$ be the set of all binary relations defined on a fixed set U. Show that $\mathfrak{R}$ is a lattice and interpret $\rho \cup \sigma$ and $\rho \cap \sigma$ where $\rho, \sigma \in \mathfrak{R}$.

17. Let L be the set of points in the plane partially ordered by $\langle x, y \rangle \leq \langle x', y' \rangle \Longleftrightarrow (x \leq x') \wedge (y \leq y')$. Show that $\langle L, \leq \rangle$ is a lattice and interpret join and meet.

18. Repeat exercise 17 if the partial order is lexicographic order.

19. Let P be the set of prime divisors of 30 and let $\mathfrak{P}(P)$ be its power set. Let D be the set of divisors of 30 partially ordered by divisibility. Prove that $\langle \mathfrak{P}(P), \subseteq \rangle$ and $\langle D, | \rangle$ are isomorphic lattices. ($\subseteq$ is set inclusion.)

20. Prove: P is a totally unordered set if and only if $[a]\uparrow \; = [a] \; \forall \; a \in P$.

21. Determine all lattices with 5 or fewer elements. Construct their diagrams.

22. Show that there are 15 distinct lattices with 6 elements.

23. Prove: $(x \cap y) \cup (z \cap w) \leq (x \cup z) \cap (y \cup w)$.

24. Prove: $(x \cap y) \cup (y \cap z) \cup (z \cap x) \leq (x \cup y) \cap (y \cup z) \cap (z \cup x)$.

25. Show that if c covers a and b and $a \neq b$, then $c = a \cup b$.

26. Prove that a lattice with three or fewer elements is a chain.

4-6. SUBALGEBRAS

In this and the next section, we apply a few topics from universal algebra to lattice theory and partially ordered set theory. The first concept is that of a subalgebra. In general, by a subalgebra of an algebraic system we mean a subset of the fundamental set which itself forms an algebraic system of the same type with respect to the same relations and operations of the system. Thus any operations performed within the subset must produce elements in the subset; *i.e.*, the subset must be closed with respect to the operations of the system. Furthermore, elements of the subset which are related within the system must remain related as elements of the subsystem. The first specific case is that of a sub-partially ordered set. If $\langle P, \leq \rangle$ is any partially ordered set, and if Q is a subset of P such that if $a, b \in Q$ and $a \leq b$ in P, then $a \leq b$ in Q, then $\langle Q, \leq \rangle$ is called a **sub-partially ordered set** of $\langle P, \leq \rangle$. The partial order relation $\leq$ is, of course, not the same as $\leq$ in P, since $\leq$ in Q is a subset of $Q \times Q$ while $\leq$ is a subset of $P \times P$; *i.e.*, $\leq$ in Q is a restriction of $\leq$ in P. In general, the same symbolism is used for both partial orders, since little confusion is apt to occur. We therefore write $\langle Q, \leq \rangle$. Thus in figure 4-1(a) if $\langle L, \leq \rangle$ is the partially ordered set shown, and if $N = \{a, b, d\}$ where $\leq$ in N is defined by $a \leq d$ and $b \leq d$ (as well as $x \leq x \; \forall \; x$), then $\langle N, \leq \rangle$ is a sub-partially ordered set of $\langle L, \leq \rangle$. On the other hand, $\langle N, \leq' \rangle$, where $\leq'$ is defined by $a \leq' d$, $x \leq' x$, is not a sub-partially ordered set, since $b \leq d$ in $\langle L, \leq \rangle$ but not in $\langle N, \leq' \rangle$ (see figure 4-4(d) and (e)). Thus a subset may be a partially ordered set without being a *sub*-partially ordered set.

The next case is that of a semi-lattice. Let $\langle L, \cup \rangle$ be a join semi-lattice and let $M \subseteq L$. Then M is called a **sub-join semi-lattice** if $x, y \in M$ implies

$M = \{a, b, c\}$

$\cup$	a	b	c	d
a	a	c	c	d
b	c	b	c	d
c	c	c	c	d
d	d	d	d	d

$(L, \cup)$

(a)

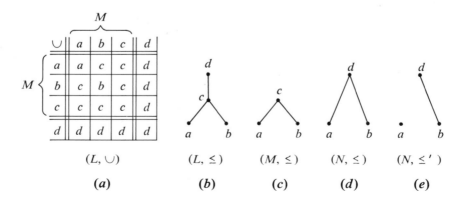

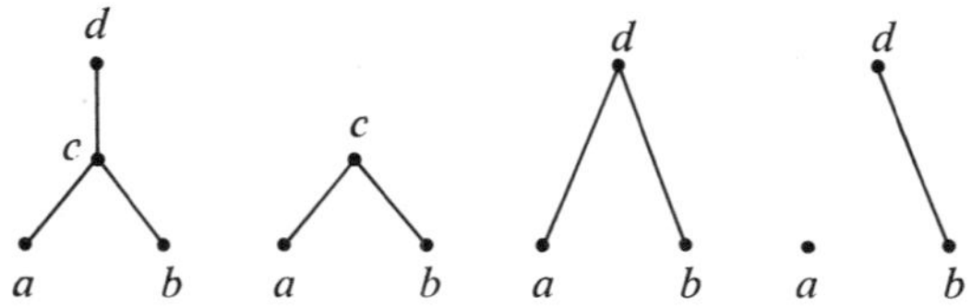

$(L, \leq)$ $(M, \leq)$ $(N, \leq)$ $(N, \leq')$

(b) (c) (d) (e)

FIGURE 4-4

$x \cup y \in M$. We write $\langle M, \cup\rangle$ again using the same notation $\cup$, for join in either L or M when it causes no confusion. The only requirement for a subalgebra in this case is the closure of M under join. The postulates for a join semi-lattice, commutativity, associativity and idempotence, are automatically satisfied, since they hold within L. We say that they are inherited from L. In figure 4-1(a) the set $M = \{a, b, c\}$ is a sub-semi-lattice under join, since the join of any pair of elements of M is again within M, join being determined by $\langle L, \cup\rangle$. If an operation table is constructed for $\langle L, \cup\rangle$ as in figure 4-4, then the subset M determines a subtable; *i.e.*, entries corresponding to pairs of elements of M lie in M as shown in the first three columns and rows of the table. Note, however, that if N is the subset $\{a, b, d\}$ discussed above, then $\langle N, \leq\rangle$ is a sub-partially ordered set of $\langle L, \leq\rangle$, but not a sub-join semi-lattice. Thus in $\langle L, \cup\rangle$, $a \cup b = c$ whereas in $\langle N, \leq\rangle$, $a \cup b = d$. Further, in the table the columns and rows corresponding to a, b and d do not form a subtable since the entry for $a \cup b$ is not within N. Thus care must be taken to distinguish between a sub-join semi-lattice and a sub-partially order set.

The conditions for a sub-join semi-lattice are actually stronger than those for a sub-partially ordered set; *i.e., every sub-join semi-lattice is automatically a sub-partially ordered set.* If $\langle M, \cup\rangle$ is a sub-semi-lattice of $\langle L, \cup\rangle$, then $\langle M, \leq\rangle$ is a sub-semi-lattice of $\langle L, \cup\rangle$, and also $\langle M, \leq\rangle$ is a sub-partially ordered set of $\langle L, \leq\rangle$. For if $x \leq y$ in L, $x, y \in M$, then $x \cup y = y$. But since M is closed under $\cup$, $x \cup y = y$ in M, and therefore $x \leq_M y$ in $\langle M, \leq\rangle$. Again we could have avoided some confusion by writing $\cup_M$ instead of $\cup$, but the subscripts are generally omitted.

We can define a **sub-meet semi-lattice** dually, but the details are left to the reader. Finally, a sub-lattice is defined similarly; *i.e.*, $\langle M, \cup, \cap\rangle$ is called a **sub-lattice** *of* $\langle L, \cup, \cap\rangle$ *if M is closed simultaneously under both $\cup$ and $\cap$.* Hence a sub-lattice is simultaneously both a sub-join semi-lattice and a sub-meet semi-lattice. We leave it to the exercises to show that the converse is not true in general; *i.e.*, a subset may be a sub-semi-lattice without being a sub-lattice.

As further examples of subalgebras, any interval of a lattice is a sub-lattice. Hence every principle filter or ideal is a sub-lattice. If, for example, $\langle L, \cup\rangle$ is a join semi-lattice and $a \in L$, then $[a]\uparrow$ is a sub-join semi-lattice. If U is any set and $\mathfrak{P}(U)$ is its power set, then $\langle\mathfrak{P}(U), \cup, \cap\rangle$ is a lattice under set union and intersection. If now A is a fixed subset of U, then $[A]\uparrow$ is the set of all subsets of U which contain A. By the example above, this family of subsets is a sub-lattice. Hence the set of subsets of U which contain a fixed set form a lattice under set union and intersection. Note, however, that although $\mathfrak{P}(U)$ and $[A]\uparrow$ both have least elements, these elements are not the same. The null set is the least element or zero of $\mathfrak{P}(U)$, whereas the set A is the least element or zero of $[A]\uparrow$. If we consider a lattice $\langle L, \cup, \cap, 0, 1\rangle$ *with units* as an algebra of type $\langle 2, 2, 0, 0\rangle$ with two binary operations and two nullary operations, then the lattice $\langle [A]\uparrow, \cup, \cap, A, U\rangle$ is an algebra of the same type as $\langle \mathfrak{P}(U), \cup, \cap, \emptyset, U\rangle$, but it is not a subalgebra, since it is not closed with respect to the nullary operation corresponding to the lower unit. The lower unit in the first case is A, while in the second it is the null set $\emptyset$. This example points out the need of being careful to specify the type of an algebra, particularly when considering nullary operations. A lattice with units, $\langle L, \cup, \cap, 0, 1\rangle$, is quite a different type of algebra from a lattice, $\langle L, \cup, \cap\rangle$, even though the latter may contain a least and greatest element. These same remarks apply when discussing homomorphisms and direct products below.

As one of the most important examples of the above concepts, we consider the family of subalgebras of some given algebraic system. Thus if $\langle L, \cup\rangle$ for example, is a join semi-lattice and $\langle M, \cup\rangle$ and $\langle N, \cup\rangle$ are two sub-join semi-lattices, then we can define a partial order relation between them by set inclusion. Hence the family $\mathfrak{L}(L)$ of all sub-join semi-lattices of L is itself a partially ordered set, $\langle \mathfrak{L}(L), \subseteq\rangle$. In fact $\mathfrak{L}(L)$ is a sub-partially ordered set of the power set $\mathfrak{P}(L)$ of all subsets of L. We can now investigate the operations of greatest lower and least upper bounds within $\langle \mathfrak{L}(L), \subseteq\rangle$. We first consider the meet operation. Let $\langle M, \cup\rangle$ and $\langle N, \cup\rangle$ be two subalgebras, and let $M \cap N$ be their point set intersection. Then if $x, y \in M \cap N$, we have both $x, y \in M$ and $x, y \in N$. Hence by the closure of M and N separately, $x \cup y \in M$ and $x \cup y \in N$. Therefore $x \cup y \in M \cap N$. Hence $M \cap N$ is also closed under $\cup$, so that $\langle M \cap N, \cup\rangle$ is also a sub-join semi-lattice; *i.e.*, an element of $\mathfrak{L}(L)$. Hence $\langle \mathfrak{L}(L), \subseteq, \cap\rangle$ is also a meet semi-lattice under $\cap$ and in fact a sub-meet semi-lattice of $\mathfrak{P}(L)$. This situation generalizes to arbitrary subalgebras of any abstract system; *i.e.*, the family of subalgebras of a fixed algebraic system $\langle A, \mathfrak{F}\rangle$ form a meet semi-lattice under set inclusion and set intersection. For example, the sub-lattices of a lattice form such a meet semi-lattice. On the other hand, the dual is not true in that the set union of two subalgebras of an algebra is not necessarily a subalgebra, so that $\mathfrak{L}(L)$ is not a lattice under set union as the second operation. If $M \cup N$ is the set union of M and N and $x, y \in M \cup N$, then there is no guarantee that $x \cup y$ will be in either M or N. x may be in M and y in N, but $x \cup y$ in neither. We leave the appropriate example to the exercises. However, we may still define a least upper bound within $\langle \mathfrak{L}(L), \subseteq\rangle$. This should be the smallest subalgebra of $\langle L, \cup\rangle$ which contains both $\langle M, \cup\rangle$ and $\langle N, \cup\rangle$. We leave the proof that such a sub-join semi-lattice always exists to a later section (section 4-8), but for now we merely note that $\langle \mathfrak{L}(L), \leq\rangle$ is a lattice, although join is different from set union.

As a second example of these arguments, we may again examine the case of the family $\mathfrak{L}(V_3)$ of linear subspaces of a linear vector space, say V_3, the usual three-dimensional space. Here the subspaces are the subsets closed under the operations of vector addition and scalar multiplication. They are the lines through the origin, the planes through the origin, the origin itself, and the whole space V_3 as we have already noted above. The set of subspaces $\mathfrak{L}(V_3)$ is partially ordered by set inclusion, and the meet of two subspaces is exactly the set intersection. Thus the meet of two planes is their line of intersection. However, the join of two subspaces is not the set union, but the smallest subspace which contains them both. In the case of two distinct lines, this is the plane generated by them. Hence $\langle \mathfrak{L}(V_3), \leq, \cup, \cap \rangle$ is a lattice where $\cup$ is the least upper bound under $\leq$, set inclusion, and $\cap$ is set intersection. $\mathfrak{L}(V_3)$ is therefore a sub-meet semi-lattice but not a sub-lattice of $\mathfrak{P}(V_3)$.

4-7. HOMOMORPHISMS, CONGRUENCE RELATIONS, FILTERS AND IDEALS

The next concept of importance is that of a homomorphism. First if $\langle L, \circ \rangle$ and $\langle M, \cdot \rangle$ are two algebraic systems of type $\langle 2 \rangle$ and ϕ is a map on L onto M such that $x \circ y$ maps onto $\phi(x) \cdot \phi(y)$, then ϕ is a homomorphism. In our case we apply this definition to the theory of partially ordered sets and lattices.

Definition 4-4. *If $\langle P, \leq \rangle$ and $\langle Q, \leq \rangle$ are two partially ordered sets and ϕ is a map on P onto Q, then ϕ is called an* **order homomorphism (monotone map, isotone, order preserving map)** *if $x \leq y$ implies $\phi(x) \leq \phi(y)$. Similarly, if $x \leq y$ implies $\phi(y) \leq \phi(x)$, then ϕ is called an* **order-inverting homomorphism (antitone mapping, dual homomorphism)**. *If $\langle L, \cup \rangle$ and $\langle M, \cup \rangle$ are two join semi-lattices and ϕ is a map on L onto M such that $\phi(x \cup y) = \phi(x) \cup \phi(y)$, then ϕ is called a* **join homomorphism**. *Similarly, a meet homomorphism is a mapping ϕ from $\langle L, \cap \rangle$ onto $\langle M, \cap \rangle$ preserving meets. If L and M are lattices and ϕ preserves both $\cup$ and $\cap$, then ϕ is called a* **lattice homomorphism**.

Again the notation is somewhat confusing, since we have used the same symbols for the partial orders in both P and Q as well as the same operations in both L and M. However, if necessary we can use subscripts to distinguish the two. We also note that the four concepts defined here are all distinct, as was the case of subalgebras. In general, an order homomorphism is weaker than a semi-lattice homomorphism, which in turn is weaker than a lattice homomorphism, as might be expected. For example, if $\langle L, \leq \rangle$ is the partially ordered set of figure 4-1(a) and M is a three element chain $M = \{a^*, c^*, d^*\}$ where $a^* \leq c^* \leq d^*$ with $\phi(a) = \phi(b) = a^*, \phi(c) = c^*$ and $\phi(d) = d^*$, then ϕ is an order homomorphism. However, ϕ is not a join homomorphism, even though L and M are both join semi-lattices, since $\phi(a) \cup \phi(b) = a^* \cup a^* = a^*$ whereas $\phi(a \cup b) = \phi(c) = c^*$. If we add a zero element 0 at the bottom of this figure and $\phi(0) = a^*$, then ϕ is a meet homomorphism, but not join-preserving, and hence not a lattice homomorphism. Thus the three concepts of homomorphism as applied to partially ordered sets, semi-lattices, and lattices are definitely distinct. Conversely however, every lattice homomorphism is obviously a semi-lattice homomorphism under both join and meet. Furthermore, every semi-lattice homomorphism is a partial order homomorphism. The proof is left as an exercise. In the special case of an isomorphism, the situation is somewhat simpler and we can obtain a stronger result. Here *if both ϕ and ϕ^{-1} are order preserving, then ϕ preserves both joins and meets whenever they exist.* Again the proof is left as an exercise.

As an example, let L be a lattice and let a be a fixed element. Then the set $M = [a]\downarrow$ is a sublattice as we saw above. Let ϕ be the mapping $\phi: x \to \phi(x) = x \cap a$. Then ϕ is defined on all of L onto M. The elements of M are all left fixed by ϕ since $x \cap a = x$ for $x \in [a]\downarrow$. Furthermore, ϕ is a meet homomorphism, since $x \cap y \leq \phi(x \cap y) = (x \cap y) \cap a = (x \cap a) \cap (y \cap a) = \phi(x) \cap \phi(y)$. However, in general ϕ fails to be a join homomorphism, since $\phi(x \cup y) = (x \cup y) \cap a$ is not necessarily equal to $\phi(x) \cup \phi(y) = (x \cap a) \cup (y \cap a)$. We shall see later that the distributive law for $\cap$ and $\cup$ does not always hold in an arbitrary lattice. However, in the special case where $L = \mathfrak{P}(U)$, then ϕ maps each subset X of U onto its intersection $X \cap A$ with A. Since $\mathfrak{P}(U)$ is distributive as we saw in Chapter 2, ϕ is a lattice homomorphism in this case.

A concept closely related to that of a homomorphism is the concept of a congruence relation. Reviewing Chapter 2, we defined an equivalence relation as any relation that is reflexive, symmetric and transitive. We also learned that any equivalence relation $\equiv$ on a set U determines a partition of U into non-overlapping equivalence classes or cosets. We then defined the quotient set as the set of these classes. If x is an element of U, its equivalence class is denoted by $\bar{x}$ while $\bar{U}$ designates the quotient set, $U/\equiv$. If now the set U has some sort of algebraic structure imposed on it such as a partial order or a semi-lattice, then we would like to impose a similar structure on the quotient set. If $\bar{x}$ and $\bar{y}$ are two cosets, we would like to be able to relate them whenever x and y are related. However, if s and t are distinct elements in $\bar{x}$ and $\bar{y}$ respectively, we would need to be sure that the relation between x and y is the same as that between s and t. In order to induce a structure on $\bar{U}$, it is necessary that equivalent elements in U behave alike. If this is the case, we call the equivalence relation a congruence relation with respect to the relations and operations involved. Again our interest centers on the case of partially ordered sets and lattices as in:

Definition 4-5. *If $\langle P, \leq \rangle$ is a partially ordered set and $\equiv$ is an equivalence relation defined on P such that $s \equiv x$, $t \equiv y$ and $x \leq y$ imply $s \leq t$, then $\equiv$ is called an* **order congruence relation**. *If $\langle L, \cup \rangle$ is a join (meet) semi-lattice* *and* $\equiv$ *is an equivalence relation such that* $x \equiv y$ *implies* $x \cup z \equiv y \cup z$ $\forall$ $z \in L$, $(x \cap z \equiv y \cap z)$, *then* $\equiv$ *is called a* **join congruence (meet congruence)**. *If both conditions are met* $\equiv$ *is called a* **lattice congruence**. *We also say that* $\equiv$ *has the* **substitution property** *with respect to* $\leq$, $\cup$, *or* $\cap$.

We can now define an algebraic structure on the quotient set $\bar{P} = P/\equiv$ by writing $\bar{x} \leq \bar{y}$ if and only if $x \leq y$ in P. The substitution property then guarantees that this partial order in $\bar{P}$ is well-defined; *i.e.*, independent of the representatives chosen in writing $\bar{x} \leq \bar{y}$. We call the partially ordered set $\langle \bar{P}, \leq \rangle$ the *quotient algebra* of $P \bmod \equiv$. Similarly if $\langle L, \cup \rangle$ is a semi-lattice and $\equiv$ is a congruence relation then we can define a join operation on $\bar{L} = L/\equiv$ by choosing representatives x and y from two cosets $\bar{x}$ and $\bar{y}$ respectively, forming their join in L, $x \cup y$, and then taking the coset containing this join; *i.e.*, we let $\bar{x} \cup \bar{y} = \overline{x \cup y}$. Again the substitution property makes the result independent of the particular representatives chosen. $\bar{L}$ then becomes a join semi-lattice in which the validity of the postulates in $\bar{L}$ is inherited from the validity in L. Similar remarks hold for lattices.

As in Chapter 2 for general algebras, we can now relate the two concepts of homomorphism and congruence relation by noting that the definition $\bar{x} \cup \bar{y} = \overline{x \cup y}$ is the condition for a homomorphism. We simply define a mapping from L onto $\bar{L}$ by mapping each element onto the coset containing it; *i.e.*, $\phi(x) = \bar{x}$ $\forall$ $x \in L$. The equation $\bar{x} \cup \bar{y} = \overline{x \cup y}$ becomes $\phi(x \cup y) = \phi(x) \cup \phi(y)$, which makes ϕ a homomorphism. We call ϕ the *natural homomorphism* of L onto $\bar{L}$. $\bar{L}$ is a homomorphic image of L and ϕ preserves whatever structure is imposed on L. Thus every congruence relation determines a homomorphism. As a second example, if $\langle L, \cup, \cap \rangle$ is a lattice and $\equiv$ is a congruence relation on L, then the quotient set $\bar{L} = L/\equiv$ is a lattice under $\bar{x} \cup \bar{y} = \overline{x \cup y}$ and $\bar{x} \cap \bar{y} = \overline{x \cap y}$. The natural homomorphism ϕ: $x \to \bar{x}$ is a lattice homomorphism and $\bar{L}$ is a homomorphic image of L.

In general the converse is not true for partial order homomorphisms, but is true for semi-lattice and lattice homomorphisms; *i.e.*, a lattice homomorphism determines a congruence relation.

Theorem 4-5. *If* $\langle L, \cup \rangle$ *and* $\langle L^*, \cup \rangle$ *are two semi-lattices and* ϕ *is a homomorphism on* L *onto* L^*, *then* ϕ *determines a congruence relation on* L *such that* $x \equiv y \bmod \phi$ *if and only if* $\phi(x) = \phi(y)$. *Furthermore* $\bar{L} = L/\equiv$ *is then isomorphic to* L^*.

Proof. The proof that $\equiv$ is an equivalence relation is left to the reader. To show that it is a congruence, let $x \equiv y$. Then $\phi(x \cup z) = \phi(x) \cup \phi(z) = \phi(y) \cup \phi(z) = \varphi(y \cup z)$. Hence $x \cup z \equiv y \cup z$. The coset $\bar{x}$ of L mod ϕ is then the set $x = \{t | t \equiv x \bmod \phi\} = \{t | \phi(t) = \phi(x)\}$; *i.e.*, $\bar{x}$ is just the set of inverse images of $x^* = \phi(x)$ in L. Thus we may define the map $\bar{x} \to x^*$. It will be a map on $\bar{L}$ onto L^*, which is one-to-one. Hence $\bar{L}$ and L^* are isomorphic.

We may therefore identify $\bar{x}$ and x^* in the future and replace ϕ by the natural homomorphism of L onto $\bar{L}$. The same results hold for meet semi-lattices or lattices in general. However, they do not hold for partially ordered sets. Let $\langle N, \leq' \rangle$ be the partially ordered set of figure 4-4(e) and let ϕ map N onto a two element chain $\{a^*, d^*\}$ where $a^* \leq d^*$ such that $\phi(a) = \phi(b) = a^*$ and $\phi(d) = d^*$. ϕ is then an order homomorphism and defines an equivalence relation on N where $a \equiv b$. But $\equiv$ is not a congruence relation, since $a \equiv b$ and $b \not\leq d$ but $a \leq d$.

A final concept closely related to homomorphisms and congruences is that of a filter. For the present, we restrict the discussion to that of a lattice $\langle L, \cup, \cap \rangle$ with an upper unit, 1. Let ϕ be a homomorphism of L onto a second lattice $\bar{L}$ with upper unit $\bar{1}$. Then the set of elements of L which map onto $\bar{1}$ in $\bar{L}$ is called the **kernel** of ϕ, designated by K_ϕ; *i.e.*, $K_\phi = \phi^{-1}(\bar{1})$ is the inverse image of $\bar{1}$ under ϕ. We can now show that $\langle K_\phi, \cup, \cap \rangle$ is a sub-lattice of L. Let $x, y \in K_\phi$. Then $\phi(x) = \phi(y) = \bar{1}$. Hence $\phi(x \cap y) = \phi(x) \cap \phi(y) = \bar{1} \cap \bar{1} = \bar{1}$. Hence $x \cap y \in K_\phi$ and K_ϕ is a meet semi-lattice. The same proof also goes for $x \cup y$, but in this case we can strengthen the result and only require that $x \in K_\phi$ in the hypothesis. Thus $x \in K_\phi$ and $y \in L$ imply $\phi(x) = \bar{1}$. Hence $\phi(x \cup y) = \phi(x) \cup \phi(y) = \bar{1} \cup \phi(y) = \bar{1}$. Thus K_ϕ is a special type of sub-lattice of L. It is called a filter. Formally:

Definition 4-6. *If $\langle L, \cup, \cap \rangle$ is a lattice with an upper unit, 1, then a non-empty subset K of L is called a* **filter** *if it satisfies:*

(*i*) *$x \in K$ and $y \in L$ imply $x \cup y \in K$,*
(*ii*) *$x, y \in K$ implies $x \cap y \in K$.*

Dually, K is called an **ideal** *in L if it satisfies the dual conditions to* (*i*) *and* (*ii*).

The condition (*i*) can be slightly rewritten as in the following theorem:

Theorem 4-6. *K is a filter in a lattice with upper unit if*

(*ia*) *$x \in K$ and $x \leq y$ imply $y \in K$,*
(*ii*) *$x, y \in K$ implies $x \cap y \in K$.*

Proof. Exercise.

Corollary. *If K is a filter in L, then $1 \in K$.*

Theorem 4-7. *If ϕ is a homomorphism of a lattice L with unit 1 onto a lattice $\bar{L}$ with unit $\bar{1}$, then the kernel of ϕ is a filter in L.*

Corollary. *If L is a lattice with unit 1 and* $\equiv$ *is a congruence relation on L, then the set* $K = \{t | t \equiv 1\}$ *is a filter in L.*

The terminology for filter or ideal theory is taken from the theory of rings. In a ring an ideal is characterized as the kernel of a homomorphism; *i.e.*, the inverse image of the unit in the ring. In the case of rings the correspondence between homomorphisms, congruence and ideals is complete and each determines the other. If $\langle R, +, \cdot \rangle$ is a ring, then an ideal in R may be characterized by the two properties $x, y \in K$ implies $x + y \in K$ and $x \in K$ and $y \in R$ imply $x \cdot y \in K$ (for R commutative). If $+$ is interpreted as $\cap$ and $\cdot$ as $\cup$, this is exactly the same as the conditions of definition 4-6, so that the analogy of ring ideals and lattice ideals is even stronger. However, in lattice theory the converse of Theorem 4-7 does not always hold. We may have distinct homomorphisms on L with the same kernel. Figure 4-5 shows a simple example. Here the kernels of ϕ and ψ are the same, but ϕ and ψ are distinct homomorphisms. Later we shall study special cases, where distinct ideals determine distinct homomorphisms. In the theory of groups, the role of the kernel of a homomorphism is played by the normal subgroup, so that normal subgroups in group theory have a position analogous to ideals in rings and lattices.

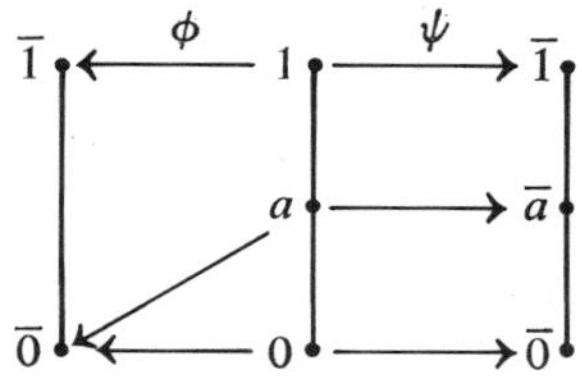

FIGURE 4-5

As an example of an ideal in a lattice, we can consider the set $[a] \uparrow$ already introduced above. This is called the principle filter generated by a as previously defined. $[a] \uparrow$ is a filter since $x \in [a] \uparrow$ implies $a \leq x$, and $x \leq y$ in turn implies $a \leq y$, so that $y \in [a] \uparrow$. Thus (*ia*) holds. Also $x, y \in [a]$ implies $a \leq x, y$ so that $a \leq x \cap y$. Hence $x \cap y \in [a] \uparrow$.

As another example of the ideas of this section, we return to our example of the power set algebra. Let U be a fixed set and $\mathfrak{P}(U)$ be its power set lattice. Let A be fixed in $\mathfrak{P}(U)$. Then its power set $\mathfrak{P}(A)$ is also a lattice and is furthermore an ideal in $\mathfrak{P}(U)$. We consider the homomorphism ϕ defined above by $X \to X \cap A$. Then ϕ determines the congruence relation $X \equiv Y \bmod \phi$ if and only if $X \cap A = Y \cap A$. Each coset of $\mathfrak{P}(U) \bmod \phi$ contains exactly one element of $\mathfrak{P}(A)$, since if $X \subseteq A$, then $X \cap A = X$. Thus the set of subsets of A is a complete set of representatives of $\mathfrak{P}(U) \bmod \phi$. Furthermore, the meet and join of two cosets is the coset determined by the meet and join respectively of these representatives, so that $\mathfrak{P}(U) \bmod \phi$ is isomorphic to $\mathfrak{P}(A)$. The kernel of ϕ is the set of subsets of U which do not intersect A; *i.e.*, $K_\phi = \{X \subseteq U | X \cap U = \emptyset\}$. But as we saw in Chapter 2, this is exactly the power set of $A' = U - A$, the complement of A in U. We also saw that A' can be defined as the largest element of this family of sets. Thus $K_\phi = \{X \subseteq$

$U|X \subseteq A'\}$. But this is exactly the principal ideal generated by A', $[A']\downarrow$. Hence the kernel of ϕ is the ideal $\mathfrak{P}(A')$. The cosets can now be written $X = \{T|T = X \cup Z \text{ for } Z \subseteq A'\}$, where $X \subseteq A$; *i.e.*, sets of the form $X \cup Z$ where Z is any subset not intersecting A. If X is any element, not necessarily a subset of A, then its coset is the set of sets of the form $Z \cup (X \cap A)$. The situation is illustrated in figure 4-6 where (*a*) shows the lattice diagram while

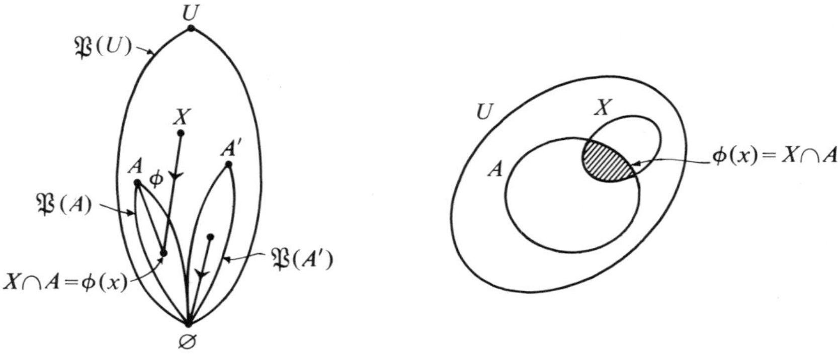

(*a*) (*b*)

FIGURE 4-6

(*b*) is a Venn diagram. Note also that $\mathfrak{P}(A)$ and $\mathfrak{P}(A')$ have no non-empty elements in common so that $\mathfrak{P}(A) \cap \mathfrak{P}(A') = \{\varnothing\}$. Later we shall discuss the family of all ideals for this case and show that it is a lattice in which the join of $\mathfrak{P}(A)$ and $\mathfrak{P}(A')$ is the whole system $\mathfrak{P}(U)$. Thus the ideals $\mathfrak{P}(A)$ and $\mathfrak{P}(A')$ are complementary ideals.

The reader familiar with group theory will notice a striking similarity with the discussion here and the discussion of homomorphism, congruence and normal subgroups of a group. In fact, in this case they are identical. In Theorem 2-13 corollary 3 of Chapter 2, we saw that the power set $\mathfrak{P}(U)$ is a group under symmetric difference. Further, $\mathfrak{P}(A)$ is closed under symmetric difference since $X, Y \in A$ implies $X \,\Delta\, Y = (X \cap Y') \cup (X' \cap Y) \subseteq A$ (Proof: exercise). Hence $\langle \mathfrak{P}(A), \Delta \rangle$ is a subgroup of $\langle \mathfrak{P}(U), \Delta \rangle$, and, in fact, a normal subgroup since Δ is commutative. The unit of $\langle \mathfrak{P}(U), \Delta \rangle$ is the null set since $X \,\Delta\, \varnothing = \varnothing$ as we saw earlier. The mapping ϕ: $X \to X \cap A$ is now a group homomorphism since $\phi(X \,\Delta\, Y) = (X \,\Delta\, Y) \cap A = (X \cap A) \,\Delta\, (Y \cap A) = \phi(X) \,\Delta\, \phi(Y)$. The proof is again left to the exercises. The kernel of the homomorphism is exactly the same as in the case of lattice theory; *i.e.*, the power set of A'. But $\mathfrak{P}(A')$ is also a normal subgroup of $\langle \mathfrak{P}(U), \Delta \rangle$. The cosets are families of sets of the form $\bar{X} = X \Delta K_\phi = X \Delta \mathfrak{P}(A')$; *i.e.*, $Y \in \bar{X}$ if and only if $Y = X \Delta Z$ for some $Z \subseteq A'$. In group theory, we frequently start with a normal subgroup and then define a congruence relation by $X \equiv Y$ if and only if $X \Delta Y$ is in this subgroup. Hence the congruence and therefore the homomorphism is determined by the normal subgroup and we write $\mathfrak{P}(U)$ mod $\mathfrak{P}(A')$ instead of $\mathfrak{P}(U)$ mod ϕ. We then call the quotient set a factor group. The isomorphism theory for group theory then states that $\mathfrak{P}(U)/\mathfrak{P}(A') \cong \mathfrak{P}(A)$, which is exactly the same result that we obtained in lattice theory above. Thus the analogy between homomorphisms, congruences and ideals in lattice theory and homomorphisms, congruences and normal subgroups in group theory is justified. Further details are contained in the exercises.

EXERCISES

1. Find all the possible sub-semi-lattices and sub-lattices of the lattice of figure 4-1(*d*).
2. Give an example of a lattice and a sub-join semi-lattice which is not a sub-lattice.
3. Write out the definition of sub-meet semi-lattice.
4. If A is any subset of a join semi-lattice show that $[A] \uparrow$ and $[A] \downarrow$ are both sub-join semi-lattices.
5. Let $U = \{0, a, b, 1\}$ be a set of four elements. Construct the diagram for the power set $\mathfrak{P}(U)$ of U. Compare with figure 2-2 of Chapter 2. Encircle the subsets of U which are sub-lattices of the lattice of figure 4-1(*d*); *i.e.*, the elements of the lattice $\mathfrak{L}(U)$. Show wherein $\mathfrak{L}(L)$ is not a sub-lattice of $\mathfrak{P}(U)$.
6. Prove that every lattice homomorphism and every semi-lattice homomorphism is an order homomorphism.
7. Prove that if ϕ is an order homomorphism from a join semi-lattice to a join semi-lattice, then $\phi(x) \cup \phi(y) \leq \phi(x \cup y)$.
8. If L and $\bar{L}$ are lattices and ϕ is an order isomorphism from L onto $\bar{L}$, show that ϕ is a lattice homomorphism if and only if ϕ^{-1} preserves order. Use a counter example for the "only if" part.
9. Show that the set of fixed elements under a lattice homomorphism forms a sub-lattice.
10. If ϕ is a lattice homomorphism from L onto $\bar{L}$, show that the relation $x \equiv y$ if and only if $\phi(x) = \phi(y)$ is an equivalence relation.
11. If $\equiv$ is a lattice congruence show that $x \equiv y$ implies $x \cup y \equiv x \cap y$.
12. A subset C of a partially ordered set $\langle P, \leq \rangle$ is called **convex** if $x, y \in C$ and $x \leq z \leq y$ imply $z \in C$; *i.e.*, if x and y are any two elements of C, then C contains the interval $[x, y]$. Show that every coset of a lattice modulo *a* lattice congruence is a convex subset of the lattice.

13. Show that every interval of a lattice is a sub-lattice.

14. Let U be any set and $\mathfrak{F}(U)$ the set of finite subsets of U. Show that $\mathfrak{F}(U)$ is a convex sub-lattice of $\mathfrak{P}(U)$, but that $\mathfrak{F}(U)$ is not an interval.

15. Show that if ϕ is a lattice homomorphism on a lattice L with unit, then the image of L under ϕ has a unit (upper or lower).

16. Show that the mapping of the lattice $\mathbf{R}$, onto $\mathbf{R}^+$, given by $\phi(x) = e^x$ (where $\mathbf{R}^+$ is the set of positive reals) is an order homomorphism. Is it a lattice homomorphism?

17. Show that the set of open sets of a topological space is a lattice. The same for the closed subsets (see Appendix 2).

18. Show that the mapping $A \to A'$ of $\mathfrak{P}(U)$ onto $\mathfrak{P}(U)$ is antitone.

19. Prove that if $\equiv$ is a congruence relation on a lattice L, then $x \equiv s$ and $y \equiv t$ imply $x \cup y \equiv s \cup t$ and $x \cap y \equiv s \cap t$; *i.e.*, the substitution property applies to both terms of $x \cup y$ and $x \cap y$ simultaneously.

20. Show that every ideal of a lattice is a convex sub-lattice.

21. If $\langle \mathbf{Z}, +, \cdot \rangle$ is the ring of integers and (m) is the set of multiples of m, show that (m) is an ideal. Show that (m) determines a ring congruence relation where $x \equiv y \bmod m$ if and only if $x - y \in (m)$. Let $\bar{x}$ be the coset of this congruence containing x and ϕ the natural homomorphism $x \to \bar{x}$. Show that the kernel of ϕ is (m). Exemplify by the case $m = 5$ and compare with lattice theory.

22. If ϕ and ψ are two lattice homomorphisms on a lattice L onto a lattice $\bar{L}$, we can define a partial order by $\phi \leq \psi$ if and only if $x \equiv y \bmod \phi$ implies $x \equiv y \bmod \psi$. This is the usual partial order for relations considered as a subset of $L \times L$. Show that the set of all such homomorphisms is a lattice and determine the nature of $\phi \cup \psi$ and $\phi \cap \psi$. This is the lattice $\mathfrak{H}(L)$. What are the least and greatest elements of $\mathfrak{H}(L)$?

23. If U is any set and A is a fixed subset, prove that $\mathfrak{P}(A)$ is closed under symmetric difference in $\mathfrak{P}(U)$.

24. Prove that meet (intersection) distributes with respect to symmetric difference.

25. Prove that the inverse of X in the group $\langle \mathfrak{P}(A), \Delta \rangle$ is X itself. Hence prove that if $X, Y \in \mathfrak{P}(A)$ are given, then the solution of the equation $X \Delta Z = Y$ is $Z = X \Delta Y$.

26. Let $X \equiv Y \bmod \mathfrak{P}(A)$ if and only if $X \cap A' = Y \cap A'$. Prove that $X \equiv Y \bmod \mathfrak{P}(A)$ if and only if $X \Delta Y \in \mathfrak{P}(A)$.

27. Using the definition of exercise 26, prove that $X \equiv Y \bmod \mathfrak{P}(A)$ if and only if $\exists\, Z \in \mathfrak{P}(A)$ such that $Y = X \Delta Z$.

28. State and discuss results similar to the theory of the group $\langle \mathfrak{P}(U), \Delta \rangle$ for the group $\langle \mathfrak{P}(U), \leftrightarrow \rangle$ where $\leftrightarrow$ is the set operation of equivalence. Show that in this case, the relation $X \equiv Y \bmod [A]\uparrow$ holds if and only if the element $X \leftrightarrow Y$ lies in $[A]\uparrow$.

29. Show that K is an ideal if and only if $x \cap y \in K \Leftrightarrow x \in K$ and $y \in K$.

4-8. COMPLETENESS

In section 4-5 we defined a join semi-lattice as a partially ordered set in which every pair of elements has a least upper bound. By induction we can prove that every finite subset of a join semi-lattice has a least upper bound; *i.e.*, if $A = \{a_1, a_2, \ldots, a_n\}$ is a finite subset of $\langle L, \cup\rangle$ then there exists an element $a = \bigcup_{i=1}^{n} a_i$ in L. However, we cannot in general extend this result to infinite sets. For example, in the lattice $\langle \mathbf{N}, |\rangle$ of the positive integers ordered by divisibility, every finite set of integers determines a least common multiple, but the set $A = \{2^n \mid n \in \mathbf{N}\}$ of powers of 2 does not have a common multiple. In general, we call a semi-lattice complete under join if every arbitrary subset has a least upper bound.

Definition 4-7. *A partially ordered set $\langle P, \leq\rangle$ is called* **join-complete, meet-complete** *or* **complete** *according as every subset A of P has a least upper bound, greatest lower bound, or both, respectively.*

Clearly a join-complete partially ordered set is a join semi-lattice, but as in the example above, a partially ordered set may be a lattice which is meet-complete without being join-complete, even though it is closed under join. The power set $\mathfrak{P}(U)$ of a set U is always a complete lattice since set intersection and union are always defined for any arbitrary collection of subsets of U. On the other hand, there are sublattices of $\mathfrak{P}(U)$ which are not complete. For example, let $\mathfrak{F}(U)$ be the set of finite subsets of U. Then $\mathfrak{F}(U)$ is closed under intersection and union and is even complete under intersection, but the infinite join of a family of finite sets is not necessarily finite.

It is possible to define a number of degrees of completeness between that of closure and completeness, as in definition 4-7. These are defined by limiting the size of the sets which are required to have joins or meets. Thus in closure we only require that finite sets have joins and meets. If we extend the requirement to denumerably infinite sets of elements, then we call the semi-lattice or lattice sequentially complete; *i.e.*, a partially ordered set is called **sequentially join-complete** if every denumerable subset has a least upper bound. Thus let $A = \{a_1, a_2, a_3, \ldots\}$ be a sequence of elements of $\langle P, \leq\rangle$, then if P is sequentially join-complete, P will contain the element $\bigcup_{i=1}^{\infty} a_i$. We also call P σ-complete if P is sequentially complete under both join and meet. The idea can be extended even further by requiring that all sets up to a certain "size" have least upper bounds. If $\mathfrak{a}$ is any cardinal number, then P is called $\mathfrak{a}$- *join-complete* if every set A such that A has cardinality $\leq \mathfrak{a}$ has a least upper bound. $\mathfrak{a}$-*meet-completeness* and $\mathfrak{a}$-*completeness* are defined similarly. Completeness in general therefore means $\mathfrak{a}$-completeness for any $\mathfrak{a}$.

We can now return to the lattice of subalgebras of an arbitrary algebra and define the union operation. We first extend the results on intersection of two subalgebras to intersections of any set of subalgebras.

Theorem 4-8. *If L is any algebra (join semi-lattice, lattice, group, etc) then the lattice $\mathfrak{L}(L)$ of subalgebras is meet-complete under set intersection.*

If $\mathfrak{A}$ is any family of subalgebras, then the intersection $\bigcap_{A \in \mathfrak{A}} A$ is also a subalgebra. The proof is exactly the same as for two subalgebras. We can now use this result to define the union of an arbitrary family of subalgebras and prove that $\mathfrak{L}(L)$ is join-complete. We first prove an auxiliary theorem that is important in its own right in lattice theory.

Theorem 4-9. *If $\langle L, \cup \rangle$ is a join-complete semi-lattice and A is any subset of L which has a lower bound, then A has a greatest lower bound in L.*

Proof. By hypothesis the set $A\downarrow$ is non-empty. Hence $A\downarrow$ has a least upper bound $g = \bigcup_{x \in A\downarrow} x$. Then since $x \leq a \; \forall \; a \in A, g \leq a \; \forall \; a \in A$. Hence g is itself a lower bound for A; *i.e.*, $g \in A\downarrow$. If now x is any other lower bound, then $x \leq g$ since $g = \bigcup_{x \in A\downarrow} x$. Therefore, g is the greatest lower bound of A.

Corollary. *If $\langle L, \cup \rangle$ is a join-complete semi-lattice with lower unit, then L is a complete lattice. Dually, if $\langle L, \cap \rangle$ is meet-complete with an upper unit, then L is a complete lattice.*

If L fails to have an upper unit, then we can still obtain the results of the corollary by adjoining an upper unit. Thus if $\langle P, \leq \rangle$ is any partially ordered set (with or without an upper unit), then we form a new partially ordered set $\langle P^*, \leq^* \rangle$ whose elements are the elements of P plus a single additional element I. The partial order in $\langle P^*, \leq^* \rangle$ is defined by setting $x \leq^* y$ for $x, y \in P$ if and only if $x \leq y$ in $\langle P, \leq \rangle$, and then setting $x \leq^* I$ for every $x \in P$, and finally setting $I \leq^* I$. $\langle P, \leq \rangle$ is then a sub-partially ordered set of $\langle P^*, \leq^* \rangle$ and the latter has a unit. We can therefore apply theorem 4-9 and its corollary to $\langle P^*, \leq^* \rangle$. For example, the set $\mathfrak{F}(U)$ of finite subsets of U was seen to be a meet-complete lattice. If we extend $\mathfrak{F}(U)$ to a new set $\mathfrak{F}^*$ by adjoining an upper unit I, then, according to Theorem 4-9, we obtain a complete lattice. In this case, the join of any infinite family of sets which is not finite becomes I and is not the set union. A more familiar example of this process is given by the real numbers $\langle \mathbf{R}, \leq \rangle$. This is a lattice, but not a complete lattice since it contains no units. However, we can extend it to a complete lattice by the adjunction of two units, $+\infty$ and $-\infty$. We therefore define $-\infty < x < +\infty \; \forall \; x \in \mathbf{R}$. The extended system is known as the extended real number system. Note that although it has advantages from the point of view of lattice theory, it loses some of its properties from the ring theoretic point of view. For example, it is no longer a ring.

We can now extend Theorem 4-8 and prove that $\mathfrak{L}(L)$ is a complete lattice.

Theorem 4-10. *If L is any algebra, then the family of subalgebras $\mathfrak{L}(L)$ is a complete lattice.*

To complete the proof, we need only note that L is itself a sub-lattice and therefore an upper unit. Hence by Theorem 4-9, corollary, the result follows. We note that the proof includes the proof of the closure of $\mathfrak{L}(L)$ under join. Thus if M and N are two subalgebras of L, then their union is the set intersection of all those subalgebras which contain both M and N. In general this will not be the set union of M and N, since the point set union is not a subalgebra in all cases. We can also think of $M \cup N$ as the smallest subalgebra of L which contains both M and N; *i.e.*, $M \cup N = \bigcap_{A \in \{M,N\}\uparrow} A$. More generally, if we have any collection of subalgebras, then their *join is the set intersection of the family of all subalgebras which contain every algebra in the given family.* Note that care must be taken in speaking of the join of two subalgebras to distinguish between the join as defined here and the point set union of the two sets. Frequently the notation $M \cup N$ is used for both and may cause trouble.

We can use the same technique developed here to define the subalgebra generated by a subset of an algebra. Thus if L is any algebra and A is an arbitrary subset, not necessarily a subalgebra, then the intersection of all such subalgebras of L which contain A will itself be a subalgebra of L, which will also contain A. In fact, it will be the smallest such subalgebra. Hence, we call it the **subalgebra generated by** A and designate it by $[A]$. Thus $[A] = \bigcap \{B \mid B \leq L$ and B is a subalgebra of $L\}$. Note that since L is itself a subalgebra of L and $A \leq L$, the class of subalgebras containing A is non-empty and hence $[A]$ always exists for any set A. This is a special case of Theorem 4-9 where $\mathfrak{L}(L)$ is partially ordered by "is a subalgebra of," and not set inclusion. The most familiar example is the lattice of subspaces of a vector space V already discussed above. For example, if A is any collection of vectors of a vector space V, then the space spanned by A is the smallest subspace of V containing A. It is the intersection of all subspaces containing A and is also characterized as the set of all linear combinations of vectors from A.

EXERCISES

1. Show that every complete lattice has a greatest and least element.
2. Show that the set of rational numbers in the closed interval [0, 1] is a lattice but is not a complete lattice. What is the smallest lattice which contains this lattice?

Do the real numbers in the open interval (0, 1) form a complete lattice? Explain. Can this lattice be embedded in a complete lattice?

3. Let $\langle X, \mathfrak{T} \rangle$ be a topological space on the carrier set X with topology $\mathfrak{T}$ and $\mathfrak{P}(X)$ the power set of X. Show that $\mathfrak{T}$ is a union-complete lattice and hence a complete lattice. Show also that $\mathfrak{T}$ is a sublattice of $\mathfrak{P}(X)$ which is a sub-union-complete sublattice, but $\mathfrak{T}$ is not a sub-meet-complete sublattice of $\mathfrak{P}(X)$. Let A° be the interior of A; *i.e.*, the union of all open sets contained in A. Show that in $\mathfrak{T}$ treated as complete lattice, the lattice operations are given by $\bigsqcap_\alpha G_\alpha = \bigcap_\alpha G_\alpha$ and $\bigsqcup_\alpha G_\alpha = (\bigcup_\alpha G_\alpha)^\circ$ where $\cap$ and $\cup$ are point set intersection and union. See Appendix 2.

4. Using the previous example, show that a meet-homomorphism on a lattice may not preserve infinite meets by showing that the mapping $A \to A^\circ$ is a meet-homomorphism which does not necessarily preserve infinite meets. Give an example on the real line. A homomorphism which preserves arbitrary meets is called a *meet-complete homomorphism.* Dualize.

5. Show that the set of subalgebras of any algebraic system $\langle A, \mathfrak{F} \rangle$ is a complete lattice. Describe the meaning of infinite meets and infinite joins in this lattice.

6. A partially ordered set is said to satisfy the *descending chain condition* if it does not contain any infinite descending chains; *i.e.*, chains of the form $a_1 > a_2 > \cdots$. Show that if a lattice satisfies the descending chain condition, then it is meet-complete. Dualize. Show that a lattice which satisfies both chain conditions is complete, but give an example to show that the converse is not true.

7. Generalize the distributive inequalities to the form:

   (*i*) $x \cup \bigcap_\alpha y_\alpha \leq \bigcap_\alpha (x \cup y_\alpha)$;

   (*ii*) $\bigcup_\alpha (x \cap y_\alpha) \leq x \cap \bigcup_\alpha y_\alpha$.

8. Generalize the distributive laws to the minimax theorem: $\bigcup_\beta \bigcap_\alpha x_{\alpha\beta} \leq \bigcap_\alpha \bigcup_\beta x_{\alpha\beta}$.

9. Show that distributive inequality $(x \cap y) \cup (y \cap z) \cup (z \cap x) \leq (x \cup y) \cap (y \cup z) \cap (z \cup x)$ can be obtained as a special case of the minimax theorem of exercise 7 by letting $\alpha, \beta \in \{1, 2, 3\}$.

10. Prove the following *fixed point theorem*: If L is a union-complete lattice and ϕ is an order homomorphism of L into itself (endomorphism), then ϕ has a fixed point. *Hint*: Let $A = \{x \in L | x \leq \phi(x)\}$ and let $a = \bigcup_A x$. Prove that $\phi(a) = a$.

4-9. CLOSURE OPERATIONS, KURATOWSKI SPACES*

By a **closure operation** *on a partially ordered set,* $\langle X, \leq \rangle$ *we mean a unary operation* $x \to \bar{x}$, *of X into itself satisfying:*

$$K0:\ x \leq y \Rightarrow \bar{x} \leq \bar{y},\ (isotone),$$

$$K1:\ x \leq \bar{x},\ (extensive),$$

$$K2:\ \bar{\bar{x}} = \bar{x}\ (idempotent).$$

*The reader may wish to read Appendix 2 at this point.

Dually, an **interior operation**, $x \to x^\circ$, *satisfies K0 and K2 and*

K1a: $x^\circ \leq x$, *(intensive).*

An element of X is **closed** *if* $x = \bar{x}$ *and* **open** *if* $x = x^\circ$. We designate the set of closed elements of X by F and the open elements by G. Clearly, x is closed if and only if $x = \bar{y}$ for some y and dually for open elements. If x contains a greatest element, then it is necessarily closed. Next we note that if a set, $\{x_\alpha\}$, of closed elements has a meet in X, then this meet is also closed, but the corresponding result may fail for union. More specifically:

Theorem 4-11. *If* $\langle L, \cup, \cap \rangle$ *is a complete lattice with a closure operation,* $x \to \bar{x}$, *then the set, F, of closed elements is a complete lattice under the operations*

$$\sqcap_\alpha x_\alpha = \bigcap_\alpha x_\alpha \text{ and } \sqcup_\alpha x_\alpha = \overline{\bigcup_\alpha x_\alpha}.$$

Proof. (*i*) $\bigcap_\alpha x_\alpha \leq x_\alpha \Rightarrow \overline{\bigcap_\alpha x_\alpha} \leq \bar{x}_\alpha = x_\alpha \ \forall \alpha$, whence $\overline{\bigcap_\alpha x_\alpha} \leq \bigcap x_\alpha$. But $\bigcap_\alpha x_\alpha \leq \overline{\bigcap_\alpha x_\alpha}$, so that $\overline{\bigcap_\alpha x_\alpha} = \bigcap_\alpha x_\alpha$. Thus $\bigcap_\alpha x_\alpha$ is closed, if the x_α are closed.

(*ii*) Since $x_\alpha \leq \bigcup_\alpha x_\alpha$, then $\bar{x}_\alpha = x_\alpha \leq \overline{\bigcup_\alpha x_\alpha}$. But $\overline{\bigcup_\alpha x_\alpha} \in F$, so that it is an upper bound for the x_α within F. If now $x_\alpha \leq f = \bar{f}$ for any $f \in F$, then $\bigcup_\alpha x_\alpha \leq f$ and hence $\overline{\bigcup_\alpha x_\alpha} \leq \bar{f} = f$, so that $\overline{\bigcup_\alpha x_\alpha}$ is a least upper bound of the x_α in F.

We call $\sqcup_\alpha x_\alpha$ the **normalized union** of the x_α. Similar results for open elements are left to the exercises. It follows next that $\bar{x}$ is the smallest closed element containing x; *i.e.*, the meet of all closed elements containing x. Dually, x° is the largest open element contained in x.

Corollary. $\overline{(x \cap y)} \leq \bar{x} \cap \bar{y}$; $\bar{x} \cup \bar{y} \leq \overline{x \cup y}$, $x, y \in L$;
$x^\circ \cup y^\circ \leq (x \cup y)^\circ$; $(x \cap y)^\circ \leq x^\circ \cap y^\circ$.

If the inequality $\bar{x} \cup \bar{y} \leq \overline{x \cup y}$ for the closure operation, ϕ: $x \to \bar{x}$, is an equality and the further condition is added that 0 is closed (if P has 0), then we call this operation a **Kuratowski closure operation**; *i.e.*, ϕ is called a **Kuratowski closure operation** *if it satisfies:*

K3: $\overline{x \cup y} = \bar{x} \cup \bar{y}$, *and*

K4: $\bar{0} = 0$.

The most significant examples are, of course, the topological spaces. In fact, *K1–K4* constitute the Kuratowski closure axioms for a topological space. Thus, by a Kuratowski space we shall mean a set X together with a closure operation: $A \to \bar{A}$ on $\mathfrak{P}(X)$, satisfying *K0–K4*. The closed elements of a

Kuratowski space then form a lattice which is complete under arbitrary point set intersections. In addition $\bar{X} = X$, so that X and $\emptyset$ are closed. Hence the closed elements of a Kuratowski space satisfy the three laws:

F1: F_1, F_2 *closed imply* $F_1 \cup F_2$ *closed;*

F2: F_α *closed implies* $\bigcap_\alpha F_\alpha$ *closed, for an arbitrary index set;*

F3: X *and* $\emptyset$ *are closed.*

We can now define an open set as any set whose point set complement is closed. Then by duality the set, $\mathfrak{T}$, of open sets of X will satisfy the three usual postulates for a topological space:

T1: The union of any number of open sets is open;

T2: The intersection of a finite number of open sets is open;

T3: $\emptyset$ *and* X *are open (cf: Kelley).*

Hence any Kuratowski space becomes a topological space under the above definitions. Conversely, every topological space satisfying *T1–T3* becomes a Kuratowski space if we define a closed set as the complement of any open set and define the closure of a set as the smallest closed set containing it. It only remains to show that this operation: $A \to \bar{A} = \bigcap \{F | F' \in \mathfrak{T} \text{ and } A \subseteq F\}$, is a closure operation satisfying *K0–K4*, and that the closed elements under this closure operation are exactly the original closed sets. The details are left to the exercises. Clearly, the entire process outlined here can also be dualized. Thus we can define an interior operation dual to a Kuratowski closure operation, and then use it to define a topological space using the open sets under the interior operation as the members of the topology. Again, the details are exercises.

4-10. GALOIS CONNECTIONS

Given two partially ordered sets, $\langle X, \leq \rangle$ and $\langle Y, \leq \rangle$ and two mappings, σ and τ from X into Y and from Y into X, respectively, then we call the pair (σ, τ) a Galois connection between X and Y if:

(*i*) σ *and* τ *are antitone,*
(*ii*) $x \leq \sigma \circ \tau(x) \; \forall \; x \in X$ *and* $y \leq \tau \circ \sigma(y) \; \forall \; y \in Y$.

For example, if X and Y are any two sets and ρ is a relation on X into Y, then we can define a Galois connection between their power sets, $\mathfrak{P}(X)$ and $\mathfrak{P}(Y)$, in the following fashion: Let $A \in \mathfrak{P}(X), A \neq \emptyset$ and let $\sigma(A) = \{y \in Y | \langle x, y \rangle \in \rho \; \forall \; x \in A\}$, and let $\tau(B) = \{x \in X | \langle x, y \rangle \in \rho \; \forall \; y \in B\}$ for $B \in \mathfrak{P}(Y), B \neq \emptyset$. Also, let $\sigma(\emptyset) = Y$ and $\tau(\emptyset) = X$. Then the pair (σ, τ) is a Galois connection between $\mathfrak{P}(X)$ and $\mathfrak{P}(Y)$ which is called the *Galois connection induced by the relation* ρ. Clearly σ is defined on all of $\mathfrak{P}(X)$ into $\mathfrak{P}(Y)$ and conversely, τ is defined on $\mathfrak{P}(Y)$ into $\mathfrak{P}(X)$. To verify (*i*), let $A_1 \subseteq A_2 \in \mathfrak{P}(X)$ and let $y \in \sigma(A_2)$. Then $\langle x, y \rangle \in \rho \; \forall \; x \in A_2$ whence $\forall x \in A_1$. Thus $y \in \sigma(A_1)$ so that $\sigma(A_2) \subseteq \sigma(A_1)$; *i.e.*, σ is antitone. Similarly, τ is antitone. To prove (*ii*), let $x \in A$ and let $B = \sigma(A)$. Then $\langle x, y \rangle \in \rho \; \forall \; y \in \sigma(A) = B$. Hence $x \in \tau(B) = \sigma \circ \tau(A)$. Thus $A \subseteq \sigma \circ \tau(A)$. If $A = \emptyset$, clearly $A \subseteq \sigma \circ \tau(A)$. Similarly, $B \subseteq \tau \circ \sigma(B) \; \forall \; B \in \mathfrak{P}(Y)$.

Theorem 4-12. *If* (σ, τ) *is a Galois connection between* X *and* Y, *then* $\sigma \circ \tau$ *is a closure operation in* X *and* $\tau \circ \sigma$ *is a closure operation in* Y.

Proof. *K0*: Let $\sigma \circ \tau(x) = \bar{x}$. Then the antitone law for both σ and τ implies that $\sigma \circ \tau$ and $\tau \circ \sigma$ are both isotone; *i.e.*, $x_1 \leq x_2 \Rightarrow \bar{x}_1 \leq \bar{x}_2$.

K1: $x \leq \sigma \circ \tau(x)$ by (*ii*) of the definition; *i.e.*, $x \leq \bar{x}$.

K2: $x \leq \bar{x} \Rightarrow \bar{x} \leq \bar{\bar{x}}$. But $x \leq \bar{x}$ also implies $\sigma(\bar{x}) \leq \sigma(x)$. Furthermore, $\sigma(\bar{x}) = \sigma(\tau \circ \sigma(x)) = \tau \circ \sigma(\sigma(x)) \geq \sigma(x)$. Hence $\sigma \circ \tau(\bar{x}) \leq \sigma \circ \tau(x)$; *i.e.*, $\bar{\bar{x}} \leq \bar{x}$, whence $\bar{\bar{x}} = \bar{x}$. Therefore $x \to \bar{x}$ is a closure operation on X. Similarly, $\tau \circ \sigma$ is a closure operation on Y.

Theorem 4-13. *If* X *and* Y *are complete lattices, then the sets* $F_X = \{x \in X | x = \bar{x}\}$ *and* $F_Y = \{y \in Y | y = \bar{y} = \tau \circ \sigma(y)\}$ *of closed elements of* X *and* Y *respectively, are complete lattices and* σ *and* τ *are dual isomorphisms between them.*

Proof. Theorem 4-11 already shows that F_X and F_Y are complete lattices. Hence we need to show that σ and τ are dual isomorphisms between them. First, if $x \in F_X$, then $x = \sigma \circ \tau(x)$. Hence if $y = \sigma(x)$, then $y = \sigma \circ \tau \circ \sigma(x)$ and $\tau \circ \sigma(y) = \sigma \circ \tau \circ \sigma \circ \tau \circ \sigma(x) = \sigma \circ \tau \circ \sigma(x) = y$, so that $y \in F_Y$. Hence σ maps F_X into F_Y. Similarly, τ maps F_Y into F_X. Furthermore, $x \in F_X$ implies $\sigma \circ \tau(x) = x$, so that $\sigma \circ \tau = \Delta_{F_X}$ is the identity on F_X. Similarly, $\tau \circ \sigma = \Delta_{F_Y}$ is the identity on F_Y. Hence both σ and τ are one-to-one and onto maps. Finally, the fact that they are isotone means that they are dual order isomorphisms. Hence they are dual lattice isomorphisms.

We shall see in the next section how the results of this theorem permit us to embed any partially ordered set in a complete lattice by means of Dedekind cuts.

4-11. DEDEKIND CUTS

We saw earlier that the set of rational numbers under their usual order do not form a complete lattice. They do form a lattice where $a \cup b$ is the maximum of a and b and $a \cap b$ is their minimum, but this lattice is not complete. For example, the set $A = \{x | x^2 < 2\}$ has a real least upper bound, $\sqrt{2}$, but this number is not rational. It is, of course, true that the reals also do not form a complete lattice, since there is no greatest or least real number. However, the extended reals, $\mathbf{R}^* = \mathbf{R} \cup \{+\infty, -\infty\}$, do form a complete lattice. Furthermore, this lattice contains a sub-lattice isomorphic to the rationals $\mathbf{Q}$. $\mathbf{R}^*$ is therefore a complete embedding lattice for the reals. The method by which the reals are created out of the rationals was originally due to Dedekind by means of so-called Dedekind cuts. We shall show how this same method can be used to extend any partially ordered set to a complete lattice. This extension of the methods of Dedekind to arbitrary partially ordered sets was originally due to MacNeille (*cf:* MacNeille).

If $\langle X, \leq \rangle$ is any partially ordered set and A is any subset of X, then we have already defined the sets $A\uparrow = \{x \in X | a \leq x \ \forall \ a \in A\}$ and $A\downarrow = \{x \in X | a \geq x \ \forall \ a \in A\}$. The operations: $A \rightarrow A\uparrow$ and $A \rightarrow A\downarrow$ are then defined from $\mathfrak{P}(X)$ into $\mathfrak{P}(X)$. In fact, they form a Galois connection from $\mathfrak{P}(X)$ to $\mathfrak{P}(X)$, namely, the Galois connection induced by the relation $\leq$ within $\mathfrak{P}(X)$. Hence, we can apply Theorem 4-13 to show that the set, $\mathfrak{F}_X$, of closed elements of $\mathfrak{P}(X)$ forms a complete lattice. In this case, an element $A \in \mathfrak{P}(X)$ is closed if $A = A\uparrow\downarrow$. We call such elements (subsets of X) *Dedekind cuts.* Then Theorem 4-13 tells us that the class of Dedekind cuts of X forms a complete lattice. We now show that this lattice contains a sub-partially ordered set isomorphic to the original set $\langle X, \leq \rangle$. Hence we have obtained an embedding lattice for X.

Theorem 4-14. (**MacNeille**) *If $\langle X, \leq \rangle$ is any partially ordered set, then $\langle X, \leq \rangle$ can be embedded in the complete lattice of all its Dedekind cuts.*

Proof. We have already seen that $\mathfrak{F}_X$ is a complete lattice. Let $x \in X$. Then we saw in Chapter 1 that $\{x\}\uparrow\downarrow = [x]\downarrow$ is the principal lower ideal generated by x. But $[x]\uparrow\downarrow = [x]\downarrow$, so that $[x]\downarrow \in \mathfrak{F}_X$. Hence the mapping $x \rightarrow [x]\downarrow$ maps X into $\mathfrak{F}_X$. Furthermore, this mapping is isotone, so that it is an order isomorphism. Thus the set of principal lower ideals of X is a sub-partially ordered set of $\mathfrak{F}_X$ isomorphic to $\langle X, \leq \rangle$.

Corollary 1. *If $\{x_\alpha\}$ is a set of elements of $\langle X, \leq \rangle$ which has a least upper bound, $\bigcup_\alpha x_\alpha$ in X, then the union of the $[x_\alpha]\downarrow$ in $\mathfrak{F}_X$ is given by $\bigsqcup_\alpha [x_\alpha]\downarrow = [\bigcup_\alpha x_\alpha]\downarrow$. Dually, if $\{x_\alpha\}$ has a greatest lower bound, $\bigcap_\alpha x_\alpha$, then in $\mathfrak{F}_X$ we have $\bigsqcap_\alpha [x_\alpha]\downarrow = [\bigcap_\alpha x_\alpha]\downarrow$.*

Proof. Let $y \in \bigsqcup_\alpha [x_\alpha]\downarrow$, then $y \in [x_\alpha]\downarrow$ for some α. Hence $y \leq x_\alpha$. Therefore $y \leq \bigcup_\alpha x_\alpha$, so that $y \in [\bigcup_\alpha x_\alpha]\downarrow$. Each step is reversible so that the result follows.

Corollary 2. *Every lattice can be embedded in a complete lattice.*

We note that these results allow us to embed any lattice in a complete lattice. They do not, however, imply that every property of the original lattice is preserved in the embedding lattice. For example, this process embeds the rationals considered as a partially ordered set into the complete lattice of the extended reals, but it does not extend the algebraic properties of the rationals. Further work must be done before we can show that even the reals form a field and certainly, the field properties cannot be extended to $+\infty$ and $-\infty$. Again, when we extend other special lattices later to complete lattices, we cannot always guarantee that these special properties will apply within the embedding lattice.

EXERCISES

1. Prove: If $\langle X, \leq \rangle$ is a partially ordered set with an interior operation: $x \to x^\circ$, then x is open $\leftrightarrow x = y^\circ$ for some $y \in X$.
2. Show that x° is the largest open element contained in x.
3. Show that *K0* can be derived from *K1*–*K3*. (*Hint*: $x \leq y \leftrightarrow x \cup y = y$.)
4. Dualize Theorem 4-11.
5. Formulate the dual concept to a Kuratowski closure operation.
6. Show that if $\langle X, \mathfrak{T} \rangle$ is a topological space and the closure of A is defined as the smallest closed set containing A, then the operation, $A \to \bar{A}$, satisfies *K1*–*K4*. Show that the closed elements under this closure operation are exactly the closed elements in $\langle X, \mathfrak{T} \rangle$.
7. Show how an interior operation dual to a Kuratowski closure operation can be used to define a topological space.
8. Show that if $\langle X, \leq \rangle$ is a partially ordered set with a closure operation, then if $\{x_\alpha\}$ is a set of closed elements whose greatest lower bound exists in X, $\bigcap_\alpha x_\alpha$ is closed.
9. Prove in detail that σ and τ are dual isomorphisms.
10. Show that if $\langle X, \leq \rangle$ is a complete lattice, then the lattice of Dedekind cuts is isomorphic to X itself.
11. If V is a vector space and $A \subseteq V$ is any subset of V, then the operation $A \to [A]$, where $[A]$ is the space spanned by A, is a closure operation.
12. Generalize the preceding example to an arbitrary abstract algebraic system.
13. Show that if X is the real plane and $\mathfrak{P}(X)$ is its power set, then the mapping ϕ: $A \to \phi(A)$ where $\phi(A)$ is the smallest convex set containing A (the **convex hull** of A) is a closure operation. What are the closed elements? Describe the normalized sum of a set of closed sets, and show that it is not necessarily the same as the set union.

14. Let G be a group and ρ be the relation defined by $x\rho y \Longleftrightarrow xy = yx$; *i.e.*, x and y are ρ-related if they commute. Determine the induced Galois connection of ρ.

15. If $\langle x, y \rangle$ is a topological space and A° is the largest open set contained in A while A^- is the least closed set containing A, show that $A^\circ = A'^{-'}$ and $A^- = A'^{\circ'}$.

16. Show that if $a \to a^-$ is a closure operation and $a \to a^\circ$ is an interior operation, then $a^{-\circ}$ is *regularly open* in the sense that it is equal to the interior of its closure; *i.e.*, $a^{-\circ-\circ} = a^{-\circ}$. Dually, show that $a^{\circ-}$ is *regularly closed.*

17. Show that in a lattice with closure and interior operations, it is possible to obtain seven distinct elements from a given element, but no more, using these operations. Show that these elements have a diagram as shown in figure 4-7 (*cf:* Kelly or Halmos).

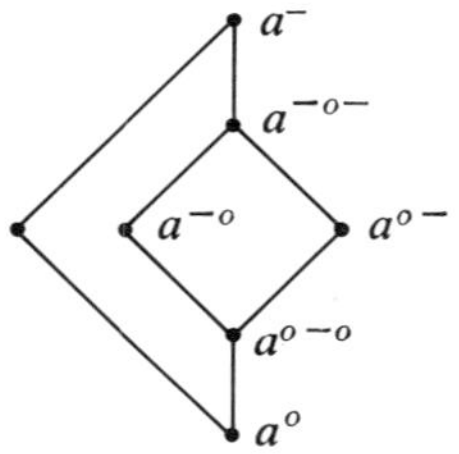

FIGURE 4-7

4-12. MAXIMALITY CONDITIONS AND ZORN'S LEMMA

We complete this chapter with a discussion of some equivalents of the axiom of choice involving partially ordered sets. In Chapter 3 we proved that the axiom of choice was equivalent to the statement that any set can be well-ordered. This is a powerful tool in proving theorems in mathematics, since it enables us to apply methods of transfinite induction to sets of arbitrary cardinality. In fact, up until the development of the theory of partially ordered sets in the 1930's, this was the standard technique for proving many of the more difficult theorems of analysis. However, during this period both Kuratowski and Zorn independently discovered new and powerful techniques which avoid the necessity of well-ordering a set at the beginning, so that more recently these techniques have almost completely replaced the method of proof by transfinite induction. In this section we shall discuss three alternatives to the well-ordering theorem which are, of course, equivalent to the axiom of choice, since the well-ordering theorem was equivalent to it. The first is due to Hausdorff and asserts the existence of maximal chains in arbitrary partially ordered sets. The second is known as Zorn's lemma and again involves maximality conditions in partially ordered sets, while the third, due to Tukey, gives a variant in terms of finiteness properties.

In order to present Hausdorff's maximality condition, we recall that a chain in a partially ordered set $\langle P, \leq\rangle$ is a sub-partially ordered set $\langle G, \leq\rangle$ in which every element is comparable to every other element. We write $a \sim b$ *if* a *is comparable to* b*; i.e., either* $a \leq b$ *or* $b \leq a$ and $a \sim A$ *if* $a \sim x \; \forall \; x \in A$. If $a \sim A$, then a may lie above all elements of A, between members of A or below all members of A. A chain is called **maximal** if it is not a proper subchain of any large chain; *i.e.*, $\langle C_m, \leq\rangle$ *is maximal* $\leftrightarrow a \sim C_m \Rightarrow a \in C_m$. Hausdorff's maximality condition now states that every partially ordered set must contain some maximal chain; *i.e.*,

Hausdorff's Maximality Principle. *Every partially ordered set,* $\langle P, \leq\rangle$, *contains a maximal chain* $\langle C_m, \leq\rangle$.

Theorem 4-15. *Zermelo's well-ordering principle implies Hausdorff's maximality principle.*

Proof. Let $\langle P, \leq\rangle$ be a partially ordered set. We apply Zermelo's well-ordering principle to the set P to obtain a well-ordered set $\langle P, \leq_w\rangle$. Note, however, that the ordering $\leq_w$ is not to be confused with the partial order in $\langle P, \leq\rangle$. Let a_0 be the first element of $\langle P, \leq_w\rangle$ (under $\leq_w$). Then trivially $\langle C_\circ, \leq\rangle = \langle\{a_0\}, \leq\rangle$ is a subchain of $\langle P, \leq\rangle$. If there are no elements of $\langle P, \leq\rangle$ comparable with a_0, then $\langle C_0, \leq\rangle$ is the required maximal chain. Otherwise, we consider the second element a_1 of $\langle P, \leq_w\rangle$. If $a_1 \sim \{a_0\}$, (under $\leq$), then we accept it and otherwise reject it. If accepted, then $C_1 = \langle\{a_0, a_1\}, \leq\rangle$ is an enlarged chain containing $C_\circ$. We proceed by transfinite induction to define an acceptance function (procedure) ϕ such that $\phi(a) = 1$ if a is accepted and $\phi(a) = 0$ otherwise. We assume that ϕ is defined for all x preceding a in $\langle P, \leq_w\rangle$; *i.e.*, $\forall \; x \in I_a = \{x \in P \,|\, x <_w a\}$ and that $C_a = \{x \in I_a \,|\, \phi(x) = 1\}$ is a subchain of $\langle P, \leq\rangle$; *i.e.*, the accepted elements preceding a form a chain. The definition of ϕ is then given by:

$$\phi(a) = \begin{cases} 1 \text{ if } a \sim C_a, \\ 0 \text{ if } a \not\sim C_a. \end{cases}$$

If $\phi(a) = 1$, the set $C_a \cup \{a\}$ will then form an enlarged chain under $\leq$ containing C_a. By induction, ϕ is defined for all $a \in P$. We now let $C_m = \{a \in P \,|\, \phi(a) = 1\}$. It remains to show that $\langle C_m, \leq\rangle$ is the required maximal chain. If not, then there exists a chain $\langle C, \leq\rangle$ properly containing $\langle C_m, \leq\rangle$ within $\langle P, \leq\rangle$. Hence $C - C_m \neq \emptyset$. Let b_0 be the first element of $C - C_m$ under $\leq_w$. If $x < b_0$ and $\phi(x) = 1$, then $x \sim C_m$, so that $\phi(b_0) = 1$. Therefore, $b_0 \in C_m$, which is a contradiction.

Using Hausdorff's maximality principle, we can now state and prove Zorn's lemma. It simply states that if every chain of a partially ordered set is bounded above, then there must exist at least one maximal element.

Zorn's Lemma. *If $\langle P, \leq \rangle$ is a partially ordered set such that every chain $\langle C, \leq \rangle$ in $\langle P, \leq \rangle$ is bounded, then $\langle P, \leq \rangle$ contains a maximal element.*

Theorem 4-16. *Hausdorff's maximality principle implies Zorn's lemma.*

Proof. We are given that any chain $\langle C, \leq \rangle$ in $\langle P, \leq \rangle$ has an upper bound a_C; *i.e.*, $x \leq a_C \ \forall \ x \in C$. We wish to find an element m in P such that $m \leq x$ for any $x \in P \Rightarrow m = x$. By Hausdorff's principle there exists a maximal chain $\langle C_m, \leq \rangle$. By hypothesis, this chain has an upper bound m. If $x \in P$ and $m < x$, then $t \leq m < x$ implies $t \sim x \ \forall \ t \in C_m$. Hence, $x \sim C_m$ and $\langle C_m \cup \{x\}, \leq \rangle$ is a chain which properly contains $\langle C_m, \leq \rangle$ contrary to the maximality condition. Therefore, m is a maximal element as required.

The most usual technique for applying Zorn's lemma is to consider a family $\mathfrak{F}$ of subsets of a fixed set A such that $\mathfrak{F}$ contains the union of any chain of its elements. This union is then an upper bound for the chain, so that we can apply Zorn's lemma and assert the existence of a maximal set in the family $\mathfrak{F}$. Specifically, we say that the family $\mathfrak{F}$ has **Zorn's property**; if $\mathfrak{C} = \langle \{C_\alpha\}, \subseteq \rangle$, $C_\alpha \in \mathfrak{F}$ is a chain, then the union $\mathbf{U}_\alpha \, C_\alpha$ is in $\mathfrak{F}$; *i.e., the union of any chain of sets in* $\mathfrak{F}$ *is in* $\mathfrak{F}$. Zorn's lemma now gives the following corollary:

Corollary. *If $\mathfrak{F}$ is a family of subsets of a set A which has Zorn's property, then $\mathfrak{F}$ has a maximal set M.*

We can illustrate this technique by a proof of the third equivalent to Hausdorff's maximality principle and Zorn's lemma. It is known as Tukey's finiteness principle. If A is a fixed set, then we say that *a property $p(X)$ defined for subsets X of A is of* **finite character**, *if X has property p if and only if every finite subset of X has this property.*

Tukey's Principle. *If A is a fixed set and $p(X)$ is a property applicable to subsets X of A and $p(X)$ is a property of finite character, then there exists a maximal subset M of A with property p.*

Theorem 4-17. *Zorn's lemma implies Tukey's principle.*

Proof. Let $\mathfrak{F}$ be the family of all subsets of A with property p, partially ordered by set inclusion. Let $\mathfrak{C} = \{C_\alpha\}$ be a chain in $\langle \mathfrak{F}, \leq \rangle$, and let $C = \mathbf{U}_\alpha \, C_\alpha$. We wish to show that $C \in \mathfrak{F}$. Let F be a finite subset of C, $F = \{x_1, x_2, \ldots, x_n\}$. Then for each i there exists $C_i \in \mathfrak{C}$ such that $x_i \in C_i$. But since $\mathfrak{C}$ is a chain, one of the C_i is maximal, say C_{i_0}. Hence $C_i \subseteq C_{i_0}$, so that $x_i \in C_{i_0} \ \forall \ i$. Therefore, $F \subseteq C_{i_0}$, whence F has property p, since it is a finite subset of C_{i_0}. But this shows that C has property p, since F was any finite subset of C. We have, therefore, proven that $\mathfrak{F}$ has Zorn's property, from which Zorn's lemma implies that there exists a maximal set in $\mathfrak{F}$, with property p.

We can complete the cycle by showing that Tukey's principle implies Hausdorff's principle.

Theorem 4-18. *Tukey's principle implies Hausdorff's maximality principle.*

Proof. Let $\langle P, \leq \rangle$ be any partially ordered set. Then the property of being a chain within $\langle P, \leq \rangle$ is a property of finite character. For a subset C is a chain if and only if every finite (two-element) subset of C is a chain. (We say in this case that the property of being a chain is of character 2.) Hence there exists a maximal subset of P which is a chain.

We have now shown that the three principles here attributed to Hausdorff, Zorn and Tukey are all equivalent to one another. We have also shown that they can all be derived from the axiom of choice via Zermelo's well-ordering principle. It therefore remains only to derive the axiom of choice from one of these three equivalent principles. Before proceeding to this point, we first state some apparently stronger forms of Hausdorff's principle and Zorn's lemma. The first states that if C is a given chain in a partially ordered set, then C can be embedded in a maximal chain. This is known as the strong form of Hausdorff's principle, but is actually equivalent to it, as we shall see. The second form of Zorn's lemma states that if we are given a fixed element x of a partially ordered set, then we can find a maximal element *which contains this* x.

Strong Form of Hausdorff's Principle. *If $\langle P, \leq \rangle$ is a partially ordered set and $\langle C, \leq \rangle$ is any chain in $\langle P, \leq \rangle$, then there exists a maximal chain $\langle C_m, \leq \rangle$ such that $\langle C, \leq \rangle \subseteq \langle C_m, \leq \rangle$.*

Proof. Clearly the strong form implies the weak form. On the other hand, if $\langle C, \leq \rangle$ is a chain in $\langle P, \leq \rangle$, let Q be the set of all elements of P which are comparable to every element of C; *i.e.*, $Q = \{x \mid x \sim C\}$. Then Q is a partially ordered set containing C. By the weak form of Hausdorff's principle, there exists a maximal chain $\langle C_m, \leq \rangle$ in $\langle Q, \leq \rangle$. We have to show that $\langle C_m, \leq \rangle$ is maximal in $\langle P, \leq \rangle$. But if $\langle K, \leq \rangle$ is any chain in $\langle P, \leq \rangle$ which contains $\langle C_m, \leq \rangle$, then K is in Q, since every element of K is comparable to every element of C. Hence by the maximality in Q, $C_m = K$.

Strong Form of Zorn's Lemma. *If $\langle P, \leq \rangle$ is a partially ordered set in which every chain is bounded and if x is a fixed element of P, then there exists a maximal element m in $\langle P, \leq \rangle$ such that $x \leq m$.*

Proof. Exercise.

Theorem 4-19. *Hausdorff's maximality principle implies Zermelo's well-ordering principle.*

Proof. We are given a set A and wish to find a choice function f defined for all subsets X of A with values in A such that $x = f(X) \in X$. Thus f is a mapping from $\mathfrak{P}^{-}(A)$ into A, where $\mathfrak{P}^{-}(A)$ is the family of *all non-empty* subsets of A. The basic idea of the proof is to consider subfamilies $\mathfrak{F}$ of $\mathfrak{P}^{-}(A)$ for which a choice function does exist, say $f_{\mathfrak{F}}$. $f_{\mathfrak{F}}$ is then defined for all members X of $\mathfrak{F}$ and satisfies $f_{\mathfrak{F}}(X) \in X$. We then partially order these families and apply Hausdorff's principle within the resulting partially ordered set. To define a partial order for the families over which choice functions are defined, we write:

$$\mathfrak{F} \sqsubseteq \mathfrak{G} \leftrightarrow \mathfrak{F} \subseteq \mathfrak{G} \text{ and } f_{\mathfrak{F}} = f_{\mathfrak{G}}|_{\mathfrak{F}};$$

i.e., $\mathfrak{F}$ precedes $\mathfrak{G}$ if $\mathfrak{F}$ is a subfamily of $\mathfrak{G}$ and the associated choice function for $\mathfrak{G}$ is an extension of the associated choice function for $\mathfrak{F}$, or $f_{\mathfrak{F}}$ is the restriction of $f_{\mathfrak{G}}$ to $\mathfrak{F}$. Hausdorff's maximality principle now asserts the existence of a maximal chain Γ within the collection $\sum$ of families with associated choice functions. We claim $\mathfrak{P}^{-}(A)$ is a member of Γ. Let the members of Γ be designated by $\mathfrak{F}_\alpha$, with associated choice functions f_α. Then if $\mathfrak{P}^{-}(A) \notin \Gamma$, there will exist a set $X_0 \in \mathfrak{P}^{-}(A)$ not in any $\mathfrak{F}_\alpha$; *i.e.*, $X_0 \notin \bigcup_\alpha \mathfrak{F}_\alpha$. Furthermore, $X_0 \neq \emptyset$, so that there exists $x_0 \in X_0$. Therefore the family $\mathfrak{F}_0 = \bigcup_\alpha \mathfrak{F}_\alpha \cup \{X\}$ is not in Γ. Yet we can define a choice function f_0 for this family by:

$$f_0(X) = \begin{cases} f_\alpha(X) \text{ if } X \in \mathfrak{F}_\alpha, \\ x_0 \text{ if } X = X_0. \end{cases}$$

f_0 is then an extension of each f where we leave it as an exercise to show that f_0 is independent of the particular α used in its definition. By adjoining $\mathfrak{F}_0$ to Γ we therefore obtain an enlarged chain, contrary to the maximality property of Γ.

We close by indicating how the process of proof by transfinite induction can be extended to partially ordered sets. We say that a partially ordered set $\langle P, \leq \rangle$ *satisfies the* **descending chain condition** *if it fails to contain any infinite descending chains; i.e.*, if in P there does not exist an infinite sequence $\cdots a_2 < a_1 < a_0$. The principle of induction can be extended to the following form.

Theorem 4-20. Principle of Extended Induction. *If $\{p_\alpha\}$ is a set of statements indexed by a partially ordered set $\langle P, \leq \rangle$ which satisfies the descending chain condition and if the truth of the statement p_α follows from the truth of the statements p_β for all $\beta < \alpha$, then p_α is true for all p_α, $\alpha \in P$.*

Proof. Exercise.

EXERCISES

1. Prove the strong form of Zorn's lemma.
2. Prove Theorem 4-20.
3. Prove that the definition of f_0 in Theorem 4-19 is independent of the parameter α.
4. Give a direct proof of the well-ordering theorem from Zorn's lemma.
5. Prove that a partially ordered set satisfies the descending chain condition if and only if every subset has a minimum element.
6. Prove that a partially ordered set satisfies the descending chain condition if and only if every chain is well-ordered.
7. Prove that a partially ordered set satisfies the descending chain condition if and only if every subset does.
8. Show that the partially ordered sets, $\langle \mathbf{N}, \leq \rangle$ and $\langle \mathbf{P}, | \rangle$ satisfy the descending chain condition but neither satisfies the ascending chain condition.
9. *An element of a union semi-lattice is called* **join irreducible** *if it cannot be written as the union of two lesser elements; i.e.,* $x \neq y \cup z$ *where* $y, z < x$. Show that *if a join semi-lattice satisfies the descending chain condition, then every element can be written as a finite union of join irreducible elements.*
10. Prove the following fixed point theorem: *If* $\langle P, \leq \rangle$ *is a partially ordered set and* f *is an injection of* P *into itself such that* $x \leq f(x)$, *then* f *has a fixed point* x_0 *such that* $f(x_0) = x_0$.

5

DISTRIBUTIVE AND MODULAR LATTICES

5-1. DISTRIBUTIVE LATTICES

In Chapter 2 we saw that, within a power set algebra, the intersection and union operations are interrelated by the two distributive laws. We also saw that, in any lattice, the distributive inequalities always hold in the form:

$$D1a\colon\ x \cup (y \cap z) \leq (x \cup y) \cap (x \cup z),$$

$$D2a\colon\ (x \cap y) \cup (x \cap z) \leq x \cap (y \cup z).$$

On the other hand, numerous examples show that not every lattice satisfies the reverse inequalities. The two simplest examples are given by figure 5-1 (*a*) and (*b*). Thus in the lattice D_5 of figure 5-1, $a \cup b = a \cup c = 1$, so that

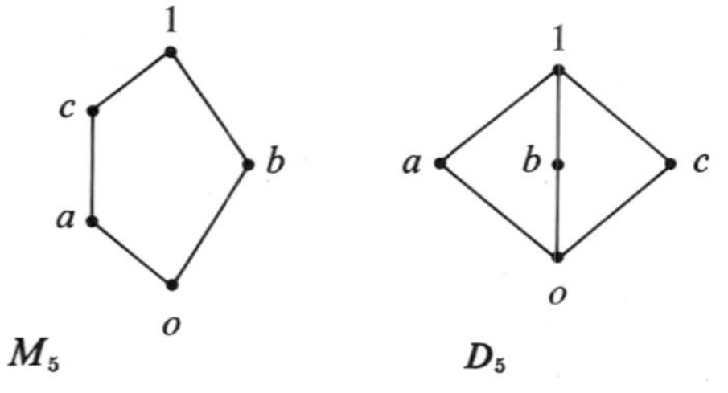

(*a*) (*b*)

FIGURE 5-1

$(a \cup b) \cap (a \cup c) = 1$. But $b \cap c = 0$, so that $a \cup (b \cap c) = a \neq 1$. The lattice M_5 of figure 5-1 is left to the exercises. The class of all those lattices for which $\cup$ and $\cap$ distribute with respect to one another forms one of the most important classes of lattices. We call them distributive lattices. Thus:

Definition 5-1. *A lattice* $\langle L, \cup, \cap\rangle$ *is called* **distributive** *if it satisfies:*

$$D1:\ x \cup (y \cap z) = (x \cup y) \cap (x \cup z),$$

$$D2:\ x \cap (y \cup z) = (x \cap y) \cup (x \cap z).$$

The power set algebra $\langle \mathfrak{P}(U), \cup, \cap\rangle$ of a fixed set U or any of its sub-lattices is an example. Moreover, any chain is a distributive lattice. Hence, the lattices $\langle \mathbf{N}, \leq\rangle$ or $\langle \mathbf{R}, \leq\rangle$ are both distributive. Less obvious is the case of the positive integers partially ordered by divisibility; *i.e.*, $\langle \mathbf{P}, |\rangle$. We leave the verification to the exercises.

We note that *D1* and *D2* are not independent of another; and, in fact, we can derive each from the other. We can use this fact along with the known inequalities *D1a* and *D2a* to shorten the work in verifying that a lattice is distributive as seen in:

Theorem 5-1. *A lattice* $\langle L, \cup, \cap\rangle$ *is distributive if and only if it satisfies either:*

$$D1b:\ (x \cup y) \cap (x \cup z) \leq x \cup (y \cap z), \text{ or}$$

$$D2b:\ x \cap (y \cup z) \leq (x \cap y) \cup (x \cap z).$$

Proof. Assuming *D1b* and applying *D1a* we have *D1*. Hence $(x \cap y) \cup (x \cap z) = [(x \cap y) \cup x] \cap [(x \cap y) \cup z] = x \cap [x \cup z) \cap (y \cup z)] = [x \cap (x \cup z)] \cap (y \cup z) = x \cap (y \cup z)$ by applying the commutative, associative, and absorption laws.

We next note that *D1* and *D2* are dual to each other, so that *the principle of duality extends to distributive lattices.* A more symmetric form of the distributive conditions is given in the following theorem, known as the symmetric distributive law.

Theorem 5-2. *A lattice* $\langle L, \cup, \cap\rangle$ *is distributive if and only if it satisfies:*

$$SD:\ (x \cap y) \cup (y \cap z) \cup (z \cap x) = (x \cup y) \cap (y \cap z) \cap (z \cup x).$$

Proof. (*i*) Assuming *D1* and *D2*, we have $(x \cap y) \cup (y \cap z) \cup (z \cap x) = [(x \cap y) \cup (z \cap y)] \cup (x \cap z) = [(x \cup z) \cap y] \cup (x \cap z) = [(x \cup z) \cup (x \cap z)] \cap [y \cup (x \cap z)] = (x \cup z) \cap [(y \cup x) \cap (y \cup z)] = (x \cup y) \cap (y \cup z) \cap (z \cup x)$.

(*ii*) Conversely, $SD \Rightarrow D1$. For let $r = (x \cup y) \cap (x \cup z)$. We then apply *SD* to the triple x, $y \cup z$ and r. Thus

(1): $(x \cup y \cup z) \cap (y \cup z \cup r) \cap (r \cup x) = [x \cap (y \cup z)] \cup [(y \cup z) \cap r] \cup (r \cap x)$.

But $r \cup x = r$, since $x \leq r$. Furthermore, $r \leq x \cup y \cup z$ and $r \leq r \cup y \cup z$, so that the left side of (1) reduces to r. But $(y \cup z) \cap r = (y \cup z) \cap (x \cup y) \cap$

$(x \cup z) = (y \cap z) \cup (x \cap y) \cup (x \cap z)$ by SD, while $r \cap x = x$. Hence the right hand side is $[x \cap (y \cup z)] \cup [(y \cap z) \cup (x \cap y) \cup (x \cap z)] \cup x = x \cup (y \cap z)$, since x absorbs all the other terms.

In general, if x, y and z are any three elements of a distributive lattice, then the element:

$$m(x, y, z) = (x \cap y) \cup (y \cap z) \cup (z \cap x)$$

is called the **median** of x, y and z. Hence, the mapping $\langle x, y, z\rangle \to m(x, y, z)$ is a ternary operation within L. It is interesting to note that a distributive lattice can be characterized entirely in terms of such an operation. The details are contained in the exercises.

An important technique of determining when a lattice is distributive is to examine its sub-lattices to see whether the diagram contains a sub-lattice isomorphic to figure M_5 or D_5.

Theorem 5-3. *A lattice is distributive if and only if it fails to contain a sub-lattice isomorphic to* M_5 *or* D_5 *of figure 5-1.*

Proof. We have already seen that the lattices of figure 5-1 are not distributive, so that we must now show, conversely, that if L is non-distributive, then it must contain a five element sub-lattice isomorphic to one of the two lattices of figure 5-1. Using SD, a lattice will be non-distributive if it contains three elements a, b, c such that

$$s = (a \cap b) \cup (b \cap c) \cup (c \cap a) < r = (a \cup b) \cap (b \cup c) \cap (c \cup a).$$

We may assume that a, b and c are all distinct. For, if $a = b$, for example, then $s = a \cup (a \cap c) = r$, contrary to our hypothesis. We next consider the case when two of a, b and c are comparable, say $a < c$. Then $s = (a \cap b) \cup (b \cap c) \cup a = a \cup (b \cap c)$ while $r = (a \cup b) \cap (b \cup c) \cap c = (a \cup b) \cap c$. We then consider the five element subset $S = \{b \cap c, b, a \cup b, s, r\}$ as show in figure 5-2. First, $b \cap c < b$. For otherwise if $b \cap c = b$, then $b \leq c$ and $s = a \cup b$ while $a, b \leq c$ imply $a \cup b \leq c$, so that $r = a \cup b$, again contrary to hypothesis. Similarly, $b < a \cup b$. Next, $b \cap c$ and s must be distinct. For if $s = b \cap c$, then $a \leq b \cap c \leq b$, so that $s = a \cup (b \cap c) = b \cap c = r$. Similarly, $r < a \cup b$. Finally, $s \cup b = (a \cup b) \cap (b \cap c) = a \cup b$, while $r \cap b = b \cap c$. Hence S is isomorphic to M_5 of figure 5-1.

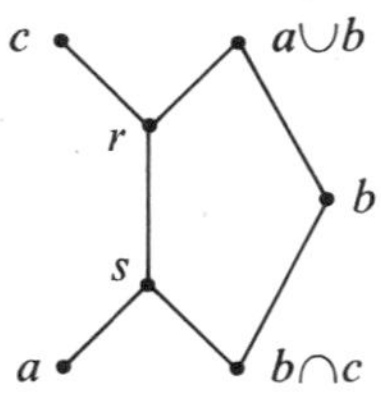

FIGURE 5-2

Thus we may henceforth assume that if $a \leq c$, then $a \cup (b \cap c) = (a \cup b) \cap c$ for any three elements, a, b and c. We now apply this rule to $s < r$. We then obtain:

$$x = s \cup (a \cap r) = (s \cup a) \cap r,$$
$$y = s \cup (b \cap r) = (s \cup b) \cap r, \text{ and}$$
$$z = s \cup (c \cap r) = (s \cup c) \cap r.$$

Using these three elements, x, y and z, we have $a \cap r = a \cap (a \cup b) \cap (b \cup c) \cap (c \cup a) = a \cap (b \cup c)$ by the absorption law. Hence, $x = s \cup [a \cap (b \cup c)]$. Similarly, $y = s \cup [b \cap (c \cup a)]$. Thus $x \cup y = s \cup \{[a \cap (b \cup c)] \cup [b \cap (c \cup a)\} = s \cup (\{[a \cap (b \cup c)] \cup b\} \cap (c \cup a))$, since $a \cap (b \cup c) \leq c \cup a$. Therefore $x \cup y = s \cup (\{b \cup [a \cap (b \cup c)]\} \cap (c \cup a)) = s \cup [(b \cup a) \cap (b \cup c) \cap (c \cup a)] = s \cup r = s$. Similarly, $y \cup z = z \cup x = s \cup r$ and dually $x \cap y = y \cap z = z \cap x = s \cap r = r$. If follows that the five element subset $S = \{s, x, y, z, r\}$ is isomorphic to D_5.

We can use this theorem to give another alternative characterization of the conditions that a lattice be distributive, in the form of a cancellation law.

Theorem 5-4. *(i) If $\langle L, \cup, \cap \rangle$ is distributive, then $a \cap x = a \cap y$ and $a \cup x = a \cup y$ imply $x = y$.*

(ii) If $a \cap x = a \cap y$ and $a \cup x = a \cup y$ $\forall$ $a, x, y \in L$, then L is distributive.

Proof. (*i*) Assuming the distributive laws, we have $x = x \cup (a \cap x) = x \cup (a \cap y) = (x \cup a) \cap (x \cup y) = (a \cup y) \cap (x \cup y) = (a \cap x) \cup y = (a \cap y) \cap y = y$.

(*ii*) Assuming the cancellation laws, we must show that L is distributive. But if L is not distributive, then by the preceding theorem it must contain a sub-lattice similar to M_5 or D_5 of figure 5-1. However, in both of these lattices $a \cup b = c \cup b$ and $a \cap b = c \cap b$, whereas $a \neq c$.

In section 5-1 we defined a distributive lattice by the two distributive laws *D1* and *D2*. These laws can be extended as in the exercises to arbitrary finite unions and meets (exercises 11, 13 and 14). On the other hand, exercise 12 shows that the finite distributive laws do not always extend to infinite unions or meets. Thus in the lattice $\langle \mathbf{N}, 1 \rangle$ partially ordered as in this exercise, the infinite distributive law $x \cap \bigcup_{n=1}^{\infty} x_n = \bigcup_{n=1}^{\infty} (x \cap x_n)$ fails. On the other hand, the distributive law $x \cup \bigcap_{n=1}^{\infty} x_n = \bigcap_{n=1}^{\infty} (x \cup x_n)$ does hold. Hence *D1* and *D2* do not imply arbitrary distributivity, nor does one infinite distributive law imply the other, as was the case for *D1* and *D2*. In infinite lattices we must postulate whatever degree of distributivity we want. First a lattice is called *sequentially-meet distributive* (**σ-meet distributive**) if the distributive law:

$$D1\sigma\colon\ x \cap \bigcup_{n=1}^{\infty} x_n = \bigcup_{n=1}^{\infty} (x \cap x_n)$$

holds for any infinite sequence of elements, $x_1, x_2, \ldots$ of L provided the indicated meets exist in L. Dually, L is **σ-union distributive** if:

$$D2\sigma\colon\ x \cup \bigcap_{n=1}^{\infty} x_n = \bigcap_{n=1}^{\infty} (x \cup x_n)$$

holds. More generally, we can replace σ by any cardinal and say that L is

α-**distributive** if:

$$D1\alpha\colon\ x \cup \bigcap_{\beta \le \alpha} x_\beta = \bigcap_{\beta \le \alpha} (x \cup x_\beta) \text{ and}$$

$$D2\alpha\colon\ x \cap \bigcup_{\beta \le \alpha} x_\beta = \bigcup_{\beta \le \alpha} (x \cap x_\beta),$$

whenever the index sets have cardinality α, (assuming the proper meets and unions exist). Thus σ-distributivity is $\aleph_0$-distributivity. If *D1* and *D2* hold regardless of the size of the index sets, then L is called **completely distributive.** However, even this type of distributivity is not completely general, since it only implies the distributivity of a *single* element onto an arbitrary set of elements. It does not permit the laws of exercise 13 of the preceding section to be stated for arbitrary cardinality. To introduce the more general concept we extend exercise 13 of the last section so that a set of α-meets will distribute onto a set of β-unions. We then call L **α-β distributive.** For more details and applications of such general distributivity, we refer the reader to Sikorski.

EXERCISES

1. Show that every chain is a distributive lattice.

2. Show that the lattice $\langle \mathbf{P}, | \rangle$ is distributive.

3. Write out the proof that *D2* implies *D1*.

4. Show that the lattice M_5 of figure 5-1*b* is not distributive.

5. Show that the lattice of figure 5-3 is not distributive.

6. Construct a lattice diagram illustrating the elements x, y, z, r and s used in the proof of Theorem 3.

7. Prove that a lattice is distributive if and only if the inequalities $a \cup x \le b \cup x$ and $a \cap x \le b \cap x$ hold if and only if $a \le b$.

8. Show that in a distributive lattice $m(a, x, b) = x \leftrightarrow a \cap b \le x \le a \cup b$.

9. Show that in a distributive lattice, every finite subset generates a finite sub-lattice.

10. Show that the homomorphic image of a distributive lattice is distributive.

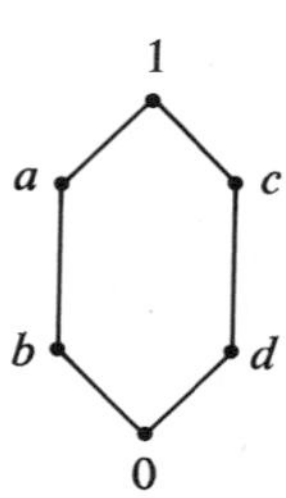

FIGURE 5-3

11. Show that in a distributive lattice $x \cap \bigcup_{i=1}^{n} y_i = \bigcup_{i=1}^{n} (x \cap y_i)$ and $x \cup \bigcap_{i=1}^{\infty} y_i = \bigcap_{i=1}^{n} (x \cup y_i)$ where n is finite.

12. Let $\mathbf{P}$ be the lattice of positive integers under divisibility. Let $\mathbf{N}$ be the set $\mathbf{P} \cup \{0\}$ of natural numbers where we define $x|0\ \forall\ x \in \mathbf{N}$. Show that $\langle \mathbf{N}, | \rangle$ is a complete lattice with greatest element 0 and least element 1. Let $x_n = 2^n$ and

$x = 3$. Show that $x \cap \bigcup_{n=1}^{\infty} x_n \neq \bigcup_{n=1}^{\infty} (x \cup x_n)$. Hence the distributive laws for infinite sets may not hold in a distributive lattice.

13. Generalize the symmetric distributive law SD to the form

$$\bigcup_{i=1}^{n} \bigcap_{j \neq i}^{n} x_j = \bigcap_{i<j} (x_i \cup x_j).$$

14. Formulate an expression for $\bigcap_{i=1}^{n} \bigcup_{j=1}^{n_i} x_{ij}$ as a union of meets.

15. If L is a distributive lattice with units and $m(a, b, c)$ is the median of a, b and c, show that m satisfies:

(*i*) $m(0, a, 1) = a$,
(*ii*) $m(a, b, a) = a$,
(*iii*) $m(a, b, c) = m(b, a, c)$,
(*iv*) $m(a, b, c) = m(c, a, b)$,
(*v*) $m(m(a, b, c), x, y) = m(m(a, x, y), b, m(c, x, y))$.

16. If m is the median operation in a distributive lattice, showth at $m(a, 1, b) = a \cup b$ and $m(a, 0, b) = a \cap b$.

17. If $\langle L, m(a, b, c)\rangle$ is a system with a carrier set L and a ternary operation satisfying the conditions (*i*)-(*v*) of exercise 15 and $a \cup b$ and $a \cap b$ are defined as in exercise 16, show that:

(*a*) $\cup$ and $\cap$ are idempotent, commutative, and distribute with respect to one another;
(*b*) $a \cup 1 = 1$ and $a \cap 1 = a$;
(*c*) prove the absorption laws (*Hint*: $a \cup (a \cap b) = (a \cap 1) \cup (a \cap b)$);
(*d*) if $r = (a \cup b) \cup c$, prove that $a = a \cap r$, $b = b \cap r$ and $c = c \cap r$;
(*e*) let $s = a \cup (b \cup c)$ and use (*d*) to prove that $r = s \cap r = r \cap s = r$.

Hence prove the associative laws for $\cup$ and $\cap$. Therefore (*i*)-(*v*) of exercise 15 constitute a set of postulates for a distributive lattice.

18. Show that if L is a distributive lattice, then the mappings $x \to a \cap x$ and $x \to a \cup x$ where a is fixed, are lattice endomorphisms from L into itself; *i.e.*, homomorphisms from L into the ideal $[a]\downarrow$ and dual ideal $[a]\uparrow$ respectively.

19. If L is a distributive lattice and $H_{a,b} = \{x | a \cup x = b \cup x\}$, prove that $H_{a,b}$ is a filter in L.

20. Show that the lattice $\mathbf{N}$ of exercise 12 is σ-union distributive.

5-2. MODULAR LATTICES

Although distributive lattices are among the more common as well as important lattices, many lattices which arise in practice are not distributive. One of the simplest and best known examples is given by a projective plane. Let π be a projective plane, and let L be the set of points of π plus the lines of π together with π itself and the empty set, $\emptyset$. Then L is a lattice under the partial order given by the incidence relation; *i.e.*, $p \leq l$ if p is a point and lies on l;

otherwise, we write $x \leq x, \emptyset \leq x \leq \pi \ \forall \ x \in L$. The union of two distinct points is then the line joining them, and the meet of two distinct lines is their point of intersection. Meet and join otherwise have their usual meaning. If now p, q and r are three distinct points on a given line l, then the five elements $\emptyset, p, q, r$, and l form a sub-lattice of L isomorphic to figure 5-1(b). Hence, L is not distributive. On the other hand, if p is a point on the line l and q is a point not on l, then the following special case of the distributive law does hold: $p \leq l$ and $p \cup (q \cap l) = (p \cup q) \cap (p \cup l) = (p \cup q) \cap l$ (Fig. 5-4). Furthermore, it is fairly easily to verify that this same case of the distributive law always holds for any three elements within L as long as the relation $x \leq z$ holds; *i.e*, $x \cup (y \cap z) = (x \cup y) \cap (x \cup z) = (x \cup y) \cap z$. Many other important lattices also satisfy this special distributive law. Such lattices were originally discovered by Dedekind and are sometimes known as Dedekind structures, but are more frequently called modular lattices, as in:

Definition 5-2. *A lattice* $\langle L, \cup, \cap \rangle$ *is called* **modular** *if it satisfies:*

$$M: x \leq z \Rightarrow x \cup (y \cap z) = (x \cup y) \cap z.$$

As in the case of distributive lattices, the definition can be weakened somewhat by noting that in any lattice the modular inequality holds in the form:

$$Ma: x \leq z \Rightarrow x \cup (y \cap z) \leq (x \cup y) \cap z.$$

We also note that the modular law is self-dual (exercise) so that *the principle of duality applies to modular lattices.*

Clearly every distributive lattice is modular. Furthermore,the non-distributive lattice of figure 5-1(b) is modular, but the lattice of figure 5-1(a) is not. We can extend Theorem 5-3 to its counterpart for modular lattices.

Theorem 5-5. *A lattice is modular if and only if it fails to contain a sublattice isomorphic to the lattice* M_5 *of figure 5-1.*

The proof is contained in that of Theorem 5-4 where the modular case of the distributive law was first used. Theorem 5-4 also has a counterpart for modular lattices in the form:

Theorem 5-6. (*i*) *If* L *is a modular lattice and* $x \leq y$, *then* $x \cup a = y \cup a$ *and* $x \cap a = y \cap a$ *imply* $x = y$.

(*ii*) *If* $a \cup x = a \cup y$ *and* $a \cup x = a \cap y$ *imply* $x = y$ *for all* a, x, y *in* L *such that* $x \leq y$, *then* L *is modular.*

The proof is left for the reader. Figure 5-4 now shows lattice diagrams for a projective line and plane alongside the usual projective figures. In general, the theory of modular lattices plays a key role in the theory of projective

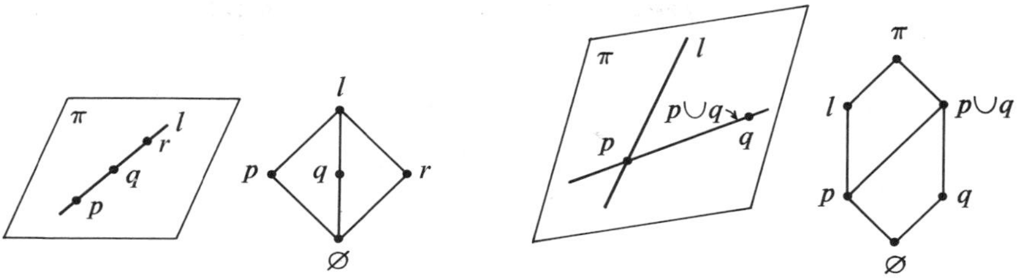

(*a*) (*b*)

FIGURE 5-4

geometries. In fact, a projective geometry can be completely characterized as a special type of modular lattice as we shall see later on. Again if V_n is an n-dimensional vector space, we have seen that the set $\mathfrak{V}_n$ of subspaces of V_n is a lattice. This lattice is isomorphic to the set of elements of an $n - 1$ dimensional projective geometry, so that $\mathfrak{V}_n$ is also a modular lattice. Other special types of modular lattices play important roles in the theory of linear operators in Hilbert spaces and in general analysis. One of the earliest known examples which served as an inspiration for much of the general theory of modular lattices is the lattice of normal subgroups of a group. Thus, let G be any group, and let $\mathfrak{N}(G)$ be the set of its normal subgroups. Then $\mathfrak{N}(G)$ can be partially ordered by the relation "is a normal subgroup of." Thus, if H and K are normal subgroups of G, then $H \cup K$ will be the smallest normal subgroup which contains H and K, while $H \cap K$ is their point set intersection. $H \cup K$ can then be characterized as the set HK of products hk where $h \in H$ and $k \in K$; *i.e.*, $H \cup K = HK$. For if $h_1, h_2 \in K$, then $(h_1k_1)(h_2k_2) = h_1(k_1h_2)k_2 = h_1(h_2'k_1)k_2 = (h_1h_2')(k_1k_2) \in HK$. If now H, K and L are normal subgroups of G, and $H \subseteq L$, then let $x \in (H \cup K) \cap L$; *i.e.*, $x = hk$ where $h \in H$ and $k \in K$ and $hk \in L$. But $H \subseteq L \Rightarrow h \in L$. Hence, since L is a subgroup, $h^{-1} \in L$, and $k = h^{-1}x \in L$, so that $k \in K \cap L$. Thus $x = hk \in H \cup (K \cap L)$. It follows that $(H \cup K) \cap L \subseteq H \cup (K \cap L)$. Therefore $\mathfrak{N}(G)$ is modular.

We note that normality is necessary, and that the theorem is not true in general for all subgroups. In fact, most of the significant theorems on the structure of normal subgroups are essentially lattice-theoretic in nature, depending on the modular law. Conversely, many of the most important results in the theory of modular lattices were originally inspired by theorems in group theory.

One of the most significant theorems concerning modular lattices is illustrated by figure 5-1(*b*), which is a modular but not distributive lattice. In figure

5-1(a), which is non-modular, it is possible to establish two chains connecting 0 and 1 which are both maximal in length but have different lengths. Thus the chains $0 < a < c < 1$ and $0 < b < 1$ contain four and three elements respectively, yet it is not possible to intersperse any further elements within either chain. However, in figure 5-1(b) this not the case, and the three possible maximal chains, $0 < a < 1, 0 < b < 1$ and $0 < c < 1$ all have the same length. We shall see that this property holds within any modular lattice and is one of its most important features. However, before going into the details, we first develop some other theorems for modular lattices, necessary to obtain our desired results.

Theorem 5-7. *If a and b are any two elements of a modular lattice, L, then the two intervals* $[a \cap b, b]$ *and* $[a, a \cup b]$ *are isomorphic.*

Proof. We consider the two mappings, $\phi: x \to b \cap x$ for $x \in [a, a \cup b]$ and $\psi: y \to a \cup y$ for $y \in [a \cap b, b]$ and show that they are inverse isomorphisms. First, $x \in [a, a \cup b] \Rightarrow a \leq x \leq a \cup b$, and hence $b \cap a \leq b \cap x \leq b \cap (a \cup b) = b$, so that ϕ maps $[a, a \cup b]$ into $[a \cap b, b]$. Similarly, ψ maps $y \in [a \cap b, b]$ into $[a, a \cup b]$. Next $\phi \circ \psi$ maps $x \to b \cap x \to a \cup (b \cap x) = (a \cup b) \cap x = x$, since $a \leq x \leq a \cup b$. Hence $\phi \circ \psi = \Delta_1$ where Δ_1 is the identity on $[a, a \cup b]$. Similarly $\psi \circ \phi = \Delta_2$ is the identity on $[a \cap b, b]$. But these are exactly the conditions that ϕ and ψ be one-to-one and onto mappings. Thus they are inverse mappings. Finally, $a \leq x_1 \leq x_2 \leq a \cup b \Rightarrow a \cap b \leq \phi(x_1) = b \cap x_1 \leq \phi(x_2) = b \cap x_2 \leq \phi(a \cup b) = b$, so that ϕ is isotone. But a one-to-one order-preserving homomorphism is at the same time a lattice homomorphism (isomorphism). Therefore $[a, a \cup b] \cong [a \cap b, b]$. See figure 5-5.

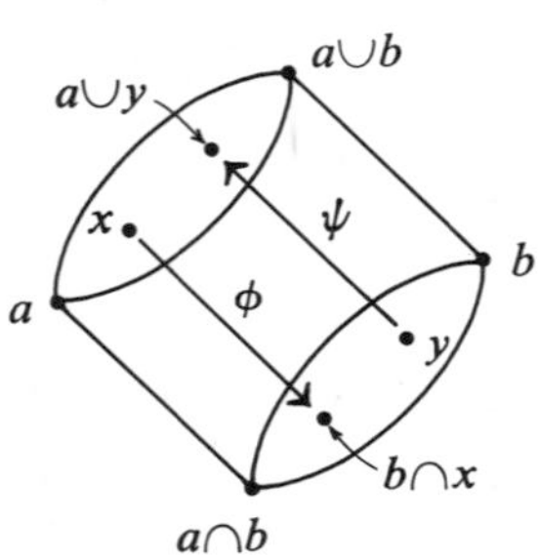

FIGURE 5-5

An important special case of this theorem is given by:

Corollary. *If* $\langle L, \cup, \cap \rangle$ *is a modular lattice and* $a, b \in L$ *are such that* $a \cup b$ *covers* a, *then* b *covers* $a \cap b$.

In general, $a \leq b$ and $c \leq d$ are elements of L, then we call the intervals $[a, b]$ and $[c, d]$ **transposed intervals** (***perspective***) if $a = b \cap c$ and $d = b \cup c$. We then write $[a, b] \approx [c, d]$. Thus $[a, b]$ and $[c, d]$ are transposes of each other if they form a figure similar to figure 5-5. For example, if π is the projective plane and p is any point of π while l is a line not containing p, then the intervals $[0, l]$ and $[p, \pi]$ are transposed intervals, since $p \cap l = 0$ and $p \cup l = \pi$. The mapping ϕ described in the proof of Theorem 5-7 from $q \in [0, l]$

to $q \cup p \in [p, \pi]$ maps the family of points on l into the family of lines through p as well as mapping 0 onto p and l onto π. We say in geometry that the family of points is perspective with the family of lines. The situation is illustrated in figure 5-6. Similarly, in a projective 3-space ϕ will define a perspectivity between points

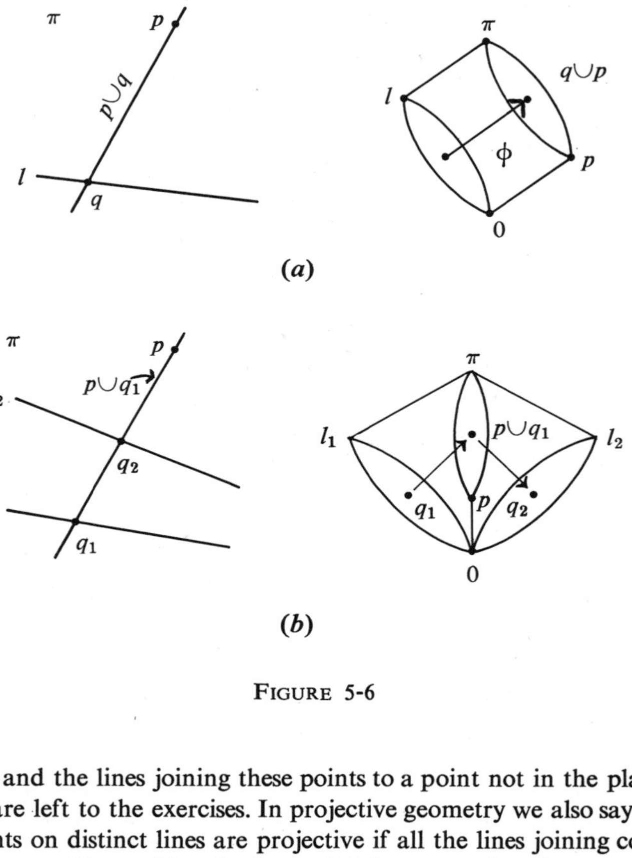

FIGURE 5-6

of a plane and the lines joining these points to a point not in the plane. Other examples are left to the exercises. In projective geometry we also say two families of points on distinct lines are projective if all the lines joining corresponding points are collinear. Thus in figure 5-6(b) we say that the points of l_1 and l_2 are projective with center of projectivity p. Hence the points of l_1 are perspective with the lines through q which in turn are perspective with the points on l_2. Hence the two families of points on l_1 and l_2 are projective if one set can be obtained from the other by a set of perspectivities. We use this idea to define the concept of a projectivity within a modular lattice in general. Thus we say that *two intervals* $[a, b]$ *and* $[c, d]$ *are* **projective** *if there exists a finite sequence of intervals* $[x_1, y_1] = [a, b] \approx [x_2, y_2] \approx \cdots \approx [x_n, y_n] = [c, d]$. We then write $[a, b] \sim [c, d]$. It therefore follows from Theorem 5-6 that projective intervals are always isomorphic. Furthermore, we call two elements a and b

projective, if the intervals $[0, a]$ and $[0, b]$ are projective. We note, for example, that two points or two lines of a projective plane are always projective. We shall see later that two elements of a projective geometry are usually projective when they have the same dimension. In fact, we shall use the theory of transposed intervals to introduce a concept of dimension into an arbitrary modular lattice. However, we first prove a lemma due to Zassenhaus, originally developed for group theory.

Theorem 5-8. **(Zassenhaus Lemma)** *If L is a modular lattice and $a \leq b$ and $c \leq d$, then*

$$[(a \cup c) \cap b, (a \cup d) \cup b] \sim [(a \cup c) \cap d, (b \cup c) \cap d].$$

Proof. $c \leq d \Rightarrow a \cup c \leq a \cup d \Rightarrow (a \cup c) \cap b \leq (a \cup d) \cap b$. Also $a \leq b \Rightarrow a \cup c \leq b \cup c \Rightarrow (a \cup c) \cap d \leq (b \cup c) \cap d$. Hence $(a \cup c) \cup [b \cap (a \cup d)] = (a \cup c \cup b) \cap (a \cup d) = (b \cup c) \cap (a \cup d)$ while $(a \cup c) \cap [b \cap (a \cup d)] = (a \cup c) \cap b$. Therefore the intervals $[(a \cup c) \cap b, (a \cup d) \cap b]$ and $[(a \cup c), (a \cup d) \cap (b \cup c)]$ are transposes of one another. Similarly, $[(a \cup c) \cap d, (b \cup c) \cap d] \approx [(a \cup c), (a \cup d) \cap (b \cup c)]$, so that $[(a \cup c) \cap b, (a \cup d) \cap b]$ and $[(a \cup c) \cap d, (b \cup c) \cap d]$ are projective. See figure 5-7.

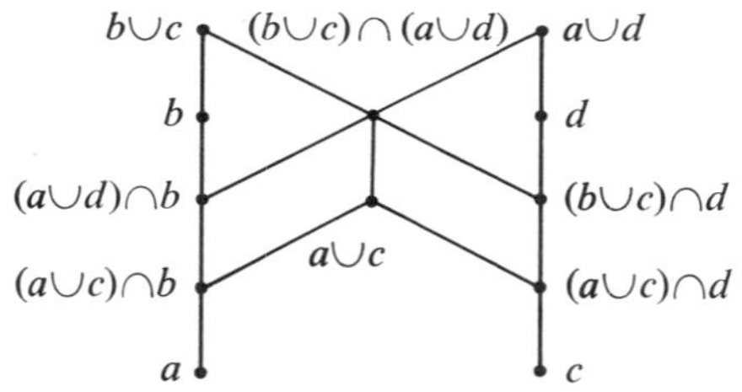

FIGURE 5-7

On the basis of the Zassenhaus lemma, we can now prove a theorem of Schreier concerning two chains connecting the same elements. Thus if $a, b \in L$ where L is any lattice and $a = x_1 < x_2 < \cdots < x_n = b$ is a chain, C_1, of distinct elements connecting a and b, then we call a second chain, C_2, a **refinement** of C_1, if C_1 is a sub-partially ordered set C_2; *i.e.*, C_2 can be obtained from C_1 by interspersing elements between the elements of C_1. A chain, C, is called *maximal* between a and b, if L contains no chains between a and b which are proper refinements of C. Finally, two chains are called **equivalent**, if there is a one-to-one correspondence between the members of the chains such that corresponding intervals are projective, We can now show that if L is modular and C_1 and C_2 are two chains connecting the same two points, then we can find refinements for both chains such that these refinements are equivalent.

Theorem 5-9. **(Schreier's Theorem)** *If L is a modular lattice and $a < b \in L$, then any two chains, C_1 and C_2, connecting a and b have equivalent refinements.*

Proof. Let C_1: $a = a_0 < a_1 < a_2 < \cdots < a_n = b$ and C_2: $a = b_o < b_1 < \cdots < b_m = b$ be the two given chains. Define elements $a_{ij} = (a_i \cup b_j) \cap a_{i+1}$, for $i = 0, \ldots, n-1$, and $j = 0, \ldots, m$; $b_{ij} = (a_i \cup b_j) \cap b_{j+1}$ for $i = 0, \ldots, n$ and $j = 0, \ldots, m-1$. Then $a = a_o = a_{oo} < a_{01} < a_{02} < \cdots a_{om-1} < a_{om} = a_{10} = a_1 < a_{11} < \cdots < a_2 < \cdots < a_{(n-1)m} = b$ is a refinement of C_1 connecting a and b. Similarly, $a = b_0 = b_{00} < b_{10} < b_{20} < \cdots < b_{(n-1)0} = b_1 < b_{11} < \cdots < b_m = b$ is a refinement of C_2. Furthermore, both chains have the same number of links, nm. But $a_i < a_{i+1}$ and $b_j < b_{j+1}$ imply by the Zassenhaus lemma that $[a_{ij}, a_{ij+1}] = [(a_i \cup b_j) \cap a_{i+1}, (a_i \cup b_{j+1}) \cap a_{i+1}] \sim [a_i \cup b_j) \cap b_{j+1}, (a_{i+1} \cup b_j) \cap b_{j+1}] = [b_{ji}, b_{ji+1}]$. Hence the intervals of the refined chains are isomorphic in pairs. (Note that the projective pairs do not occur in the same order in both chains). See figure 5-8.

We next note that if C: $a_1 < a_2 < \cdots < a_i < \cdots < a_n$ is a maximal chain in any partially ordered set, then each a_{i+1} covers a_i. For otherwise, we could obtain a proper refinement of C which contradicts the maximality condition. By the **length of a chain,** C, we mean the *number l of links in the chain*; *i.e.*, $n - 1$ in this case or $+\infty$ if C is infinite. By the *length of a partially ordered set* we shall mean the length of the longest chain in the set. We denote the length of C by $l(C)$. Furthermore, we say that p is *locally finite* if every chain connecting two arbitrary points is finite, i.e., if every bounded chain is finite. Our next result shows that if L is a modular lattice, and if two finite chains connecting the same elements are both maximal, then they must have the same number of elements. Again, this theorem was originally discovered in connection with the theory of subgroups of a group quite early in the history of lattice theory by Jordan and Dedekind.

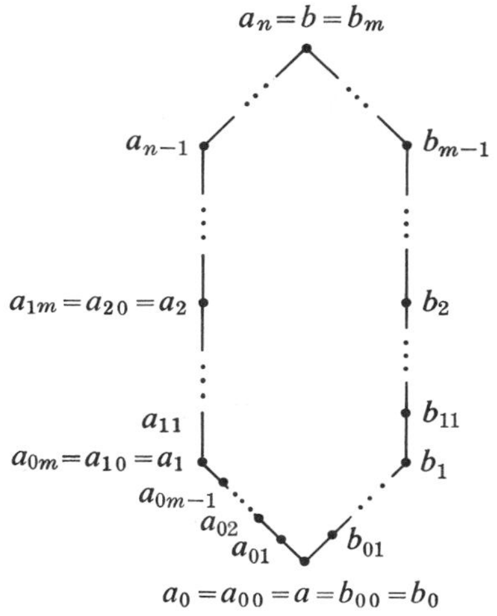

FIGURE 5-8

Theorem 5-10. **(Jordan-Hölder Theorem)** *If $a < b$ are two elements of a modular lattice and if C_1 and C_2 are two finite maximal chains connecting a and b of lengths n and m respectively, then $n = m$, and there is a $1 - 1$ correspondence between the intervals of C_1 and C_2 such that corresponding intervals are projective.*

Proof. We use induction of the length of a maximal chain connecting a and b. If $n = 1$, then b covers a and the theorem is obviously true. Hence assume that the theorem is true for all pairs of elements which can be connected by a maximal chain of length n. Let a and b be two elements which can be connected by a maximal chain of length $n + 1$; C_1: $a_0 = a < a_1 < a_2 < \cdots < a_n < a_{n+1}$. Let C_2: $b_0 = a < b_1 < b_2 < \cdots < b_m < b_{m+1}$ be any other maximal chain connecting a and b. Then a_1 and b_1 both cover a, so that $a_1 \cup b_1$ covers both a_1 and b_1. Then the chain $a_1 < a_2 < \cdots < a_{n+1} = b$ is a maximal chain of length n connecting a_1 and b. We can now apply the Schreier theorem to obtain a refinement of the chain $a_1 < c_2 < b$, where $c_2 = a_1 \cup b_1$, between a_1 and b. Let this chain be $a_1 < c_2 < c_3 < \cdots < c_{r+1} = b$. Then by our inductive hypothesis, $n = r$. Similarly, $b_1 < b_2 < \cdots < b_{m+1}$ and $b_1 < c_2 < \cdots < c_{r+1} = b$ are two maximal chains connecting b_1 and b. Hence $m = r$. Therefore $n = m$. See figure 5-9.

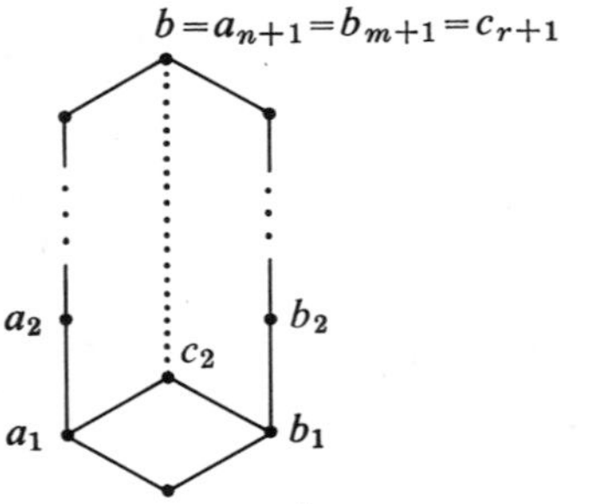

FIGURE 5-9

The particular importance of the Jordan-Hölder theorem is that it permits us to introduce a concept of dimension into an arbitrary modular lattice with 0. Thus if $\langle L, \cup, \cap, 0\rangle$ is a modular lattice of finite length with least element, 0, and if $a \in L$ then we call the *length of any chain from 0 to a* **the dimension of *a*, *d*(*a*)**. We also write $d(0) = 0$. The Jordan-Hölder theorem then guarantees that $d(a)$ is a unique integer $\forall\ a \in L$. For example, if a is an atom; *i.e.*, covers 0, then $d(a) = 1$. Again, if L has a greatest element, 1, then $d(1) = l(L)$. Also, if $a \leq b$, then $d(b) = d(a) + l(a, b)$ where $l(a, b)$ is the length of the interval sub-lattice $[a, b]$. In particular, if b covers a, then $d(b) = d(a) + 1$. The primary theorem concerning dimension in a modular lattice is the following:

Theorem 5-11. *If L is a modular lattice with 0 and $a, b \in L$, then:*

$$V1\colon\ d(a) + d(b) = d(a \cap b) + d(a \cup b).$$

Proof. Since $a \cap b \leq a, b$ we have $d(a) = d(a \cap b) + l(a \cap b, a)$. Furthermore, $b \leq a \cup b$ implies $d(a \cup b) = d(b) + l(b, a \cup b)$. But by the basic isomorphic theorem for modular lattices, $[a \cap b, a] \cong [b, a \cup b]$, so that $l(a \cap b, a) = l(b, a \cup b)$. Hence $d(a \cup b) = d(b) + l(a \cap b, a)$. Therefore $d(a) + d(b) = d(a \cap b) + l(a \cap b, a) + d(b) = d(a \cap b) + d(a \cup b)$.

For example, if L is the lattice associated with the projective plane, π, and if p and q are distinct points, then $p \cap q = 0$ while $p \cup q$ is the line joining p and q. $d(p) = d(q) = 1$ while $d(p \cap q) = 0$ and $d(p \cup q) = 2$. Therefore, $d(a) + d(b) = d(a \cap b) + d(a \cup b)$ in this case. In general, in projective geometry we define the *projective dimension, D, to be one less that the lattice dimension*, so that points have dimension 0, lines dimension 1, etc. Thus $D(a) = d(a) - 1$. However, equation *V1* still holds. We also note that if a and b are projective, then $d(a) = d(b)$. This fact is true for arbitrary projective geometries, but may not be true in general modular lattices. As a second example we may consider the lattice $\mathfrak{V}_n$ of subspaces of a finite dimensional vector space. As we have mentioned before, this lattice is isomorphic to the lattice of elements of a projective geometry. Hence the lattice of subspaces of a vector space has a dimension function which satisfies *V1*. In this case, the lattice dimension has the same meaning as the vector space dimension, so that lines have dimension 1, planes dimension 2, etc. The origin is the least element, is a point, and has dimension 0. For example, if $n = 3$, then $\mathfrak{V}_n$ is the lattice of subspaces of V_3, vector three-space. If π is a plane not passing through the origin, then every one-dimensional line of V_n; *i.e.*, line through the origin, intersects π in a point, while every plane through 0 intersects π in a line. Hence we have a one-to-one mapping of the subspaces, lines, planes, etc. of V_3 onto the points, lines, etc of π. Furthermore, this mapping is a lattice isomorphism, so that we have an isomorphism between the lattice of subspaces of V_3 and the elements of the projective plane, π. This mapping reduces the dimension by 1, which accounts for the definition given above for projective dimension.

EXERCISES

1. Show that figure 5-1(a) is non-modular.
2. Prove Theorem 5-6.
3. Show that a lattice is modular if and only if $x \leq z$ implies $(x \cup y) \cap z \leq x \cup (y \cap z)$.
4. Show that if L is a modular lattice and $a, b, c \in L$, then $m(a, b, c) = (a \cup b) \cap (b \cup c) \cap (c \cup a) = [a \cap (b \cup c)] \cup [b \cap (a \cup c)]$.
5. Show that if a, b, c are any three elements of any lattice such that $a < c$, then they generate a sub-lattice isomorphic to figure 5-10. Construct a $\cup/\cap$ table for this sub-lattice.

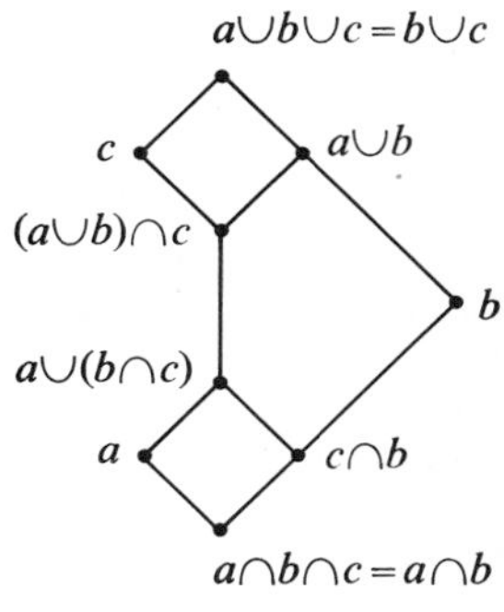

FIGURE 5-10

6. Show that if L is a modular lattice and $a, b, c \in L$ such that $a \cup (b \cap c) = (a \cup b) \cap (a \cup c)$, then a, b, c form a distributive triple in the sense that any distributive law for $\cup$ or $\cap$ onto the other involving a, b and c holds.
7. Show that every chain in the lattice of figure 5-11 is finite, but that $l(L) = \infty$. Hence, L is locally finite, but has infinite length.
8. Show that every chain connecting any pair of elements of $\langle \mathbf{P}, | \rangle$ is finite, but $\mathbf{P}$ contains infinite chains.
9. Determine the meaning of $d(a)$ in $\langle \mathbf{P}, | \rangle$.
10. Let $\langle P, \leq \rangle$ be any partially ordered set and let $\mathfrak{C}$ be the family of chains within P. Show that $\mathfrak{C}$ is partially ordered by inclusion and is a complete lattice under point set intersection and union. Show that if P is itself totally ordered, then $\mathfrak{C} = \mathfrak{P}(P)$ is the power set of P.

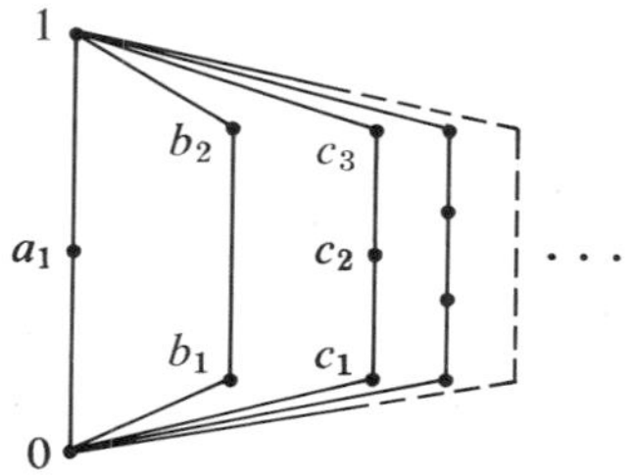

FIGURE 5-11

11. If C_0 is a fixed chain in a partially ordered set, P, let $\mathfrak{C}_0$ be the class of all chains which contain C_0. If $\{C_\alpha\}$ is any set of elements in $\mathfrak{C}_0$, show that $\mathbf{U}_\alpha C_\alpha$ is a chain which is an upper bound for all the chains, C_α, in $\mathfrak{C}_0$. Hence, use Zorn's lemma to show that C_0 can be embedded in a maximal chain. Thus show that the reference to Schreier's theorem can be avoided in the proof of the Jordan-Hölder theorem.
12. Show that if a_{ij} and b_{ij} are defined as in the proof of Schreier's theorem, then (a) $a_{ij} < a_{ij+1}$, and (b) $a_{im} = a_{i+1} = a_{i+10}$.
13. Prove that in a modular lattice $a \leq b \Rightarrow d(b) = d(a) + l(a, b)$.
14. Prove that in a modular lattice $a \leq b$ and $d(a) = d(b) \Rightarrow a = b$.
15. Prove that in a modular lattice $a \leq b$ and $d(b) = d(a) + 1 \Rightarrow b$ covers a.
16. Show that if a and b are projective, then $d(a) = d(b)$.
17. If L is a modular lattice, show that the set of elements with finite dimension forms an ideal in L.
18. Construct the lattice diagram of the subgroups of the group of even permutations on four letters. Show that it is not modular, but that the lattice of normal subgroups is.
19. Show that projectivity is an equivalence relation. If π is a projective plane what are the equivalence classes under projectivity?
20. Use the dimension theorem to show that if two planes in euclidean three space have one point in common, then they have a line in common. Show that this need not be true in euclidean four space.
21. If X is a finite set, what is the meaning of $d(A)$ for any subset A within the lattice $\mathfrak{P}(X)$?
22. If l_1 and l_2 are two skew lines of a projective 3-space, S, illustrate the concept of transposed intervals between $[0, l_1]$ and $[l_2, S]$ by constructing a projective figure and the corresponding lattice diagram.

23. Illustrate the concept of perspectivity between the family of points and lines on a fixed plane of projective 3-space and the family of lines and planes through a fixed point not on the given plane. Draw lattice diagrams and the projective figure.

24. Show that L is modular $\Leftrightarrow (x \cup y) \cap z = \{x \cup [y \cap (x \cup z)]\} \cap z$.

25. Show that if P satisfies the ascending and descending chain conditions (exercise 5, §3-8) then it has finite length.

26. Show that if d is bounded and P is locally finite, then it has finite length.

5-3. SEMI-MODULAR LATTICES

The concept of dimension for modular lattices proves satisfactory for projective planes as well as for vector spaces of finite dimension. However, if we consider the affine plane (the euclidean plane, for example) then we can still introduce a satisfactory definition of dimension, but the lattice of subspaces is no longer modular. For example, if π is an affine plane, l and m are parallel lines and p is a point on l, then $p \cup (m \cap l) = p \cup \emptyset = p$ whereas $(p \cup m) \cap l = \pi \cap l = l \neq p$. The situation is illustrated in figure 5-12.

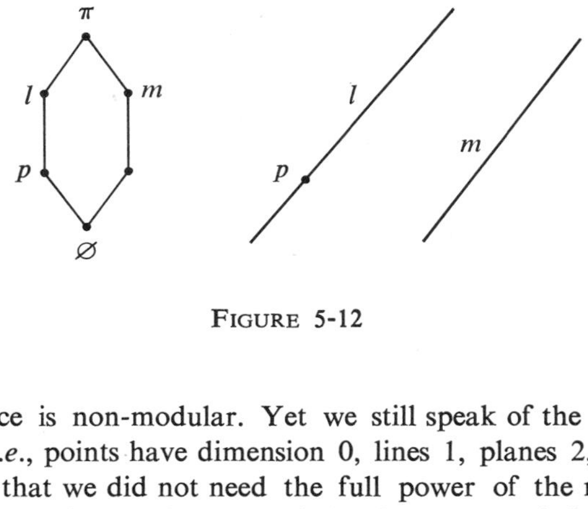

FIGURE 5-12

Hence the lattice is non-modular. Yet we still speak of the dimension of a subspace of π; *i.e.*, points have dimension 0, lines 1, planes 2, etc. The fact of the matter is that we did not need the full power of the modular law to introduce a concept of dimension. Essentially all that we needed was the Jordan-Dedekind chain condition which states that all maximal chains between fixed points have the same length. Thus if any lattice satisfies the Jordan-Dedekind chain condition; then we can define the dimension of an element, a, just as above, as the length of any maximal chain from 0 to a. The dimension function is then an integral-valued function defined on L. The only condition essential for the existence of such a function is given by the following theorem:

Theorem 5-12. *A lattice of locally finite length with least element,* 0, *satisfies the Jordan-Dedekind chain condition* $\Leftrightarrow$ *there exists an integral-valued function on L such that*

$$V2\text{: } b \text{ covers } a \Leftrightarrow d(b) = d(a) + 1.$$

Proof. (*i*) If the Jordan-Dedekind chain condition holds and b covers a, and if we define $d(a)$ as the length of any maximal chain from 0 to a, then clearly $d(b) = d(a) + 1$.

(*ii*) Let L be a lattice with a dimension function which satisfies $V2$. Let $a < b$ and let $a_0 = a < a_1 < a_2 < \cdots < a_n = b$, and $b_0 = a < b_1 < b_2 < \cdots < b_m = b$ be two maximal chains connecting a and b. Then by $V2$, $d(a_1) = d(a) + 1$, $d(a_2) = d(a_1) + 1 = d(a) + 2, \ldots, d(b) = d(a) + n$. Similarly, $d(b) = d(a) + m$. Hence $n = m$ and the Jordan-Dedekind condition is satisfied.

We note that condition $V2$ does not determine $d(a)$ uniquely, since $d(a) + k$ for any k will satisfy $V2$ equally satisfactorily. If we wish, we may add the further condition that $d(0) = 0$ and avoid this situation.

We saw in the preceding section that the dimension function in a modular lattice satisfied the dimension equation $V1$ of Theorem 5-11. This is not the case in the affine plane, however. Thus let l and m be two parallel lines and p a point on l as above. Then $d(l) = d(m) + 2$, while $d(l \cap m) = 0$ and $d(l \cup m) = 3$. Hence, $d(l \cap m) + d(l \cup m) = 3$, $d(l) + d(m) = 4$. Thus equation $V1$ is not necessary in order to obtain a satisfactory concept of dimension for geometry. If we examine the derivation of the Jordan-Hölder theorem from the modular law we notice that the only condition needed was the fact that if a_1 and b_1 cover $a = a_1 \cap b_1$ where $a_1 \neq b_1$, then $c_2 = a_1 \cup b_1$ covers both a_1 and b_1. This result followed from the corollary to Theorem 5-7 for modular lattices. We can use it here to generalize the concept of a modular lattice and yet maintain the dimension function.

Definition 5-3. *A lattice* $\langle L, \cup, \cap \rangle$ *of finite length* is called upper semi-modular if it satisfies:*

$$USM\text{: } a \cap b \prec a, b \Rightarrow a, b \prec a \cup b.$$

Dually, L is lower semi-modular if:

$$LSM\text{: } a, b \prec a \cup b \Rightarrow a \cap b \cap a, b.$$

Theorem 5-13. *Any upper semi-modular (respectively, lower semi-modular) lattice satisfies the Jordan-Dedekind chain condition and has a dimension*

*For a generalization which applies without the restriction to finite length, *Cf:* Szasz, § 45.

function $d(a)$ which is integral-valued and satisfies:

$$V1\text{a}: d(a \cap b) + d(a \cup b) \leq d(a) + d(b),$$

$$(\text{respectively: } V1b: d(a) + d(b) \leq d(a \cap b) + d(a \cup b)),$$

$$V2: a \prec b \Rightarrow d(b) = d(a) + 1.$$

Proof. We have already seen that the Jordan-Dedekind chain condition which, being self-dual, applies to either upper or lower semi-modular lattices, is equivalent to $V2$. Hence, we need only verify $V1a$. Let $a_0 = a \cap b < a_1 < a_2 < \cdots < a_n = a$ and $b_0 = a \cap b < b_1 < b_2 < \cdots < b_m = b$ be two maximal chains from $a \cap b$ to a and b, respectively. We first show that $a \cup b_1$ either covers a or equals a. For since $a_0 \prec a_1, b_1$, either $a_1 = b_1 = a_1 \cup b_1$ and $a \cup b_1 = a$ or $a_1 \neq b_1$, in which case $a_1 \cup b_1$ covers a_1. Again, either $a_2 = a_1 \cup b_1 = a_2 \cup (a_1 \cup b_1)$ and $a \cup b_1 = a$, or else $a_2 \neq a_1 \cup b_1$ and $a_2 \cup (a_1 \cup b_1)$ covers a_2. Proceeding in this way by induction, either $a \cup b_1 = a$ or $a \cup b_1$ covers a. Similarly, using b_2 we again find that either $a \cup b_2 = a \cup b_1$ or $a \cup b_2$ covers $a \cup b_1$. Continuing, we see that the chain $a = a \cup b_0 \leq a \cup b_1 \leq a \cup b_2 \leq \cdots \leq a \cup b_m = a \cup b$ consists of either equalities or coverings. Hence $l(a, a \cup b) \leq m = l(a \cap b, b)$. Therefore $d(a \cup b) = d(a) + l(a, a \cup b) \leq d(a) + m$ while $d(b) = d(a \cap b) + m$, so that $d(a \cup b) + d(a \cap b) \leq d(a) + m + d(b) - m < d(a) + d(b)$. See figure 5-13.

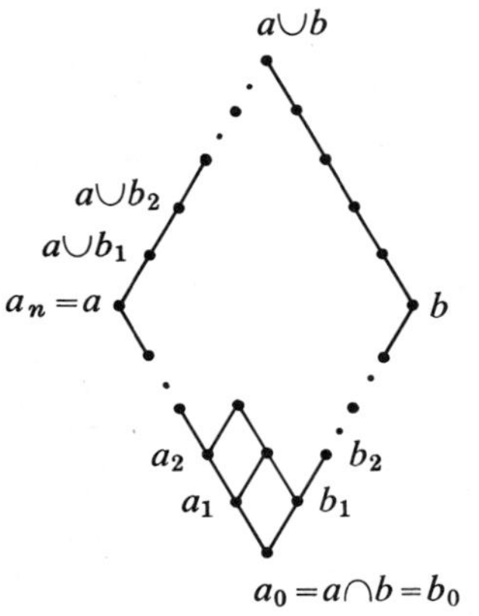

FIGURE 5-13

The reverse inequality for lower semi-modular lattices follows by duality.

Thus either upper or lower semi-modularity is sufficient for the existence of a dimension function and the Jordan-Dedekind chain condition. Clearly every modular lattice of finite length is both upper and lower semi-modular, and in the next section we shall show the converse.

5-4. METRIC LATTICES

The concept of a dimension function as a real valued function on a lattice which satisfies the dimension equation $V1$ of Theorem 5-11 is similar to many other functions in mathematics which satisfy this same condition. In general, a real valued function which satisfies $V1$ is called a valuation; *i.e.*, a **valuation** *on a lattice is a real valued function, $v(a)$, which satisfies:*

$$V1:\ v(a) + v(b) = v(a \cap b) + v(a \cup b),$$

It is **isotone** if:

$$V2:\ a \leq b \Rightarrow v(a) \leq v(b).$$

For example, if U is any set, and $c(A)$ is the cardinality of any subset A of U, then $c(A)$ satisfies $V1$. The proof is left to the exercises. Again if U is a set on which a measure function is defined such that every subset of U is a measurable set, then this measure function, $m(A)$, will be a valuation on the power set lattice of U. Also, in probability theory if an experiment is performed, then the class of possible events which can occur forms a lattice where $E_1 \cup E_2$ is the event "either E_1 occurs or E_2 occurs" and $E_1 \cap E_2$ is the event that "both E_1 and E_2 occur." The probability $p(E)$ that a given event occurs is then a valuation on this lattice.

In the first example cited, if U is a finite set, then the cardinality function satisfies the additional condition that if A is a proper subset of B, then $c(A) < c(B)$; *i.e.*, $c(A)$ is *strictly isotone*. In this case we call $c(A)$ a positive valuation. In particular, $A \neq \emptyset$ implies $c(A) > 0$. In general, *any valuation which satisfies*

$$V3:\ a < b \Rightarrow v(a) < v(b) \textit{ is called a } \textbf{positive valuation.}$$

If $\langle L, v(a) \rangle$ is a lattice with an isotone valuation, then L is called a **quasimetric lattice**, while if the valuation is positive, then it is called a **metric lattice.** A modular lattice of finite length is therefore a metric lattice under the dimension function $d(a)$. We can now show that the converse is also true.

Theorem 5-14. *Every metric lattice is modular.*

Proof. Let L be a metric lattice with valuation $v(a)$. If L is non-modular, then it contains a sub-lattice isomorphic to the lattice M_5 of figure 5-1 where $a \cup (b \cap c) < (a \cup b) \cap c$. Hence if v is positive, then $v(a \cup (b \cap c)) = v(a) + v(b \cap c) - v(a \cap b \cap c) = v(a) + v(b) + v(c) - v(b \cup c) - v(a \cap b \cap c) = v(a) + v(b) + v(c) - v(a \cup b \cup c) - v(a \cap b \cap c)$, since $a \cup c = c$. Similarly, $v((a \cup b) \cap c) = v(a \cup b) + v(c) - v(a \cup b \cup c) = v(a) + v(b) + v(c) - v(a \cap b) - v(a \cup b \cup c) = v(a) + v(b) + v(c) - v(a \cap b \cap c) - v(a \cup b \cup c)$. Hence $v(a \cup (b \cap c)) = v((a \cup b) \cap c)$ contrary to the positiveness of v.

Corollary 1. *Every lattice of finite length which is both upper and lower semi-modular is metric.*

Corollary 2. *If L is a lattice of finite length, then the following three conditions are equivalent:*

(*i*) *L is modular;*

(*ii*) *L is both upper and lower semi-modular; and*
(*iii*) *L satisfies the Jordan-Dedekind chain condition and V1 holds.*

Proof. We need only show that the third alternative implies the first. The Jordan-Dedekind chain condition implies the existence of a dimension function. Now let a, b, c be any three elements of L such that $a < c$. and for which the modular law fails. Then they generate a sub-lattice of the type M_5. But in this lattice, $a \cup b = c \cup b$ and $a \cap b = c \cap b$. Hence, $d(a) + d(b) = d(a \cup b) + d(a \cap b) = d(c \cup b) + d(c \cap b) = d(c) + d(b)$. Therefore $d(a) = d(c)$ contrary to the fact that $a < c$.

Corollary 3. *A lattice of finite length is upper semi-modular if and only if* $a \cap b \prec a \Longleftrightarrow b \prec a \cup b$.

To explain why we call a metric lattice metric, we next show that we can, in fact, introduce a metric into any metric lattice in a fashion which will make L into a metric space in the usual sense of topology. Thus if X is any set and $d(a, b)$ is a real valued function defined for every pair of elements of X; *i.e.*, defined on $X \times X$, then the pair $\langle X, d \rangle$ is called a *metric space* if d satisfies:

$$M1: \ d(a, b) \geq 0 \text{ and } d(a, b) = 0 \Longleftrightarrow a = b,$$
$$M2: \ d(a, b) = d(b, a),$$
$$M3: \ d(a, b) + d(b, c) \leq d(a, c)$$

If we now let $\langle L, v \rangle$ be a metric lattice, then we can define a distance function on L by:

$$d(a, b) = v(a \cup b) - v(a \cap b).$$

The next theorem shows that d is then a metric on L.

Theorem 5-15. *Every metric lattice, $\langle L, v \rangle$ is a metric space under:*

$$d(a, b) = v(a \cup b) - v(a \cap b).$$

Proof. Clearly $d(a, b)$ is a real valued function defined on $L \times L$. Also d is positive valued, since $v(a \cup b) \geq v(a \cap b)$. Furthermore, if $a = b$, then $d(a, a) = v(a \cup a) - v(a \cap a) = 0$. Conversely, if $d(a, b) = 0$, then $v(a \cup b) = v(a \cap b)$, so that $a \cup b = a \cap b$. Thus $a = b$. Therefore $M1$ holds. $M2$ follows from the commutative laws for $\cup$ and $\cap$ in any lattice. Finally, to verify $M3$ $d(a, b) + d(b, c) = v(a \cup b) - v(a \cap b) + v(b \cup c) - v(b \cap c) = v(a \cup b \cup c) + v((a \cup b) \cap (b \cup c)) - v((a \cap b) \cup (b \cap c)) - v(a \cap b \cap b \cap c)$. But $a \cup c \subseteq a \cup b \cup c \Rightarrow v(a \cup c) \leq v(a \cup b \cup c)$, while $a \cap b \cap c \leq a \cap c \Rightarrow v(a \cap b \cap c) \leq v(a \cap c)$. Furthermore, $b \leq b \cup (a \cap c) \leq (a \cup b) \cap (b \cup c) \Rightarrow v(b) \leq v((a \cup b) \cap (b \cup c))$ and $(a \cap b) \cup (b \cap c) \leq b \cap (a \cup c) \leq b \Rightarrow v((a \cap b) \cup (b \cap c)) \leq v(b)$. Therefore $v(a \cup b \cup c) + v((a \cup b) \cap (b \cup c)) - v((a \cap b) \cup (b \cap c)) - v(a \cap b \cap c) \geq v(a \cup c) + v(b) - v(b) - v(a \cap c) = v(a \cup c) - v(a \cap c) = d(a, c)$.

EXERCISES

1. Show that a lattice is lower semi-modular (respectively, upper semi-modular) if and only if $a \prec a \cup b \Rightarrow a \cap b \prec b$ (respectively; $a \cap b \prec b \Rightarrow a \prec a \cup b$).
2. Show that L is upper semi-modular if and only if $a \prec b$ implies $a \cup x \prec b \cup x$ or $a \cup x = b \cup x \, \forall \, x \in L$.
3. Show that the lattice of figure 5-14 is upper, but not lower semi-modular. Show that this lattice can be realized as a sub-lattice of an affine plane.
4. Show that if L is a modular lattice and $\equiv$ is a congruence relation such that $x \equiv x \cup y$, then $y \equiv x \cap y$.
5. Show that in a metric lattice $a \leq b \Rightarrow d(a, b) = l(a, b)$. Hence in the chain $\langle \mathbf{R}, \leq \rangle$, $d(a, b) = |b - a|$ is the usual metric.
6. If U is a fixed set, show that $c(A) = \bar{\bar{A}}$ is a valuation on $\mathfrak{P}(U)$. Show by a counter-example that $c(A)$ is not a positive valuation if U is infinite. What is the associated metric for this lattice?
7. Show that probability is a valuation. Is it positive?
8. Show that if $a \cap b = 0$, then $v(a \cup b) = v(a) + v(b)$. Show that $d(a, b) = l(a \cap b, a \cup b)$.
9. What is the metric associated with the dimension function for the lattice of subspaces for a finite dimensional vector space?

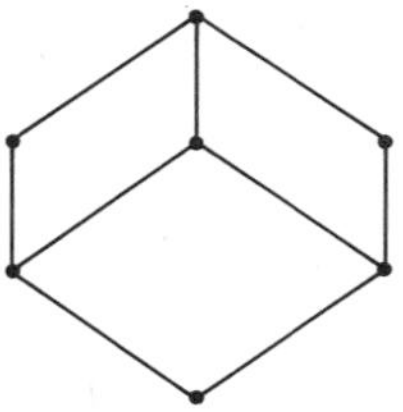

FIGURE 5-14

10. The real plane, $\mathbf{R} \times \mathbf{R}$, is a lattice under $x = (x_1, x_2) \leq y = (y_1, y_2) \Leftrightarrow x_1 \leq y_1$ and $x_2 \leq y_2$. What is the meaning of $x \cup y$ and $x \cap y$? Show that this lattice does not have a least element. If $v(x) = v((x_1, x_2)) = x_1 + x_2$, show that v is a valuation and determine the associated metric in the plane.
11. If $\langle \mathfrak{C}, X \rangle$ is the space of real continuous functions defined on the real unit interval, $X = [0, 1]$, and $f \leq g \Leftrightarrow f(x) \leq g(x) \, \forall \, x \in X$, then $\langle \mathfrak{C}, X, \leq \rangle$ is a lattice. Show that $v(f) = \int_0^1 f(x)\, dx$ is a valuation on this lattice. What is the associated metric?
12. Show that a meet semi-lattice L with units, which has no infinite chains, is a lattice. (*Hint*: let $a, b \in L$ and construct a chain in the set $\{a, b\} \uparrow$ where $x_0 = 1 > x_2 > x_3 > \cdots$ Show that this chain must have a last element which will be $a \cup b$.)
13. Construct a lattice of locally finite length which has both infinite descending and ascending chains.
14. Extend Theorem 5-12 to lattices of finite length by requiring $d(a)$ to be either a finite integer (positive or negative or $+\infty$ or $-\infty$), letting $d(x_o) = 0$ for some fixed x_o.
15. Show that the lattice of figure 5-14 contains a sub-lattice which is not upper semi-

modular. Hence, every sub-lattice of an upper semi-modular lattice need not be upper semi-modular*.

16. Show that the dual of an upper semi-modular lattice need not be upper semi-modular. Hence, the theory of upper semi-modular lattices is not self-dual, although the theory of upper semi-modular lattices is dual to the theory of lower semi-modular lattices.

17. Show that every interval, (convex) sub-lattice of an upper semi-modular lattice is upper semi-modular. (*Hint*: Let $b \underset{S}{\prec} a$ mean a covers b in the sub-lattice. Show that $b \underset{S}{\prec} a$ implies $b \prec a$ where $\prec$ is the covering relation in the original lattice.)

5-5. ATOMIC LATTICES

Another important concept of lattice theory is that of atomicity. We have already defined an atom as an element which covers 0. Also, as we have seen, every power set algebra is atomic as well as dual atomic, where the atoms are the singleton sets. On the other hand, the lattice of real numbers is not atomic since no real number covers 0 in the usual order. But the natural numbers under either $\leq$ or $|$ are both atomic lattices; in the first case 1 being the only atom, while in the second case every prime is an atom. Neither of these lattices is dually atomic, since neither has a greatest element. Not every atomic lattice has finite length, but every lattice which is of finite length is atomic. More generally, every lattice which satisfies the descending chain condition is atomic (exercise). Hence, by definition, every semi-modular lattice is atomic. In such lattices, we can arrange the elements in a diagram on levels such that 0 is at the bottom, the atoms are at the second level, etc. and all elements of a given level have the same dimension. We therefore frequently refer to the dimension of a as the *height* of a and $d(a)$ as a *height function*.

In atomic lattices we obtain a special case of the modular law called the **atomic modular law** which states:

$$AM\colon\ x \leq z \text{ and } a \text{ an atom imply } x \cup (a \cap z) = (x \cup a) \cap z.$$

In general, we know that the upper semi-modular law is weaker that the modular law; *i.e.*, the modular law does not hold in every upper semi-modular lattice. However, we can now show that the atomic modular law does follow for any semi-modular lattice as in:

Theorem 5-16. *Every upper semi-modular lattice satisfies the atomic modular law AM.*

*This implies that the class of upper semi-modular lattices can not be distinguished within the class of lattices by equational identities (*Cf:* Grätzer).

Proof. By exercise 5 section 5-2, the three elements x, z, a form a sub-lattice which is either isomorphic to figure 5-10 or is formed from it by an identification of elements; *i.e.*, is a homomorphic image of figure 5-10. If $x = a$, then clearly *AM* holds. Otherwise, $x \neq a$ and $a \cup x$ covers x, since a is an atom. If the modular law *AM* does not hold, then this figure shows that $x = x \cup (a \cap z) < (x \cup a) \cap z = x \cup a$. Hence $x \cup a \leq z$, so that $a \leq z$, whence $x \cup a = a \cup z$. Thus $x \cup (a \cap z) = x \cup a = (x \cup a) \cap z$ which is contrary to our assumption. Therefore, *AM* holds.

The lattice of figure 5-15 shows that the atomic modular is weaker than the

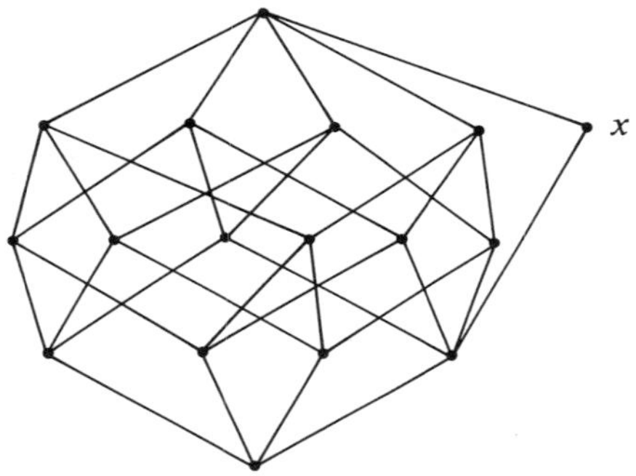

FIGURE 5-15

modular law, even in a lattice which is not upper semi-modular. However, just as the modular law implies the upper semi-modular law, the atomic modular law implies a corresponding *atomic upper semi-modular law:*

AUSM: If a is an atom and $a \cap x = 0$, then $a \cup x$ covers x.

In contrast to the general semi-modular law, the atomic law, *AUSM*, is actually equivalent to the atomic modular law, *AM*. Thus:

Theorem 5-17. *In an atomic lattice of finite length, the laws AM and AUSM are equivalent.*

Proof. (*i*) Assuming *AM*, if $x \leq t \leq a \cup x$, then $t = (x \cup a) \cap t = x \cup (a \cap t)$. But $a \cap t \leq a$, so that $a \cap t$ is either a or 0. If $a \cap t = 0$, then $t = x$, while if $a \cap t = a$, then $t = x \cup a$. Hence $x \prec a \cup x$.

(*ii*) Assuming the atomic semi-modular law, let $x < z$ and a be an atom. Then $a \cap z$ is either 0 or a. If $a \cap z = 0$, then $a \cap x = 0$ and $x \cup (a \cap z) = x$. Hence $x \prec a \cup x$, and $z \prec a \cup z$. Therefore $x \leq (x \cup a) \cap z \leq x \cup a$ implies either $(x \cup a) \cap z = x$ from which $x \cup (a \cap z) = (x \cup a) \cap z$, or

$(x \cup a) \cap z = x \cup a$. In this second case $x \cup a \leq z$, so that $x \cup a \cup z = z = z \cup a$ contrary to $z \prec a \cup z$. Finally, if $a \cap z = a$, then $a \leq z$, while $x \cup (a \cap z) = x \cup a$. But also $a \cup x \leq z \cup x = z$, so that $(x \cup a) \cap z = x \cup a$, and again $x \cup (a \cap z) = (x \cup a) \cap z$.

We shall find these results useful in the next section in the discussion of independence of atoms.

5-6. INDEPENDENCE

The concepts of dimension and atomicity are related in geometry by the concept of independence of atoms. For example, in a vector space V_n we determine the dimension of a subspace by the number of independent vectors in it. We say that a vector v is dependent on a set of vectors $v_1, v_2, \ldots, v_n$, if v can be represented as a linear combination of them; *i.e.*, if v is contained in the subspace spanned by them. To put this definition in terms of the lattice of subspace of V_n, let $[v_i]$ denote the linear subspace spanned by v_i; *i.e.*, the set of scalar multiples of v_i. Then the space spanned by the v_i's is the union of the $[v_i]$'s. Hence, to say that v is dependent on the v_i's means that $[v] \subseteq [v_1] \cup [v_2] \cup \cdots \cup [v_n]$, where $\subseteq$ and $\cup$ have their usual meaning in the lattice of subspaces. This definition is now purely lattice-theoretic in nature, and therefore suggests a generalization to arbitrary atomic lattices. More generally, the concepts of dependence and independence are even more general than lattice theory and apply to abstract set theory, and universal algebra. It therefore seems best to characterize these notions in terms of their fundamental properties before giving the specific definition for lattices. A dependence relation is a relation which relates single elements to a finite set of elements of a given set X. If $x \in X$ and F is a finite subset of X, then we say x is dependent on F and write $x \,\Delta\, F$ if the following conditions are fulfilled: (1) every element of F depends on F; (2) if every element of a set F depends on a second finite set G, and x depends on F, then x depends on G; (3) if a is independent of a set F, but x depends on $\{a\} \cup F$, then a depends on $\{x\} \cup F$. These properties serve to characterize the notion of dependence as given formally by the following definition:

Definition 5-4. *If X is any set and $\mathfrak{F}(X)$ the set of finite subsets of X, then a linear dependence relation Δ on X is a relation between elements of X and finite subsets F; i.e., Δ is a subset of $X \times \mathfrak{F}(X)$, satisfying:*

Δ1. $a \in F \Rightarrow a \,\Delta\, F$;

Δ2. $a \,\Delta\, F$ *and* $f \,\Delta\, G \;\forall\, f \in F \Rightarrow a \,\Delta\, G$;

Δ3. $a \,\Delta\, F \cup \{b\}$, *and* $a \not\Delta\, F \Rightarrow b \,\Delta\, F \cup \{a\}$.

We say that a is **dependent** *on F if $a \Delta F$, and a is* **independent** *of F if $a \not\Delta F$.*

We can now apply this concept to the set of atoms of a lattice. (It can be applied to more general elements, but we restrict the discussion to atoms here.) We would like to call an element a dependent on a set $F = \{a_1, a_2, \ldots, a_n\}$ where a and a_i are atoms, if $a \leq a_1 \cup a_2 \cup \cdots \cup a_n$. However, condition 3 is not fulfilled in an arbitrary lattice (exercise), although it will hold in an upper semi-modular lattice as given by:

Theorem 5-18. *If $\langle L, \cup, \cap, 0\rangle$ is an upper semi-modular lattice, then the relation $a \Delta F \Leftrightarrow a \leq \mathbf{U}_F f$ is a dependence relation on the set of atoms of L.*

Proof. $\Delta 1$. $a \in F \Rightarrow a \leq \mathbf{U}_F f$.

$\Delta 2$. $a \Delta F$ and $f \Delta G$ imply $a \leq \mathbf{U}_F f$ and $f \leq \mathbf{U}_G g$. Hence $\mathbf{U}_F f \leq \mathbf{U}_G g$, so that $a \leq \mathbf{U}_G g$; *i.e.*, $a \Delta G$.

$\Delta 3$. Let $x = \mathbf{U}_F f$ and let $a \Delta F \cup \{b\}$. Then $a \leq x \cup b$. Furthermore, $a \nleq x$, since $a \not\Delta F$. Since b is an atom, either $b \leq x$ or $x \cap b = 0$. If $b \leq x$, then $x \cup b = x$ and $a \leq x$, contrary to $a \nleq x$. Hence, $x \cap b = 0$. Therefore $x \prec x \cup b$ by Theorem 5-17. But $a \nleq x \Rightarrow x < a \cup x \leq b \cup x$. Thus $a \cup x = b \cup x$; *i.e.*, $b \leq a \cup x$ or $b \Delta F \cup \{a\}$.

We now call a set $F = \{a_1, a_2, \ldots, a_n\}$ **linear independent** if each a_i is independent of the remaining a_j's; *i.e.*, $a_i \not\Delta \{a_1, a_2, \ldots, a_{i-1}, a_{i+1}, \ldots, a_n\}$ for $i = 1, 2, \ldots, n$. *An arbitrary set A is then* **independent** *if every finite subset is independent*. Clearly, if F is independent, then every non-empty subset is independent. Also, every singleton $\{a\}$ is an independent set. If F is any finite set of atoms, then F contains an independent subset (exercise). We can extend this result to arbitrary subsets by use of the axiom of choice.

Theorem 5-19. *If L is a semi-modular lattice and A is any subset of L, then A contains a maximally independent subset.*

Proof. Let $A \neq \emptyset$ be any subset of L and let $\mathfrak{A}$ be the family of all subsets of A which are independent. $\mathfrak{A}$ is non-empty, since every singleton of A is an independent set. Partially order $\mathfrak{A}$ by set inclusion, and let $\mathfrak{C} = \{C_1 \subseteq C_2 \subseteq \cdots \subseteq C_\alpha \subseteq \cdots\}$ be any chain in $\mathfrak{A}$. Let $C = \mathbf{U}_\alpha C_\alpha$. Then C is independent. For if $F = \{f_1, f_2, \ldots, f_n\}$ is any finite subset of C, then each individual f_i is an element of some $C_i \in \mathfrak{C}$. But the finite family of sets C_i thus obtained must contain a maximal set, since C is a chain. Let this maximal C_i, be C_{i_0}. Then $C_i \subseteq C_{i_0}\ \forall\ i$ and $f_i \in C_{i_0}\ \forall\ i$. But C_{i_0} was independent, so that F is therefore independent. Hence C is independent. But C is an upper bound for $\mathfrak{C}$ and lies in $\mathfrak{A}$, so that $\mathfrak{A}$ satisfies the conditions of Zorn's lemma; *i.e.*, every chain is bounded. Hence by Zorn's lemma, $\mathfrak{A}$ has a maximal element; *i.e.*, A contains a maximally independent subset.

The proof of this thorem required the use of Zorn's lemma, which is a variant of the axiom of choice. It is also interesting to note that the converse is also true; *i.e.*, Theorem 5-19 is also a variant of the axiom of choice (*Cf:* Rubin and Rubin).

The following theorem now shows that we can augment an independent set by adjoining any independent element.

Theorem 5-20. *If L is an upper semi-modular lattice and a is independent of* $\{a_1, a_2, \ldots, a_n\}$ *where* $\{a_1, a_2, \ldots, a_n\}$ *is an independent set, then* $\{a, a_1, a_2, \ldots, a_n\}$ *is an independent set.*

Proof. Let $x = \bigcup_{j=1}^{n} a_j$ and $y = \bigcup_{j \neq i} a_j$. Then $y \leq x$. Hence, by the atomic modular law, $y \cup (a \cap x) = (y \cup a) \cap x = y$, since $a \cap x = 0$ (a was independent of the a_i's). Furthermore, since the a_i's are an independent set, $a_i \cap y = 0$. Also $a_i \leq x$ implies $a_i \cap (a \cup y) \leq x \cap (a \cup y) = y$. Thus $a_i \cap (a \cup y) \cap y = a_i \cap (a \cup y) = 0$. Therefore, a_i is independent of the set $\{a, a_1, \ldots, a_{i-1}, a_{i+1}, \ldots, a_n\}$. Hence the set $\{a, a_1, a_2, \ldots, a_n\}$ is an independent set. See figure 5-16.

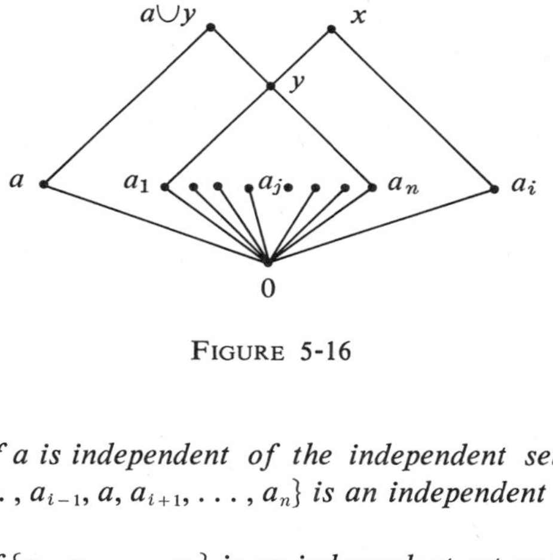

FIGURE 5-16

Corollary 1. *If a is independent of the independent set* $\{a_1, a_2, \ldots, a_n\}$, *then the set* $\{a_1, \ldots, a_{i-1}, a, a_{i+1}, \ldots, a_n\}$ *is an independent set.*

Corollary 2. *If* $\{a_1, a_2, \ldots, a_n\}$ *is an independent set and a is independent of this set, then* $a \cup \bigcup_{i=1}^{n} a_i$ *covers* $\bigcup_{j=1}^{n} a_i$.

The first corollary allows us to replace any element of an independent set by any other element independent of the set. The second enables us to relate the concept of independence to that of the dimension of an element. Thus we have:

Theorem 5-21. *If x is any element of a semi-modular lattice and $x = a_1 \cup a_2 \cup \cdots \cup a_n$ where $\{a_1, a_2, \ldots, a_n\}$ is an independent set of atoms, then $d(x) = n$.*

Proof. The sequence of elements $0 \prec a_1 \prec a_1 \cup a_2 \prec \cdots \prec a_1 \cup a_2 \cup \cdots \cup a_n = x$ is a sequence of distinct elements which form a maximal chain from 0 to x. Hence $d(x) = n$.

Corollary. *If $\{a_1, a_2, \ldots, a_n\}$ and $\{b_1, b_2, \ldots, b_m\}$ are two independent sets of atoms such that $a_1 \cup a_2 \cdots \cup a_n = b_1 \cup b_2 \cup \cdots \cup b_m$, then $n = m$. If, furthermore, L is distributive; then each a_i is a b_j.*

Proof. To prove the second statement, note that $a_i \leq \mathbf{U}_j a_j = \mathbf{U}_j b_j$ implies $a_i \cap \mathbf{U}_j b_j = \mathbf{U}_j(a_i \cap b_j) = a_i \neq 0$. Hence, $a_i \cap b_j \neq 0$ for some j. But since a_i is an atom, $a_i \cap b_j \neq 0$ implies $a_i \cap b_j = a_i$; *i.e.*, $a_i \leq b_j$. But again, b_j is an atom so that $a_i = b_j$.

We note that Theorem 5-21 allows us to determine the dimension of a union of a set of independent atoms in terms of the number of atoms contained in it. We would like to use this idea to introduce the concept of a basis similar to that used in vector spaces. However, the lattice of figure 5-14 which is upper semi-modular shows that this cannot be done without further restrictions. Thus the element x has dimension 2, but contains only one atom. Furthermore, x cannot be written as the union of any set of atoms, let alone an independent set, so that its dimension cannot be related to the number of atoms contained in it. In the next section we shall study lattices in which every element is the join of a set of atoms, so that Theorem 5-12 can be applied to any element.

5-7. GEOMETRIC LATTICES

We have seen that two of the fundamental properties of the lattice of subspaces of a finite dimensional geometry are atomicity and upper semi-modularity, but in the last section we have also seen that these properties are insufficient to characterize geometry. The added condition needed is that every element be the join of a set of atoms. Thus we make the definition:

Definition 5-5. *A lattice $\langle L, \cup, \cap, 0, 1\rangle$ is called* **geometric** *if it is upper semi-modular and every element ($\neq 0$) is the join of a set of atoms.*

In fact, the atomic modular law is also sufficient to characterize a geometric lattice if every element is the join of a finite number of atoms as in:

Theorem 5-22. *An atomic lattice of finite length is geometric if it satisfies the atomic modular law and every element, $\neq 0$, is the join of a finite number of atoms.*

Proof. (*i*) Clearly the upper semi-modular law implies the atomic upper semi-modular law which is equivalent to the atomic modular law. Furthermore, if L is of finite length and 1 is the join of a set of atoms, then, as in the proof of Theorem 5-21, 1 is the join of a finite number of atoms. Similarly, every other element is the join of a finite number of atoms.

(*ii*) Conversely, let L satisfy the atomic upper semi-modular law and let $x \cap y \prec x$. Then $x = a_1 \cup a_2 \cup \cdots \cup a_n$ and $y = b_1 \cap b_2 \cap \cdots \cap b_m$ where the a_i's and b_j's are atoms. If $\{a_i\}_i \subseteq \{b_j\}_j$, then $x \leq y$ so that $x = x \cap y$ contrary to $x \cap y \prec x$. Thus there exists an atom $a = a_{i_0} \in \{a_i\}_i$ such that $a \notin \{b_j\}_j$; *i.e.*, $a \leq x$ and $a \nleq y$. Hence $a \cap y = 0$ and $a \cap (x \cap y) = 0$. But by the atomic upper semi-modular law, this implies $x \cap y \prec a \cup (x \cap y) \leq x$, since $a \leq x$ and $x \cap y \leq x$. Hence $a \cup (x \cap y) = x$. Therefore $x \cup y = a \cup (x \cap y) \cup y = a \cup y$. But again $a \cap y = 0$, so that $y \prec a \cup y$; *i.e.*, $y \prec x \cup y$, which is the upper semi-modular law.

As the name suggests, examples of geometric lattices are given by the lattice of subspaces of a finite dimensional projective geometry, and hence the lattice of linear subspaces of a finite dimensional vector space, and the lattice of subspaces of an affine space. However, since we have restricted ourselves to a lattice of finite dimension, we exclude the lattice of subspaces of an infinite dimensional vector space as well as infinite dimensional projective geometries such as von Neumann's continuous geometries. Since this is only an introduction to geometry, we should not try to discuss such spaces here. Further examples arise in the theory of graphs which are geometric, but are not related to projective or affine geometry (*cf:* Oriore and Rota).

The importance of geometric lattices lies in the fact that every element can be written as the join of an independent set of atoms, and the number of such atoms is exactly the dimension of the element. These facts follow directly by combining the results of the last section with this section. We then therefore introduce the notion of a basis. Thus *if x is the union of a finite number of independent atoms, $a_1, a_2, \ldots, a_k$, then this set is called a* **basis** *of x. If $a_1, a_2, \ldots, a_n$ is a basis for the unit 1, then we call this set a* **basis** *for L.* Clearly a basis for L is not unique, but given any independent set, $a_1, a_2, \ldots, a_k$ we can always extend this basis to a basis for all of L, $a_1, a_2, \ldots, a_k, a_{k+1}, \ldots, a_n$. The elements $a_{k+1}, \ldots, a_n$ then generate another element $y = a_{k+1} \cup \cdots \cup a_n$ which has the two properties $x \cup y = 1$ and $x \cap y = 0$. Such a pair of elements are called *complementary* in L. Hence geometric lattices are always complemented. We shall postpone further discussion of geometric lattice until we have discussed the general class of complemented lattices.

EXERCISES

1. Show that a is independent of a set $\{a_i\}_i$ if and only if $a \nleq a_1 \cup \cdots \cup a_n$.
2. Prove that the lattice of figure 5-15 satisfies the atomic modular law, but is not

modular. Show that it is not upper semi-modular. Show that it does not have a dimension function.

3. Use figure 5-15 to show that 1 may be the union of atoms, but not every element is.
4. Show that in a distributive lattice, if 1 is the union of a finite set of atoms, then every element is.
5. Show that every lattice which satisfies the descending chain condition has a zero and is locally atomic and hence atomic.
6. Show that $a \Delta F$ if and only if $a \leq \bigcup_i a_i$ does not satisfy condition $\Delta 3$ in an arbitrary lattice.
7. Show that a sub-lattice of a geometric lattice need not be geometric.
8. Is the homomorphic image of a geometric lattice geometric?
9. Show that if a geometric lattice L contains an independent set A of atoms, then L has a sub-lattice isomorphic to $\mathfrak{P}(A)$.
10. Show that any independent set of elements in a geometric lattice can be extended to a basis for L.
11. Show that elements x and y as defined at the end of section 5-7 are complementary.
12. Show that every subset of an independent set of elements is independent.
13. Show directly that every finite set of elements in an upper semi-modular lattice contains an independent subset.
14. Show that a set $a_1, a_2, \ldots, a_n$ of elements of an upper semi-modular lattice is independent if and only if $(a_1 \cup \cdots \cup a_k) \cap a_{k+1} = 0$ for $k = 1, 2, \ldots, n$. Show that this is not true without the assumption of upper semi-modularity (use Theorem 5-16).
15. Prove that in a geometric lattice a set of elements is independent if and only if it satisfies:
$$d(a_1) + d(a_2) + \cdots + d(a_n) = n.$$
16. Give a proof of Theorem 5-19 using Tukey's lemma.

5-8. COMPLEMENTED LATTICES

Of all the types of lattices discussed so far, the power set algebra has served as a model since it satisfies all the laws introduced. However, it also satisfies additional laws, so that none of the lattices considered so far serves to characterize the algebra of sets as discussed in Chapter 2. In particular, our discussion of the algebra of sets began with the operation of set subtraction; *i.e.*, relative complementation whereas none of the lattices introduced in Chapters 3 and 4 so far have an operation of complementation. In this section, we introduce the notion of complementation into lattice theory and show that both the power set algebras as well as geometric lattices are complemented. Thus in both of these cases a complement is defined by the two equations $x \cap y = 0$ and $x \cup y = 1$. Hence we make the following definition:

Definition 5-6. *If* $\langle L, \cup, \cap, 0, 1\rangle$ *is a lattice with units and* $x \in L$ *and if there exists an element* x' *satisfying.*

$$C1:\ x \cup x' = 1,$$

$$C2:\ x \cap x' = 0,$$

then x' *is called a* **complement** *of* x. *A lattice is called* **complemented** *if every* x *in* L *has a complement.*

Note that the definition is symmetric in x and x', so that if x' is a complement of x, then x is complement of x'. Furthermore, the definition is self-dual, so that *the principle of duality applies to complemented lattices* in the form: if any statement is true in a complemented lattice, then the statement formed by replacing each element by its complement, interchanging $\cup$ and $\cap$, and reversing the direction of $\leq$ is again a true statement.

In the power set algebra of all subsets of a set X, the complement of a set A is the set of all elements of X not contained in A. Each A then has exactly one complement.

On the other hand, projective geometries are complemented but not uniquely so. For example, if π is a projective plane and p is any point of π, then any line which does not contain p is a complement of p as shown in figure 5-17,

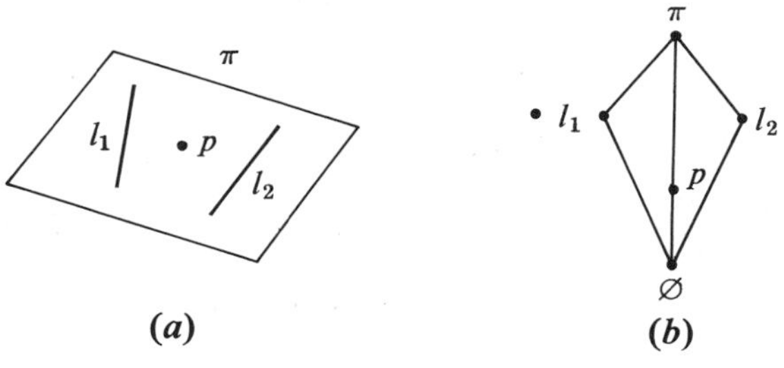

FIGURE 5-17

where l_1 and l_2 are both complements of p with respect to π. The lattice diagram is also shown. Hence p in this case has infinitely many points (if π is infinite). In the lattice M_5 of figure 5-1, b has two distinct complements, a and c, while a and c both have the same unique complement b. In D_5, however, a, b and c each have two distinct complements. Finally, in any chain with more than two elements, no element except 0 and 1 has a complement (exercise). The lattice $\langle \mathbf{N}, \leq \rangle$, for example, is not complemented. In general, the lattice $\langle \mathbf{P}_n, | \rangle$, the lattice of integral divisors of a fixed integer n is also not complemented. For example, the lattice of divisors of 12 as diagramed in figure 4-1 of Chapter 4 is not complemented since the element 2, for example, has no complement. Yet in this same lattice the elements 3 and 4 are mutual complements and unique. However, if n is square free; *i.e.*, n is not divisible by the square of any prime, and x is a divisor of n, then x and n/x are complements, so that $\langle \mathbf{P}_n, | \rangle$ is a complemented lattice. Finally the lattice $\langle \mathbf{P}, | \rangle$ is not complemented since it has no greatest element. Therefore, an element of a lattice may have zero, one, or many complements. In an arbitrary lattice, complementation does not define a unary operation; *i.e.*, the relation $x \rightarrow x'$ is not a function. About the only general statements we can make are those concerning 0 and 1 as given in:

Theorem 5-23. *In a lattice* $\langle L, \cup, \cap, 0, 1 \rangle$ *with units,* 0 *and* 1 *are uniquely complemented and* $0' = 1$ *and* $1' = 0$.

Proof. Exercise.

The concept of set subtraction in the algebra of sets is equivalent to relative complementation and suggests that we can extend the general notion of complement to that of relative complement by applying the concept to an interval sublattice. If $a \leq b$ are fixed elements of L and $x \in [a, b]$, then *the element* $x'_{a,b}$ *is called a* **complement of** x **relative to** a **and** b if:

$$RC1: \; x \cup x'_{a,b} = b, \text{ and}$$

$$RC2: \; x \cap x'_{a,b} = a.$$

A lattice is **relatively complemented** *if every interval* $[a, b]$ *is complemented.* We note that a lattice may be complemented but not relatively complemented, or relatively complemented, but not complemented. For example $M5$ is complemented, but the sublattice $[a, 1]$ is not complemented; *i.e.*, c has no complement relative to a and 1. On the other hand, if X is any infinite set and $\mathfrak{F}(X)$ is the set of finite subsets of X, then $\langle \mathfrak{F}(X), \subseteq \rangle$ is relatively complemented, but not complemented. Thus if $A, B \in \mathfrak{F}$ and $A \subseteq B$, then the set $X'_{A,B} = A \cup (B - X)$ is a unique relative complement of X relative to A and B. But $\mathfrak{F}(X)$ cannot be complemented, since it has no greatest element. However, if $\langle L, \cup, \cap, 0, 1 \rangle$ is a lattice with units which is relatively complemented, then it is obviously complemented. Note that if we extend $\mathfrak{F}(X)$ by adjoining a greatest element 1 such that $A \subseteq 1 \; \forall \; A$, then we lose the property that $\mathfrak{F}(X)$ is relatively complemented. Therefore, although it is possible to embed any lattice in a lattice with units, there is no guarantee that all the properties will hold in the extended lattice.

We now investigate what conditions are necessary to ensure that complements be unique. In fact, the uniqueness of relative complements is exactly equivalent to the distributive law. For if x_1' and x_2' are both complements of x relative to a and b, then $x \cup x_1' = b = x \cup x_2'$ and $x \cap x_1' = a = x \cap x_2'$. By Theorem 5-4, these conditions are equivalent to the distributive law. Hence we have:

Theorem 5-24. *A lattice $\langle L, \cup, \cap \rangle$ is distributive if and only if relative complements are unique.*

Corollary. *In a distributive lattice an element can have at most one complement.*

Notice, however, that a lattice can be distributive without being complemented as is seen in the case of a chain. Conversely, a lattice may be relatively complemented without being distributive as is D_5, for example. As a further corollary we note that if a lattice is both complemented and distributive, then complements are necessarily unique. It is just such lattices which will occupy us for the next two chapters, and which essentially characterize the algebra of sets. They are called Boolean algebras. First, however, we shall examine the situation if a lattice is complemented and modular.

Theorem 5-25. *Every complemented modular lattice is relatively complemented.*

Proof. Let $\langle L, \cup, \cap, 0, 1 \rangle$ be a complemented lattice and $a \leq b \in L$. Then let $x \in [a, b]$; *i.e.*, $a \leq x \leq b$, and let x' be the complement of x in L. Then $x'_{a,b} = a \cup (b \cap x')$ is a relative complement of x in $[a, b]$. Thus $x \cup x'_{a,b} = (x \cup a) \cup (b \cap x') = x \cup (x' \cap b) = (x \cup x') \cap b = b$, since $x \leq b$. Also $x \cap x'_{a,b} = [a \cup (b \cap x')] \cap x = a \cup [(b \cap x') \cap x] = a \cup 0 = a$, since $a \leq x$.

Complemented modular lattices are most useful in the theory of projectve geometry, as we shall see briefly in the next section. Affine geometries, however, are not modular as we have already seen, but are complemented; *i.e.*, they are upper semi-modular complemented lattices. More generally, semi-modular, relatively complemented lattices characterize geometric lattices, as is given by:

Theorem 5-26. *A lattice of finite length is geometric if and only if it is both upper semi-modular and relatively complemented.*

Proof. (*i*) Let $\langle L, \cup, \cap, 0, 1 \rangle$ be a geometric lattice in the sense of the definition of section 5-7, and let $a \leq x \leq b$. Then $a = a_1 \cup \cdots \cup a_k$ is the join of a set of independent atoms. Then we can extend this basis for a to a basis of x, since $a \leq x$ and write $x = a_1 \cup \cdots \cup a_k \cup a_{k+1} \cup \cdots \cup a_p$. Again, since $x \leq b$ we can further extend the basis of x to a basis of b and obtain $b = a_1 \cup \cdots \cup a_k \cup a_{k+1} \cup \cdots \cup a_p \cup a_{p+1} \cup \cdots \cup a_r$. Now let $x'_{a,b} = a_1 \cup \cdots \cup a_k \cup a_{p+1} \cup \cdots \cup a_r$, then $x'_{a,b}$ will be the desired relative complement of x relative to a and b.

(*ii*) Conversely, let L be an upper semi-modular, relatively complemented lattice. For any $b \in L$, let A_b be the set of all atoms contained in b and let $x = \mathbf{U}\, A_b$. Let $x'_{0,b}$ be a complement of x relative to 0 and b. Then if $x'_{0,b}$ contains an atom a, then $a \leq b$ and hence $a \leq x$ since x was the join of all atoms contained in b. But then $x \cap x'_{0,b} \neq 0$ contrary to the definition of relative complement. Therefore $x'_{0,b}$ cannot contain any atoms. But this is contrary to the fact that L has finite length, unless $x'_{0,b} = 0$. But $x'_{0,b} = 0$ implies that $x = b$; *i.e.*, b is the join of the set of atoms contained in it. Hence L is geometric.

Corollary 1. *An upper semi-modular lattice is complemented if and only if* 1 *is the join of atoms.*

Corollary 2. *A complemented modular lattice of finite length is geometric.*

EXERCISES

1. Prove that if L is a chain and $x \neq 0, 1$, then x cannot have a complement.
2. Prove that if n is square free and x is a divisor of n, then n/x is a complement of x in $\langle \mathbf{P}_n, | \rangle$.
3. If π is a projective line, prove that the lattice of projective subspaces of π is complemented. Describe the class of complements of a point p.
4. Show that the lattice $\langle \mathbf{N}, | \rangle$ has units, but is not complemented ($\mathbf{N} = \mathbf{P} \cup \{0\}$).
5. Show that although $\mathfrak{F}(X)$ is relatively complemented $\mathfrak{F}(X) \cup \{1\}$ is not.
6. Show that if M is the set all square free positive integers, then $\langle M, | \rangle$ is relatively complemented but not complemented.
7. Show that in a relatively complemented lattice of finite length, every element is the join of the atoms contained in it.
8. Show that any lattice with units can be embedded in a complemented lattice by adjoining a single point.
9. Show that the element $x'_{a,b}$ of Theorem 5-26 is a complement of x in $[a, b]$.
10. Show that in a complemented modular lattice every element not an atom can be decomposed into the union of two strictly smaller elements. Show that this is not true in the lattice of figure 5-14.
11. Show that in a modular lattice of finite length, if 1 is the join of atoms, then every element is.

5-9. PROJECTIVE GEOMETRY

Throughout our discussion of the various types of lattices, we have frequently used the lattice of subspaces of a projective geometry as a model. In this section we shall outline the definition of a projective geometry and indicate how projective geometries can be characterized within lattice theory. However, the subject is much too large for a complete discussion even of the various lattice theoretic aspects of projective geometry, so that this is merely an introduction. Nor shall we be able to discuss the exact relationship to vector spaces, since this would require an examination of methods of introducing coordinates into a projective space in order to show the isomorphism between the lattice of subspaces of a vector space and the lattice of "flats" of a projective space. Finally, we shall confine the discussion to finite dimensional spaces as we have been doing heretofore.

In the classical definition of a *projective geometry* a projective space P is defined as a collection of elements called *points* and a collection of subsets of these elements called *lines*. We designate points by $p, q, r, \ldots$ and lines by l_1, l_2 or pq, etc. π shall designate the collection of all points of P. A projective geometry then satisfies:

PG1: Two distinct points, p and q, determine one and only one line, $l_{pq} = pq$ such that $p, q \in l_{pq}$;

PG2: If a line l intersects two sides of a triangle not at a vertex, then it intersects the third side (the definition of a triangle is the usual one, exercise);

PG3: Every line contains at least three distinct points.

PG1 states that if $p \neq q$, then there is (*i*) at least one line containing them both and (*ii*) if $p, q \in l_1, l_2$, then $l_1 = l_2$. If *PG3* is replaced by the weaker postulate that every line contains at least two points or is omitted entirely, then we obtain generalizations of projective geometry which may again be characterized within the theory of complemented lattices. Finally, we shall need one extra axiom to insure finite dimensionality. First, however, we introduce the concept of a projective subspace or "flat." Thus a collection of points α of π is called a **flat** if whenever two points $p \neq q$ belong to α, then all the points on the line pq also belong to α; *i.e.*, if $p \neq q \in \alpha$ and $r \in pq$ then $r \in \alpha$. First, the empty set is a flat and every singleton point set $\{p\}$ is a flat. Furthermore, every line is a flat by *P1* and the definition of a flat. Finally, π is itself a flat, since every point belongs to π. We can partially order the set $L(\pi)$ of all flats, by inclusion. Thus $\alpha \leq \beta$ if every point of α is in β. We also say that α lies on β, or β passes through α. For example, if $p \in l$, then p lies on l and l passes through p. We also call $\leq$ an *incidence relation.* With respect to this partial order $L(\pi)$ has a least element $\emptyset$ and a greatest element π. Furthermore, the intersection of any set of flats is itself a flat (exercise). Hence $L(\pi)$ is a complete lattice, $\langle L, \cup, \cap, \emptyset, \pi \rangle$, by Theorem 3-9, Corollary. Here join means the smallest flat containing all flats of a given set of flats. The following theorem characterizes the join of two flats.

Theorem 5-27. *If α and β are two flats of a projective geometry P, then their join $\alpha \cup \beta$ is the set of all points r such that there exist points $x \in \alpha$ and $y \in \beta$ and $r \in xy$.*

Proof. Let γ be the sets of points r such that $r \in xy$ for $x \in \alpha, y \in \beta$. Then

(*i*) $\alpha, \beta \leq \gamma$. (exercise)

(*ii*) We next show that γ is a flat; *i.e.*, $p, q \in \gamma$ and $r \in pq \Rightarrow r \in \gamma$. There are four basic cases to be considered:

(1) $p, q \in \alpha$ or $p, q \in \beta$; (2) $p \in \alpha$ and $q \in \beta$, or $p \in \beta$ and $q \in \alpha$; (3) $p \in \alpha$ (or β), $q \notin \alpha, \beta$ or $q \in \alpha$(or β), $p \notin \alpha, \beta$; and (4) $p, q \notin \alpha, \beta$.

Case (1) follows from (*i*).

Case (2) follows directly from the definition of γ.

In case (3), let $p \in \alpha$ and $q \notin \alpha, \beta$, as in figure 5-18(*a*). Since $q \in \gamma$, there

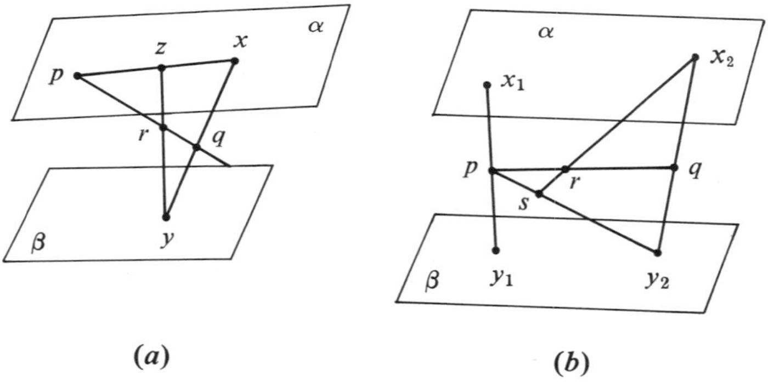

FIGURE 5-18

exists x and y in α and β respectively, such that $q \in xy$. Then $x \neq y$, since if $x = y$, then y will lie in α and therefore q will be in α. Also $q \neq x, y$ since $q \notin \alpha, \beta$. Therefore, x, y, q are all distinct. Again we assume that r, p and q are distinct, for otherwise $r \in \gamma$ directly. Hence by *P3* the line *prq* must intersect the line *px* in some point z and $z \in \alpha$. Therefore, $r \in zy$ where $z \in \alpha$ and $y \in \beta$; *i.e.*, $r \in \gamma$.

Case (4) implies there exist $x_1, x_2 \in \alpha$ and $y_1, y_2 \in \beta$ such that $p \in x_1y_1$ and

$q \in x_2y_2$ as shown in figure 5-18(*b*). Furthermore, as in case (3) x_1, y_1 and x_2, y_2 must be distinct, and we assume that p is distinct from x_1, y_1 and q is distinct from x_2 and y_2. Hence the line rx_2 intersects pq and y_2q in distinct points, and therefore by *P3* it must intersect py_2 in some point s. Therefore we can apply the results of case (*3*); *i.e.*, $x_2 \in \alpha$, $r \notin \alpha, \beta$ (otherwise apply (*i*)) $y_2 \in \beta$. Hence $r \in \gamma$. Thus γ is a flat which contains both α and β.

(*iii*) If δ is a flat and contains both α and β, let $x \in \alpha$ and $y \in \beta$ and $r \in xy$. Then $x, y \in \delta$ and hence $r \in \delta$. Therefore $\gamma \leq \delta$. Thus γ is the least upper bound of α and β in the lattice $L(\pi)$; *i.e.*, $\gamma = \alpha \cup \beta$.

This theorem can be extended to finite unions by induction. Thus if $\{\alpha_i\}_n$ is a finite set of flats, then we have $\bigcup_{i=1}^{n} \alpha_i = \bigcup_{i=1}^{n-1} \alpha_i \cup \alpha_n$. If now $\{\alpha_i\}_i$ is any collection of flats, then $\bigcup_i \alpha_i$ is the set of points p which lie on some union of a finite number of the α_i. For certainly $\bigcup_i \alpha_i$ must contain every union of a finite number of the α_i, so that all that is necessary is to show that this collection of points is a flat. We leave the details to the exercises. We can now show that the lattice of flats is modular.

Theorem 5-28. *The lattice $L(\pi)$ of flats of a projective geometry is modular.*

Proof. Let $\alpha \leq \gamma$ and β be three flats of π and let $p \in (\alpha \cup \beta) \cap \gamma$. Then $p \in \gamma$ and $p \in \alpha \cup \beta$; *i.e.*, $p \in xy$ where $x \in \alpha$ and $y \in \beta$. But $\alpha \leq \gamma \Rightarrow x \in \gamma$. The case $p = x$ is left to the reader. Otherwise, $x \cup p$ is a line in γ and $y \in xy$. Hence $y \in \gamma$. Therefore $x \in \alpha$ and $y \in \beta \cap \gamma$, so that $p \in \alpha \cup (\beta \cap \gamma)$. Therefore $(\alpha \cup \beta) \cap \gamma \subseteq \alpha \cup (\beta \cap \gamma)$, and hence $L(\pi)$ is modular since the reverse inequality holds in any lattice.

Since $L(\pi)$ is modular, the Jordan-Dedekind chain condition holds. We now introduce an axiom that restricts the geometry to a finite number of dimensions.

PG4. There exists a finite set of points $F = \{p_1, p_2, \ldots, p_N\}$ such that every flat which contains F contains every point.

PG4 states that $\pi = \bigcup_{i=1}^{N} p_i$ is the union of a finite set of atoms of $L(\pi)$, since each $\{p_i\}$ is an atom in $L(\pi)$. Therefore $L(\pi)$ is finite dimensional. But π is the greatest element of $L(\pi)$, so that $L(\pi)$ is a modular lattice in which 1 is the join of atoms. Hence $L(\pi)$ is a complemented modular lattice and every element is the join of atoms; *i.e.*, $L(\pi)$ is a geometric lattice and every element is the join of a finite set of atoms. Therefore we have:

Theorem 5-29. *The lattice of flats of a finite dimensional projective geometry is a complete complemented modular lattice of finite dimensions.*

Conversely, if we begin with a finite dimensional complemented modular lattice, then we can define a point as an atom and a line as an element which covers a point. *PG1*, *PG2* and *PG4* will then follow as in:

Theorem 5-30. *If π is the set of atoms of a finite dimensional complemented modular lattice and a line is any element of dimension 2, then PG1, PG2, and PG4 hold.*

Proof. *PG1:* If p and q are two distinct points, then the their lattice union, $p \cup q$, covers both p and q and has dimension 2. Hence $p \cup q$ is the unique line joining p and q.

PG2: Let p, q, r be three distinct atoms such that $r \nleq p \cup q$ and let $\alpha = p \cup q, \beta = p \cup r$. Let $x \leq p \cup q$ and $y \leq p \cup r$ where $x, y \neq p, q, r$ are two atoms. Then by the dimension law for modular lattices, we have:

$d[(x \cup y) \cap (q \cup r)] = d(x \cup y) + d(q \cup r) - d[(x \cup y) \cup (q \cup r)] =$

$2 + 2 - d(x \cup y \cup q \cup r)$. But $x \leq p \cup q$ and $y \leq p \cup r$, so that $x \cup y \leq p \cup q \cup r$ or $x \cup y \cup q \cup r \leq p \cup q \cup r$. Therefore $d(x \cup y \cup q \cup r) \leq d(p + q + r) = d(p) + d(q) + d(r) = 3$. Thus $d[(x \cup y) \cap (q \cup r)] \geq 2 + 2 - 3 = 1$. On the other hand, since $x, y \nleq q \cup r$ we cannot have $d[(x \cup y) \cap (q \cup r)] > 1$. Therefore $d[(x \cup y) \cap (q \cup r)] = 1$, so that the line $x \cup y$ intersects $q \cup r$ in a point.

PG4 follows directly from the finite dimensionality of the lattice.

It remains to investigate the lattice significance of *PG3* which states that every line contains at least three distinct points. Within such a line if p and q are two points and r is a third point, then r is a common relative complement of both p and q relative to the line. We can now consider the points p and q as elements of a basis for π which can be extended to a basis of all of π by adjoining independent points $p_3, p_4, \ldots, p_n$. Then the flat $\delta = \{p_3\} \cup \cdots \cup \{p_n\}$ will be independent of the two flats $\alpha = \{p\}$ and $\beta = \{q\}$. Furthermore, the flat $\delta \cup \{r\}$ will be a complement to both α and β within π. Hence, every pair of distinct atoms of $L(\pi)$ will have a common complement. Conversely, if every pair of atoms α, β of any finite dimensional complemented modular lattice have a common complement γ, then *PG3* will hold in the associated projective geometry. We leave it to the exercises to show that $(\alpha \cup \beta) \cap \gamma$ is the required point. Hence *PG3* is equivalent to the requirement that every pair of distinct atoms have a common complement.

If now γ is the common complement of the two atoms α and β, then by the fundamental isomorphism theorem of modular lattices the intervals $[0, \alpha]$ and $[0, \beta]$ are both isomorphic to the interval $[\gamma, \pi]$. Hence the atoms α and β are projective. Thus *PG3* can also be formulated in terms of the concept of projectivity by stating that ever pair of distinct atoms be projective. Hence we have:

Theorem 5-31. *A finite dimensional projective geometry is a complemented modular lattice of finite dimensions in which every pair of distinct atoms is projective.*

Thus the study of projective geometry is brought within the field of lattice theory. In general, projective geometry can be generalized by either dropping the requirement of finite dimensionality or weakening *PG3*. If we permit the dimension to be infinite, then we can bring the study of the lattice of subspaces of an infinite dimensional vector space within the realm of projective geometry. If, further, the requirement that a dimension function be integral valued is weakened to permit a continuous spectrum of dimensions, then we obtain the beginnings of the theory of continuous geometry. Finally, we replace condition *PG3* by the condition that every line contain at least two points or drop *PG3* entirely, then we obtain various types of generalized projectivities. (For further discussions of their relations to lattice theory see either Szasz, Hermes, or Birkhoff.)

EXERCISES

1. Define the term "triangle" and state the axiom *PG2* in terms of points and lines and the notion of collinearity.
2. Show that the intersection of any set of flats is a flat.
3. Show that the flats α and β of Theorem 5-27 are contained in γ.
4. Complete the details of the proof of Theorem 5-28 by treating the case $p = x$.
5. Show that if $\{\alpha_i\}_i$ is any collection of flats of a projective geometry, then the set of points such that each point lies on some finite union of the given flats is a flat.
6. Show that if α and β are two distinct atoms of a finite dimensional comlemented modular lattice which have a common complement γ, then $d[(\alpha \cup \beta) \cap \gamma] = 1$.
7. Show that the principle of duality holds in a finite dimensional projective geometry. Show that it does not hold in the lattice of subspaces of an infinite dimensional vector space.

6

BOOLEAN ALGEBRA

6-1. DEFINITION

Of all the different types of lattices discussed so far; *i.e.*, lattices, modular lattices, semi-modular lattices, distributive lattices, complemented lattices, etc., the algebra of subsets of a fixed set has always served as a prime example. Yet none of these types of lattices is sufficiently restrictive to characterize completely the algebra of subsets of a fixed set. More generally, we define a *field of sets* as a collection of subsets of some given set, which is closed under set intersection, union, and complementation. We are seeking a lattice characterization of all algebras which are isomorphic to some field of sets; *i.e.*, such that every field of sets will serve as a model for such an algebra, and, conversely, every such algebra will be representable (to within isomorphism) by some field of sets. Hence we are looking for an abstract algebra which will have all the properties of the algebra of sets discussed in Chapter 2 and essentially no others. All other types of lattices will then be generalizations of such algebras and when we complete the discussion of these algebras we will have met our essential goal for this book. The final chapter will then discuss a different way of defining Boolean algebras and offering a new generalization of them. We begin by repeating the definition of an abstract Boolean algebra as given at the end of the last chapter:

Definition 6-1. *A* **Boolean algebra** *is a complemented, distributive lattice.*

Thus a Boolean algebra is a lattice closed under two binary operations, with a least and greatest element in which every element has a complement. But we have already seen that the distributive law implies the uniqueness of complements, so that we may characterize complementation as a unary operation $a \to a'$. Hence we are dealing with an algebra $\langle B, \cup, \cap, 0, 1, ' \rangle$ defined on a carrier set B with two binary operations, two nullary operations and one unary operation. A Boolean algebra therefore has type $\langle 2, 2, 0, 0, 1 \rangle$; *i.e.*, there is a finite set of finitary operations. Furthermore, the associated lattice $\langle B, \cup, \cap \rangle$

is a distributive lattice and hence modular, so that all of the results discussed in Chapters 4 and 5 for such lattices apply within the theory of Boolean algebras. Similarly, all general theorems for complemented lattices apply. In section 6-3 we shall extend the notions of universal algebra such as sub-algebra, homomorphisms, etc., to the particular case of a Boolean algebra. If B satisfies additional conditions such as having finite length, or being atomic, then we can also apply the results for semi-modular lattices as well as geometric lattices to Boolean algebras. We note that the condition of finite length for Boolean algebras is quite restrictive and implies that B is itself finite. Furthermore, we shall also see that finite Boolean algebras have a simple structure and are relatively rare as lattices, since they must have 2^n elements for some n. Thus semi-modularity, etc. add very little and will not be discussed further.

The simplest examples of Boolean algebras are the power set algebras; *i.e.*, the algebras of *all* subsets of some fixed set X, and we shall show that every finite Boolean algebra is isomorphic to such an algebra. Again the simplest power set is the set of subsets of the empty set. In this case there is only one subset, so that the corresponding Boolean algebra consists of a single element, $0 = 1$. Such algebras are called **degenerate** and in the future we shall consider only non-degenerate algebras; *i.e.*, Boolean algebras in which 0 and 1 are distinct. In contrast to this trivial case, the next case, which arises as the algebra of subsets of a singleton set, is the most important of all algebras. Its diagram and the tables for the operations are shown in figure 6-1. We shall later see

$\cup$	0	1
0	0	1
1	1	1

$\cup$	0	1
0	0	0
1	0	1

x	x'
0	1
1	0

FIGURE 6-1.

how every finite Boolean algebra can be characterized in terms of this particular Boolean algebra. It is the only Boolean algebra which is a chain; *i.e.*, simply ordered, and is order isomorphic to the ordinal **2**. Hence we designate it by **2**. The Boolean algebra corresponding to the algebra of subsets of a pair set has already been discussed in Chapter 2 where the diagram and tables are shown. Other finite examples are left to the reader. Infinite Boolean algebras are obtained in the same way by considering the power set of an infinite set X and its various subalgebras. Many of them will occur throughout this chapter.

We conclude this section with a summary of the principal properties inherent in the definition of a complemented distributive lattice and a definition of completeness.

Theorem 6-1. *A Boolean algebra is a system* $\langle B, \cup, \cap, 0, 1, ' \rangle$ *satisfying:*

(*i*) $\langle B, \cup, \cap \rangle$ *is lattice satisfying:*

$L1$: $a \cup b = b \cup a$; $a \cap b = b \cap a$;
$L2$: $a \cup (b \cup c) = (a \cup b) \cup c$; $a \cap (b \cap c) = (a \cap b) \cap c$;
$L3$: $a \cup a = a = a \cap a$;
$L4$: $a \cup (a \cap b) = a = a \cap (a \cup b)$;

(*ii*) $\langle B, \leq \rangle$ *is a partially ordered set under:*

$a \leq b \Leftrightarrow a \cup b = b \Leftrightarrow a \cap b = a$ *where*
$P1$: $a \leq a$;
$P2$: $a \leq b, b \leq a \Rightarrow a = b$;
$P3$: $a \leq b, b \leq c \Rightarrow a \leq c$;
$B1$: $a, b \leq a \cup b$ *and* $a, b \leq x \Rightarrow a \cup b \leq x$;
$B2$: $a \cap b \leq a, b$ *and* $x \leq a, b \Rightarrow x \leq a \cap b$;

(*iii*) $\langle B, \cup, \cap \rangle$ *is distributive:*

$D1$: $a \cup (b \cap c) = (a \cup b) \cap (a \cup c)$;
$D2$: $a \cap (b \cup c) = (a \cap b) \cup (a \cap c)$;

(*iv*) $\langle B, \cup, \cap, 0, 1 \rangle$ *has a least and greatest element satisfying:*

$U1$: $0 \leq a \leq 1 \ \forall a \in B$;
$U2$: $0 \cup a = a$,
$U3$: $1 \cap a = a$;
$U4$: $0 \cap a = 0$,
$U5$: $1 \cup a = 1$;

(*v*) $\langle B, \cup, \cap, 0, 1, ' \rangle$ *is uniquely complemented such that complements satisfy:*

$C1$: $a \cup a' = 1$;
$C2$: $a \cap a' = 0$;
$C3$: $a'' = a$; $0' = 1$; $1' = 0$;
$C4$: $a \leq b \Leftrightarrow a \cap b' = 0 \Leftrightarrow b' \leq a' \Leftrightarrow a' \cup b = 1$;
$C5$: $(a \cup b)' = a' \cap b'$;
$(a \cap b)' = a' \cup b'$.

Proof. All the statements except $C4$ and $C5$ have been proven in the last chapter. $C4$ is left as an exercise as is the first part of $C3$. To prove $C5$, $(a \cup b) \cup (a' \cap b') = (a \cup b \cup a') \cap (a \cup b \cup b') = 1 \cap 1 = 1$, while $(a \cup b) \cap (a' \cap b') = (a \cap a' \cap b') \cup (b \cap a' \cap b') = 0$ so that $C5$ follows from the uniqueness of complements. The second half follows dually.

We note in passing that the definition of a Boolean algera is self-dual, so that *the principle of duality holds for Boolean algebras*. The laws $C5$ are the *de Morgan laws* for Boolean algebra and are similar to the same laws for the algebra of sets and the de Morgan laws of the predicate calculus.

We can now define a **complete Boolean algebra** as one which is complete as a lattice; *i.e.*, every subset A of B has a least upper bound and greatest lower bound. Furthermore, the complete distributive laws for meet onto an arbitrary union and its dual hold in any Boolean algebra without further assumptions on the Boolean algebra. Thus:

Theorem 6-2. *Every Boolean algebra satisfies the distributive laws:*

$$D1C\colon\ a \cup \bigcap_\alpha a_\alpha = \bigcap_\alpha (a \cup a_\alpha) \text{ and}$$
$$D2C\colon\ a \cap \bigcup_\alpha a_\alpha = \bigcup_\alpha (a \cap a_\alpha),$$

whenever the indicated unions and meets exist.

Proof. Since the distributive inequality $a \cup \bigcap_\alpha a_\alpha \leq \bigcap_\alpha (a \cup a_\alpha)$ holds in any lattice, we merely have to prove the reverse inequality. Thus let $r = \bigcap_\alpha (a \cup a_\alpha)$. Then $r \leq a \cup a_\alpha\ \forall\ \alpha$. Hence $r \cap a' \leq (a \cup a_\alpha) \cap a' = a_\alpha \cap a' \leq a_\alpha$. Therefore $r \cap a' \leq \bigcap_\alpha a_\alpha$. Furthermore, $r \leq a \cup r = a \cup (r \cap a') \leq a \cup \bigcap_\alpha a_\alpha$; *i.e.*, $\bigcap_\alpha (a \cup a_\alpha) \leq a \cup \bigcap^\alpha a_\alpha$.

Although one infinite distributive law does not necessarily follow from the other in an arbitrary distributive lattice, the second half in this case follows by duality.

Corollary: *The infinite de Morgan laws:*

$$C5\colon\ (\bigcup_\alpha a_\alpha)' = \bigcap_\alpha a'_\alpha \text{ and}$$
$$(\bigcap_\alpha a_\alpha)' = \bigcup_\alpha a'_\alpha$$

hold in any Boolean algebra whenever the indicated unions and meets exist.

Proof. Using the infinite distributive laws we have $(\bigcup_\alpha a_\alpha) \cup \bigcap_\beta a'_\beta = \bigcap_\beta ((\bigcup_\alpha a_\alpha) \cup a'_\beta) = \bigcap_\beta (\bigcup_{\alpha \neq \beta} a'_\alpha \cup a_\beta \cup a'_\beta) = \bigcap_\beta 1 = 1$, where the β's run over the same index set as the α's. The second half and the dual are similar.

Hence in any complete distributive lattice the infinite distributive and de Morgan laws hold automatically. However, we also point out without proof that these laws do *not* generalize to the distributive laws for *arbitrary* unions onto *arbitrary* meets nor the dual. Thus there are Boolean algebras which are not totally distributive in the sense described here. On the other hand, every algebra of sets does satisfy such laws, so that the isomorphism between Boolean algebra and abstract set theory does not extend to arbitrary total distributivity. For more details, the reader is referred to Sikorski.

EXERCISES

1. Construct the tables and diagram for the Boolean algebra of four, eight, and sixteen elements.

2. Prove $C4$ of Theorem 5-1.
3. Prove that $a'' = a$ in any Boolean algebra.
4. Prove that in a Boolean algebra $(\bigcup_\alpha a_\alpha) \cap (\bigcap_\alpha a'_\alpha) = 0$.
5. Prove that the set of complemented elements of a distributive lattice form a Boolean algebra.
6. Show that the set of all relations between two sets X and Y is a Boolean algebra.
7. Prove that the set of divisors of a square free integer, n, is a Boolean algebra. Show that this algebra is isomorphic to the power set of the set of m integers $\mathbf{P}_m = \{1, 2, \ldots, m\}$ where m is the number of distinct prime divisors of n.
8. Show that the mapping $a \to a'$ is a dual isomorphism of any Boolean algebra into itself.
9. Prove that in any Boolean algebra:
(*a*) $a = b \Leftrightarrow (a \cap b') \cup (a' \cap b) = 0$;
(*b*) $a = 0 \Leftrightarrow (a \cap b') \cup (a' \cap b) = b$;
(*c*) $(a \cup b') \cap (b \cup c') \cap (c \cup a') = (a' \cup b) \cap (b' \cup c) \cap (c' \cup a)$.
10. Show that a distributive lattice of finite length is a Boolean algebra if and only if every element is the join of atoms.
11. Show that the set of closed-open subsets of a topological space form a Boolean algebra (see Appendix 2).

6-2. POSTULATE SYSTEMS

Since, in Boolean algebra as in abstract set theory, there are sixteen different nullary, unary and binary operations, it is natural to expect that there are many different ways to approach the subject. From the point of view of lattice theory, it is simplest to think of a Boolean algebra as a special kind of lattice; *i.e.*, complemented and distributive, but in fact this definition has many redundancies both in terms of the number of operations as well as in the postulates. Many of these redundancies have already been discussed in the chapter on the algebra of sets. For example, the de Morgan laws can be used to express either $\cup$ or $\cap$ in terms of the other and complementation. Furthermore, some of the properties in $L1$–$L4$ of even simple lattices are redundant, as we saw in Chapter 4. From the point of view of gaining intuitions about Boolean algebras, these redundancies are not objectionable, but from the point of view of logical simplicity, it is desirable to find a simpler definition. In fact, much of the early history of Boolean algebra was devoted to just this task, and a large number of different definitions of Boolean algebra have been discovered. We shall not try to give a complete discussion of any but one or two, (*cf:* Rudeanu for a more complete list). One of the earliest leaders in this phase of the subject was Huntington, who developed a number of independent sets of postulates over a period of more than 25 years. We present here one of his sets which is quite simple and best known, having first appeared in 1904 (*cf:* Huntington).

Theorem 6-3. *A Boolean algebra is a system* $\langle B, \cup, \cap, 0, 1, ' \rangle$ *consisting of a carrier set B closed under two binary, two nullary and one unary operations satisfying:*

L1: $a \cup b = b \cup a, a \cap b = b \cap a;$
D1: $a \cup (b \cap c) = (a \cup b) \cap (a \cup c);$
D2: $a \cap (b \cup c) = (a \cap b) \cup (a \cap c);$
U2: $a \cup 0 = a \,\forall\, a \in B;$
U3: $a \cap 1 = a \,\forall\, a \in B;$
C1, C2: $a \cap a' = 0$ *and* $a \cup a' = 1.$

Proof. Clearly this set of postulates is a subset of the set of statements of Theorem 6-1, so that every Boolean algebra satisfies the conditions listed here. To prove the converse, we note that these postulates are self-dual, so that the principle of duality may be used. We therefore omit duals in the remainder of the proof.

We first remark that 0 and 1 are unique. For if 0_1 and 0_2 satisfy *U2*, then $0_1 = 0_1 \cup 0_2 = 0_2 \cup 0_1 = 0_2$. Next, complementation is unique. For if a_1' and a_2' both satisfy *C1* and *C2*, then $a_1' = a_1' \cap 1 = a_1' \cap (a \cup a_2') = (a_1' \cap a) \cup (a_1' \cap a_2') = (a \cap a_1') \cup (a_1' \cap a_2') = 0 \cup (a_2' \cap a_1') = (a_2' \cap a_1') \cup 0 = a_2' \cap a_1'$ while similarly $a_2' = a_2' \cap a_1'$. Hence $a_1' = a_2'$.

Next the idempotent laws hold. For $a \cup a = (a \cup a) \cap 1 = (a \cup a) \cap (a \cap a') = a \cup (a \cup a') = a \cup 0 = a.$

U4 follows next, since $a \cap 0 = 0 \cup (a \cap 0) = (a \cap a') \cup (a \cap 0) = a \cap (a' \cup 0) = a \cap a' = 0.$

The absorption laws now follow, since $(a \cup b) \cap a = (a \cup b) \cap (a \cup 0) = a \cup (b \cap 0) = a \cup 0 = a.$

To prove the associative laws, let $s = a \cup (b \cup c)$ and $r = (a \cup b) \cup c$. Then $a \cap s = a \cap r$, since $a \cap s = a \cap [a \cup (b \cup c)] = a$ by the absorption law, while $a \cap r = a \cap [(a \cup b) \cup c] = [a \cap (a \cup b)] \cup (a \cap c) = a \cup (a \cap c) = a$. Similarly, $a' \cap s = a' \cap r$. For $a' \cap s = a' \cap [a \cup (b \cup c)] = (a' \cap a) \cup [a' \cap (b \cup c)] = a' \cap (b \cup c)$, while $a' \cap r = a' \cap [(a \cup b) \cup c] = [a' \cap (a \cup b)] \cup (a' \cap c) = [(a' \cap a) \cup (a' \cap b)] \cup (a' \cap c) = (a' \cap b) \cup (a' \cap c) = a' \cap (b \cup c)$. But therefore, $(a \cap s) \cup (a' \cap s) = (a \cap r) \cup (a' \cap r)$. Hence $s = 1 \cap s = (a \cup a') \cap s = (a \cap s) \cup (a' \cap s) = (a \cap r) \cup (a' \cap r) = r$. Thus $\langle B, \cup, \cap, 0, 1, ' \rangle$ is a complemented, distributive lattice; *i.e.*, a Boolean algebra.

The independence of these postulates can be established by counterexamples and is left to the exercises. Huntington also lists two independent set of postulates in terms of union and complementation. Later in 1933 he added a set in which a Boolean algebra is defined as a union semi-lattice $\langle B, \cup \rangle$; *i.e.*, $\cup$ is commutative, associative and idempotent, with a complementation satisfying $(a' \cup b')' \cup (a' \cup b)' = a$. This set of postulates is not self-dual and the last postulate is not very neat. A further reduction of these postulates was made by

Byrne in 1946 to the two following laws:

$$(i)\ (a \cap b) \cap a = (b \cap c) \cap a \text{ and } (ii)\ a \cap b' = c \cap c' \leftrightarrow a \cap b = a.$$

(*cf:* Byrne.) A few other sets are found in the exercises.

All of these systems of postulates make use of at least two fundamental operations while, as we have already seen, the lattice definition uses five operations. The second Huntington set above makes a Boolean algebra an algebra of type $\langle 2, 1 \rangle$ since it involves one binary and one unary operation. Attempts to reduce the number of operations to a single binary operation led Shoeffer to a formulation in terms of the operation of joint rejection. In terms of $\cup$, $\cap$ and $'$, this is given by $a|b = (a \cup b)' = a' \cap b'$, and is called the Shoeffer stroke operation. We shall not list the postulates here since they are not very simple or intuitive, but refer the reader to Shoeffer. In terms of stroke, we can now define complementation by $a' = a|a$, while join and meet are given by $a \cup b = (a|b)' = (a|b)|(a|b)$ and $a \cap b = a'' \cap b'' = (a|a)|(b|b)$. Hence it is clear that any of the known sets of postulates can be written in terms of stroke alone. Dually the operation $a||b = a' \cup b'$ can also be used. However, it is known that none of the other single binary operations alone can serve to define a Boolean algebra of the type $\langle 2 \rangle$ (*cf:* Freudenthal).

EXERCISES

1. Use the following tables to define algebraic systems of the type $\langle 2, 2 \rangle$ which show that the Huntington postulates are independent:

	0	1
0	0	1
1	1	0

	0	1
0	0	0
1	0	1

(*a*)

	0	1
0	0	1
1	1	1

	0	1
0	1	0
1	0	1

(*b*)

	0	1
0	0	0
1	1	1

	0	1
0	0	0
1	0	1

(*c*)

	0	1
0	0	0
1	0	0

	0	1
0	0	0
1	0	1

(*e*)

	0	1
0	0	1
1	1	1

	0	1
0	0	1
1	1	1

(*g*)

(*d*) and (*f*) are the duals of (*c*) and (*e*) respectively. Each system satisfies all except one of the postulates.

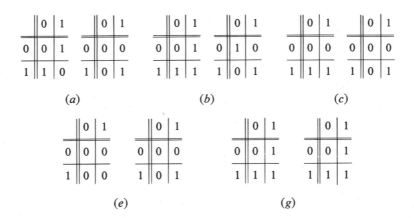

2. Given a system $\langle B, \cup, \cap, ' \rangle$ in which $\cup$ and $\cap$ are commutative, associative, absorptive, and distributive with respect to each other, and which satisfies $(a \cup a') \cap b = (a \cap a') \cup b = b$. Prove that this is a Boolean algebra. (*a*) Prove $\cup$ and $\cap$ are idempotent. (*b*) $a \cap a' = b \cap b' \; \forall \, a, b \in B$ and hence define 0. (*c*) Define 1 similarly; (*d*) Prove $a \cap b = a \Leftrightarrow a \cup b = b$ and hence define $\leq$. (*e*) show that $0 \leq a \leq 1 \; \forall \, a$.
3. Prove that the system $\langle B, \cup, ' \rangle$ is a Boolean algebra if it satisfies: $a'' = a$, $a \cup (b \cup b') = a$, $a \cup (b \cup c)' = [(b' \cup a)' \cup (c' \cup a)']'$.
4. Show how a Boolean algebra can be defined in terms of the single ternary median operation: $m(a, b, c) = (a \cap b) \cup (b \cap c) \cup (c \cap a)$. See exercise 1.17 of Chapter 5.
5. Show that the following axioms can be used to characterize Boolean algebra: (1) $a \cup b = b \cup a$; (2) $a \cup (b \cup c) = (a \cup b) \cup c$; (3) $(a' \cup b')' \cup (b' \cup b)' = a$.

6-3. BOOLEAN RINGS

In Chapter 2 we saw how a power set algebra determines a ring under the set operations of symmetric difference and intersection. In this section we obtain the same results for an arbitrary abstract Boolean algebra. Thus:

Theorem 3-4. *If $\langle B, \cup, \cap, 0, 1, ' \rangle$ is a Boolean algebra, then the system $\langle B, +, \cdot, e \rangle$ is a Boolean ring with identity under $a + b = (a \cap b') \cup (a' \cap b)$, $a \cdot b = a \cap b$ and $e = 1$.*

Proof. The properties of a Boolean ring were given in Chapter 2. Thus we first show that $\langle B, +, 0 \rangle$ is an additive commutative group with identity 0. The commutative law follows from the symmetry in the definition of $a + b$. Next $a + 0 = (a \cap 0') \cup (a' \cap 0) = a$ where the zero of the ring is the least element of the Boolean algebra. Again $a + a = (a \cap a') \cup (a' \cap a) = 0$ so that every element is its own additive inverse; *i.e.*, $-a = a$. Finally $+$ is associative:

$$\begin{aligned} \text{For } a + (b + c) &= \{a \cap [(b \cap c') \cup (b' \cap c)]'\} \cup (a' \cap [(b \cap c') \cup (b' \cap c)]\} \\ &= [a \cap (b' \cup c) \cap (b \cup c')] \cup (a' \cap b \cap c') \cup (a' \cap b' \cap c) \\ &= (a \cap b' \cap b) \cup (a \cap b' \cap c') \cup (a \cap c \cap b) \cup (a \cap c \\ &\quad \cap c') \cup (a' \cap b \cap c') \cup (a' \cap b' \cap c) \\ &= (a \cap b' \cap c') \cup (a' \cap b \cap c') \cup (a' \cap b' \cap c) \cup (a \cap b \\ &\quad \cap c). \end{aligned}$$

But this last expression is symmetric in a, b and c, so that it will also equal $(a + b) + c$.

Next the idempotent, commutative and associative laws for $\cdot$ follow from the same laws for meet. Hence we need only the distributive law $a \cdot (b + c) = a \cdot b$

$+ a \cdot c$. But

$$a \cdot (b + c) = a \cap [(b \cap c') \cup (b' \cap c)] = (a \cap b \cap c') \cup (a \cap b' \cap c).$$

Also $a \cdot b + a \cdot c = [a \cap b \cap (a \cap c)'] \cup [(a \cap b)' \cap (a \cap c)]$

$$= [a \cap b \cap (a' \cup c')] \cup [(a' \cup b') \cap (a \cap c)]$$

$$= (a \cap b \cap c') \cup (a \cap b' \cap c).$$

Hence $a \cdot (b + c) = a \cdot b + a \cdot c$. Thus $\langle B, +, \cdot \rangle$ is an idempotent, commutative ring; *i.e.*, a Boolean ring.

Finally, $e = 1$ is an identity, since $a \cdot e = a \cap 1 = a$. Hence $\langle B, +, \cdot, e \rangle$ is a Boolean ring with identity.

Corollary 1. *Every Boolean algebra determines a commutative group under symmetric difference.*

Corollary 2. *Every Boolean algebra determines a Boolean ring with identity under* $a + b = a \leftrightarrow b = (a' \cup b) \cap (a \cup b')$ *and* $a \cdot b = a \cup b$*; i.e. under equivalence and union.*

This second corollary is the dual of the theorem. To establish the converse of Theorem 6-4, we note that every Boolean ring; *i.e.*, idempotent ring, is automatically commutative and has characteristic 2; *i.e.*:

Lemma. *If* $\langle B, +, \cdot \rangle$ *is a Boolean ring, then* $a \cdot b = b \cdot a$ *and* $a + a = 0$ $\forall\, a, b \in B$.

Proof. $a + b = (a + b) \cdot (a + b) = a \cdot a + a \cdot b + b \cdot a + b \cdot b = (a + b) + (a \cdot b + b \cdot a)$, so that $a \cdot b + b \cdot a = 0$. Letting $a = b$ now gives $a \cdot a + a \cdot a = 0 = a + a$; *i.e.*, every element is its own inverse. Hence adding $b \cdot a$ to both sides of $a \cdot b + b \cdot a = 0$ gives $a \cdot b = b \cdot a$.

Theorem 6-5. *Every Boolean ring with identity* $\langle B, +, \cdot, e, 0 \rangle$ *determines a Boolean algebra under* $a \cup b = a + b + a \cdot b$, $a \cap b = a \cdot b$, $0 = 0$, $1 = e$ *and* $a' = 1 + a$.

Proof. We shall use the Huntington postulates. $\cup$ is clearly commutative from the symmetry of the definition, while the commutativity of $\cap$ follows from the same law for $\cdot$

D1: $a \cup (b \cap c) = a + b \cdot c + a \cdot b \cdot c$ while

$$\begin{aligned}(a \cup b) \cap (a \cup c) &= (a + b + a \cdot b) \cdot (a + c + a \cdot c) \\ &= a \cdot a + a \cdot c + a \cdot a \cdot c + b \cdot a + b \cdot c + b \cdot a \cdot c \\ &\quad + a \cdot b \cdot a + a \cdot b \cdot c + a \cdot b \cdot a \cdot c \\ &= a + b \cdot c + a \cdot b \cdot c\end{aligned}$$

where we have used the idempotent law for $\cdot$ and the inverse law for $+$.

$$D2\colon\ a \cap (b \cup c) = a \cdot (b + c + b \cdot c) = a \cdot b + a \cdot c + a \cdot b \cdot c.$$

On the other hand, $(a \cap b) \cup (a \cap c) = a \cdot b + a \cdot c + a \cdot b \cdot a \cdot c = a \cdot b + a \cdot c + a \cdot b \cdot c$ also, so that the two are equal.

The laws for 0 and 1 follow, since $a \cup 0 = a + 0 + a \cdot 0 = a$, while $a \cap 1 = a \cdot e = a$.

Finally, $a \cap a' = a \cdot (1 + a) = a \cdot (e + a) = a \cdot e + a \cdot a = a + a = 0$. Also $a \cup a' = a + (e + a) + a \cdot (e + a) = a + e + a + a \cdot 1 + a \cdot a = 1$. Hence $\langle B, \cup, \cap, 0, 1, ' \rangle$ is a Boolean algebra.

In the case where the Boolean ring fails to contain an identity, we can still introduce the lattice operations $\cup$ and $\cap$ exactly as in Theorem 6-5. $\langle B, \cup, \cap \rangle$ will then again be a distributive lattice with the same proofs as given there, although we must now prove the associative and idempotent laws for union separately. We leave them to the exercises. B becomes partially ordered as in any lattice by $a \leq b \leftrightarrow a \cap b = a$; *i.e.*, $a \leq b \leftrightarrow a \cdot b = a$. Then since $0 \cdot a = 0$ in any ring $0 \leq a \; \forall \; a \in B$; *i.e.*, 0 is a least element of $\langle B, \cup, \cap, 0 \rangle$. However, B will not have a greatest element, since the ring B does not contain an identity. Hence we cannot define complements in $\langle B, \cup, \cap, 0 \rangle$. However, if b is a fixed element, then we can show that the interval sub-lattice $[0, b]$ is complemented. For let $a \in [0, b]$; *i.e.*, $a \leq b$; *i.e.*, $a \cdot b = a$. Then we can show that $a + b$ is a complement of a relative to 0 and b. Thus $a \cup (a + b) = a + (a + b) + a \cdot (a + b) = (a + a) + b + a \cdot a + a \cdot b = 0 + b + a + a = b$. Furthermore, $a \cap (a + b) = a \cdot (a + b) = a \cdot a + a \cdot b = a + a = 0$. Hence $a + b = a'_b$ is a complement of a in $[0, b]$. Therefore $[0, b]$ is a Boolean algebra (but not a sub-Boolean algebra). In general a distributive lattice is called a **generalized Boolean algebra** if it contains a least element and every interval of the form $[0, b]$ is complemented. Hence our result is that every Boolean ring determines a generalized Boolean algebra, under $a \cup b = a + b + a \cdot b$, $a \cap b = a \cdot b$ and $a'_b = a + b$. A generalized Boolean algebra is a Boolean algebra if and only if it contains a greatest element.

The converse is again true. We simply replace complements by relative complements with respect to any "sufficiently large" element. We first prove:

Lemma. *In any generalized Boolean algebra, if* $a \leq b \leq c$, *then* $a'_b = a'_c \cap b$.

Proof. $a \cap (a'_c \cap b) = 0$, while $a \cup (a'_c \cap b) = (a \cup a'_c) \cap (a \cup b) = c \cap b = b$. Hence $a'_c \cap b$ is a complement of a relative to 0 and b.

Hence we can define $a + b = (a \cap b'_c) \cup (a'_c \cap b)$ where c is any element such that $a, b \leq c$. The lemma shows that if c and d both satisfy $a, b \leq c, d$, then $a \cap b'_c = a \cap b'_d$. First, consider the case where $c \leq d$. Then $a \cap b'_c = a \cap b'_d \cap c = a \cap b'_d$. Otherwise, we can refer both c and d to $c \cap d$; *i.e.*, $a \cap b'_c = a \cap b'_d = a \cap b'_{c \cap d}$. Thus we may define symmetric difference *relative to any upper bound for a and b*, and the result will be independent of this element. The proof of the Theorem 6-4 now goes through exactly as given, if we replace complementation by relative complements with respect to 0 and any element which is an upper bound for all the elements involved; for example $a \cup b \cup c$ in the associative and distributive laws. Such upper bounds always exist, since B is a lattice. Hence:

Theorem 6-6. *Every generalized Boolean algebra determines a Boolean ring and every Boolean ring determines a generalized Boolean algebra. The Boolean ring will have an identity if and only if the generalized Boolean algebra is a Boolean algebra.*

As an example of a generalized Boolean algebra which is not Boolean, we may consider the set of all finite subsets of an infinite set X; *i.e.*, $\mathfrak{F}(X)$. $\mathfrak{F}(X)$ has no greatest element, but the interval $[\emptyset, Y]$ is exactly the power set of Y for any Y in $\mathfrak{F}(X)$, so that $[\emptyset, Y]$ is complemented. Hence $\mathfrak{F}(X)$ is a generalized Boolean algebra. $\mathfrak{F}(X)$ then becomes a Boolean ring under $A + B = (A \cap B'_C) \cap (A'_C \cap B)$ where C contains A and B. In particular if $C = A \cup B$, then this reduces to $(A - B) \cup (B - A) = A \,\Delta\, B$, the usual symmetric difference. Thus the results are the same as those of Chapter 2, except that the ring has no identity and the lattice no greatest element.

EXERCISES

1. Prove that if $\langle B, +, \cdot \rangle$ is a Boolean ring and $a \cup b = a + b + a \cdot b$, then $\cup$ is idempotent and associative.
2. Prove that in any Boolean ring with identity, if $a + b + c = 0$ and $a \cdot b + b \cdot c + c \cdot a = 1$, then $a \cup b = b \cup c = c \cup a = 1$, $a' \cup b' = c$, $b' \cup c' = a$, $c' \cup a' = b$ and $a \cdot b = 1 + a + b$.
3. Prove that every finite Boolean ring has an identity e, where $e = \mathbf{U}_i \{a_i \mid \forall a_i \in B\}$. Show that e can be expressed in terms of the ring operations as:
$$e = \sum_{k=1}^{n} \sum_{i_1 < i_2 < \cdots < i_k} a_{i_1} \cdot a_{i_2} \cdots a_{i_k}$$
4. Verify that e as given in the previous exercise is a ring identity by direct substitution in $a \cdot e = a$, where $a = a_i$ for some i. Examine the case $n = 3$.
5. Show that in any Boolean ring $a \le b \Leftrightarrow a + b + a \cdot b = b \Leftrightarrow a + a \cdot b = 0$.
6. Show that if a is an atom in a Boolean algebra, then a' is a dual atom.
7. Show that if $\langle \mathbf{2}, \cup, \cap, 0, 1, ' \rangle$ is the Boolean algebra of two elements, then the corresponding Boolean ring $\langle \mathbf{2}, +, ' \rangle$ is a field, the field of integers mod 2, and that in no other case can a Boolean ring be a field. This is the field of characteristic 2.

6-4. SUBALGEBRAS

Since a Boolean algebra is a special type of algebraic system, all of the general concepts of universal algebra can be defined within the theory of Boolean algebras. More specifically, since a Boolean algebra is a lattice, these concepts can be developed from the concepts of lattice theory discussed in Chapters 4 and 5.

We define a **sub-Boolean algebra** *of a Boolean algebra* $\langle B, \cup, \cap, 0, 1, ' \rangle$ *as a system consisting of a subset A of B with operations defined on A having the same meaning as in B.* Thus A must be closed under all five operations of B. In particular, 0 and 1 must be in A. However, it is not necessary to check closure under all five operations, since they are interdependent. For example:

Theorem 6-7. *A subset A of a Boolean algebra* $\langle B, \cup, \cap, 0, 1, ' \rangle$ *is a sub-Boolean algebra of A if A is closed under* $\cup$ *and* $'$.

Proof. Exercise.

The simplest sub-Boolean algebra of any Boolean algebra is the subset consisting of 0 and 1 alone; *i.e.*, **2** is a sub-Boolean algebra of every Boolean algebra. If $a \in B$ is not 0 or 1, then the four element subset $A = \{0, 1, a, a'\}$ is again a sub-Boolean algebra. More generally, if A is any subset of B, then A generates a sub-Boolean algebra $[A]$ which is the smallest sub-Boolean algebra of B containing all the elements of A. Thus, as in universal algebra, the intersection of any collection of Boolean algebras is again a Boolean algebra (exercise), while the Boolean algebras B and **2** are greatest and least sub-Boolean algebras. Hence by Theorem 4-10 the collection $\mathfrak{S}(B)$ of all sub-Boolean algebras of B is a complete lattice. Within $\mathfrak{S}(B)$, $[A]$ is the intersection of all sub-Boolean algebras which contain A. A will therefore contain 0, and 1, and with any a and b, it must contain $a \cup b$, $a \cap b$, and a' Note, however, that every sub-lattice of B which is a Boolean algebra is not necessarily a sub-Boolean algebra. Thus if X is any set, then $\mathfrak{P}(X)$ is the Boolean algebra of all its subsets. If now A is a fixed subset, then the power set of A, $\mathfrak{P}(A)$, is a sub-lattice of $\mathfrak{P}(X)$, since it is closed under $\cup$ and $\cap$. Furthermore, $\mathfrak{P}(A)$ is itself a Boolean algebra. But the greatest element of $\mathfrak{P}(A)$ is A, which is not the greatest element of $\mathfrak{P}(X)$. Hence $\mathfrak{P}(A)$ is not a sub-Boolean algebra of $\mathfrak{P}(X)$; *i.e.*, a Boolean sub-algebra is not the same as a sub-Boolean algebra. Furthermore, the meaning of complementation within $\mathfrak{P}(A)$ is not the same as within $\mathfrak{P}(X)$.

Many of the most important types of Boolean algebras are obtained by considering sub-algebras of known Boolean algebras. For example, if we consider a power set algebra $\mathfrak{P}(X)$, then we can obtain examples by considering either sub-lattices or sub-Boolean algebras of $\mathfrak{P}(X)$. In the first case, if a collection

$\mathfrak{R}$ of subsets of X contains with any two sets A and B, their intersection and union, then $\mathfrak{R}$ is called a **lattice of sets.*** In the second case, if $\mathfrak{F}$ is closed under intersection, union and complementation, then $\mathfrak{F}$ is called a **field of sets.** $\mathfrak{P}(A)$ is therefore a lattice, but not a field of subsets of X. An important example of a field of sets is the class of all finite or cofinite subsets of X consisting of all subsets of X which are either finite or have finite complements. Note, however, that it is not complete. On the other hand, the class of finite subsets is a lattice of sets but not a field. Other examples of lattices of sets are the class of open sets or the class of closed sets of a topological space. If now $\mathfrak{R}$ is any lattice of sets, then if we consider all the elements which are complements of elements in $\mathfrak{R}$, then we obtain a second lattice of sets $\mathfrak{R}'$ (exercise). The intersection of these two lattices is itself a lattice which is closed under complementation and hence a field. Therefore $\mathfrak{R} \cap \mathfrak{R}'$ is a Boolean algebra. If we apply this result to the case of the open sets of a topological space where $\mathfrak{R}$ is the lattice of open sets, then $\mathfrak{R}'$ will be the lattice of closed sets.† Hence the field $\mathfrak{R} \cap \mathfrak{R}'$ is the class of closed-open sets. Therefore the family of closed-open subsets of any topological space is a Boolean algebra. The most important use of fields of sets will occur in section 6-5, where we shall show that every abstract Boolean algebra is isomorphic to some field of sets. Furthermore, we shall show later that every Boolean algebra can also be represented as the set of closed-open subsets of a suitably chosen topological space.

As a further example of a Boolean algebra of subsets of X which is not a field of subsets of X, we consider the class of regular open subsets of a topological space. A subset of a topological space is called **regular open** if it is open and is equal to the interior of its closure; *i.e.*, A is regular open $\leftrightarrow A = A^{-\circ}$. We then let $\mathfrak{U}$ be the set of all regular open sets of the topological space $\langle X, \mathfrak{T}\rangle$ and show that $\mathfrak{U}$ can be made into a Boolean algebra of sets by the proper definition of the operations in $\mathfrak{U}$. We do this in a series of lemmas.

Lemma 1. *If $\langle X, \mathfrak{T}\rangle$ is a topological space, then the set $\mathfrak{U}$ of regular open sets of X is a meet semi-lattice $\langle \mathfrak{U}, \cap\rangle$ under point set intersection.*

Proof. Let $A, B \in \mathfrak{U}$; *i.e.*, $A = A^{-\circ}, B = B^{-\circ}$. But we already learned that both the operations $A \to A^{\circ}$ and $A \to A^{-}$ are isotone, so that $A \cap B \subseteq A, B \Rightarrow (A \cap B)^{-\circ} \subseteq A^{-\circ}, B^{-\circ}$ and hence $(A \cap B)^{-\circ} \subseteq A^{-\circ} \cap B^{-\circ} = A \cap B$. Conversely, $A \cap B \subseteq (A \cap B)^{-}$ implies $(A \cap B)^{\circ} \subseteq (A \cap B)^{-\circ}$ where $A \cap B$ is open so that $(A \cap B)^{\circ} = A \cap B \subseteq (A \cap B)^{-\circ}$. Hence $(A \cap B)^{-\circ} = A^{-\circ} \cap B^{-\circ}$, or $A \cap B \in \mathfrak{U}$. Thus $\langle \mathfrak{U}, \cap\rangle$ is a meet semi-lattice.

*In the earlier literature, a lattice of sets was known as a ring of sets, since it is closed under the operations of union and intersection, which were treated analogously to ring addition and multiplication. However, since, more properly, ring addition corresponds to symmetric difference, a ring of sets should be defined as a family of sets closed under symmetric difference and meet. Hence we prefer the term **lattice of sets** here.

†See Appendix 2.

In general, the corresponding result for set union is false (exercise), so that $\mathfrak{U}$ is not closed under set union. However, the fact that $\langle \mathfrak{U}, \cap \rangle$ is a meet semi-lattice implies that $\mathfrak{U}$ is partially ordered under $A \leq B \Leftrightarrow A \cap B = A$. But this is precisely set inclusion, so that $\langle \mathfrak{U}, \subseteq \rangle$ is a partially ordered set. It therefore remains to determine the meaning of union; *i.e.*, we must find the smallest regular open set containing A and B.

Lemma 2. *$\langle \mathfrak{U}, \sqcup, \cap \rangle$ is a lattice under $A \sqcup B = (A \cup B)^{-\circ}$.*

Proof. We first recall from exercise 15 of section 4-11 that $A^{\circ} = A'^{-'}$. From this we show that $A^{-\circ-\circ} = A^{-\circ}$; *i.e.*, $A \to A^{-\circ}$ is involutory. First, $A \subseteq A^{-} \Rightarrow A^{\circ} \subseteq A^{-\circ}$ by the isotone law for $\circ$. Applying this to $A^{-\circ}$ gives $A^{-\circ} \subseteq A^{-\circ-\circ}$. But conversely, $A' \subseteq A'^{-} \Rightarrow A^{-'} = A''^{-'} = A'^{\circ} \subseteq A'^{-\circ} = A'^{-'-'}$. Applying $^{-}$ gives $A^{-'-} \subseteq A'^{-'-'-}$, so that $A'^{-'-'-'} \subseteq A^{-'-'}$; *i.e.*, $A^{\circ-\circ} \subseteq A^{-\circ}$. Hence $A^{-\circ-\circ} \subseteq A^{-\circ}$. Therefore, $A^{-\circ-\circ} = A^{-\circ}$. (See figure 3-15 of Chapter 3).

Applying this result to $A \cup B$ gives $(A \cup B)^{-\circ-\circ} = (A \cup B)^{-\circ}$; *i.e.*, $(A \sqcup B)^{-\circ} = A \sqcup B$, so that $A \sqcup B$ is regular open.

We next show that $A \sqcup B$ is an upper bound for A and B in $\langle \mathfrak{U}, \subseteq \rangle$. Thus $A, B \subseteq A \cup B$ implies $A^{-\circ}, B^{-\circ} \subseteq (A \cup B)^{-\circ} = A \sqcup B$.

Finallly, $A \sqcup B$ is a least upper bound. For let $A, B, C \in \mathfrak{U}$ and let $A, B \subseteq C$. Then $A \sqcup B = (A \cup B)^{-\circ} \subseteq C^{-\circ} = C$. Hence $\langle \mathfrak{U}, \sqcup \rangle$ is a union semi-lattice under $\sqcup$.

Lemma 3. *$\langle \mathfrak{U}, \sqcup, \cap, \emptyset, X, * \rangle$ is a complemented lattice with units under $A^* = A^{-'}$.*

Proof. (*i*) $\emptyset^{-o} = \emptyset$ and $X^{-o} = X$, so that $\emptyset$ and X are least and greatest elements of $\mathfrak{U}$.

(*ii*) $A^{*-o} = A^{-'-'-'} = A^{-o-'} = A^{-'} = A^*$, so that $A^* \in \mathfrak{U}$.

(*iii*) $A \subseteq A^{-} \Rightarrow A^{-'} \subseteq A'$. Hence $A \cap A^* = A \cap A^{-'} \subseteq A \cap A' = \emptyset$; *i.e.*, $A \cap A^* = \emptyset$.

(*iv*) Finally $A \sqcup A^* = (A \cup A^{-'})^{-\circ} = (A^{-} \cup A^{-'-})^{\circ} = (A^{--} \cup A^{-'-})^{\circ} = (A^{-} \cup A^{-'})^{-\circ} = X^{-\circ} = X$. Thus A^* is a complement of A in $\langle \mathfrak{U}, \sqcup, \cap, \emptyset, X, * \rangle$.

Theorem 6-8. *The set U of regular open sets of a topological space $\langle X, \mathfrak{T} \rangle$ is a Boolean algebra $\langle U, \sqcup, \cap, \phi, X, * \rangle$ where $A \sqcup B = (A \cup B)^{-\circ}$ and $A^* = A'^{-}$.*

Proof. All that remains is to prove the distributive laws. For this purpose we first prove that if A is open,

$$(1)\ A \cap B^{-} \subseteq (A \cap B)^{-}.$$

Thus let $x \in A \cap B^{-}$. Then $x \in A$ and $x \in B^{-}$. To show that $x \in (A \cap B)^{-}$, let G be an open set such that $x \in G$. Then $x \in G \cap A$ which is also open. Hence, since $x \in B^-$, $G \cap A \cap B \neq \emptyset$ which implies $x \in (A \cap B)^-$.

Applying $^\circ$ to this inequality gives $A \cap B^{-\circ} = A^\circ \cap B^{-\circ} = (A \cap B^-)^\circ \subseteq (A \cap B)^{-\circ}$, since A is open and $^\circ$ distributes onto $\cap$. Now replacing B by $B \cup C$ gives $A \cap (B \cup C)^{-\circ} \subseteq [A \cap (B \cup C)]^{-\circ} = [(A \cap B) \cup (A \cap C)]^{-\circ}$. Thus $A \cap (B \sqcup C) \subseteq (A \cap B) \sqcup (A \cap C)$. But the reverse inequality holds in any lattice, so that the distributive laws hold.

Thus $\mathfrak{U}$ determines a Boolean algebra for the regular open sets of X, but this is again not a sub-Boolean algebra of $\mathfrak{P}(X)$ nor even a field of subsets of X. It will follow from our general representation theorem in section 6-7 that $\mathfrak{U}$ is isomorphic to some field of sets but not a field of subsets of X.

6-5. HOMOMORPHISMS, CONGRUENCES, IDEALS AND FILTERS

The topics of homomorphisms, congruences and ideals carry over from the corresponding discussion of general lattices with a few extra conditions due to the Boolean character of the algebra. Thus we first define a **homomorphism** as a mapping ϕ from one Boolean algebra $\langle B, \cup, \cap, 0, 1, '\rangle$ to a second $\langle \bar{B}, \cup, \cap, \bar{0}, \bar{1}, '\rangle$ which preserves the five operations. But if we merely require that ϕ preserve either $\cup$ or $\cap$ and $'$, this will be enough, since the others can be defined in terms of these two. For example $\phi(0) = \phi(a \cup a') = \phi(a) \cup \phi(a') = \phi(a) \cup \phi(a)' = \bar{0}$, shows that ϕ carries 0 onto $\bar{0}$. We leave the rest of the proof to the exercises. Furthermore, if we have a lattice homomorphism; *i.e.*, ϕ preserves $\cup$ and $\cap$, then ϕ will preserve order. Now since $0 \leq a \;\forall\; a \in B$ we will have $\phi(0) \leq \phi(a) = \bar{a} \;\forall\; \bar{a} \in \phi(B)$. Hence 0 maps onto the least element of $\phi(B)$. Then similarly ϕ will map 1 onto the greatest element of $\phi(B)$. But now $'$ can be defined in terms of $\cup, \cap, 0$ and 1, so that ϕ will be a homomorphism from B onto $\phi(B)$. We leave the details to the reader, as well as the proof that $\phi(B)$ is a Boolean algebra. Thus every lattice homomorphism from one Boolean algebra into another is a Boolean homomorphism from B onto the set $\phi(B)$ of images in $\bar{B}$. However it is not necessarily a Boolean homomorphism of B onto $\bar{B}$, since $\phi(0)$ may not be the $\bar{0}$ of $\bar{B}$. This argument also shows that we can generate new Boolean algebras from known ones by considering lattice homomorphisms.

The concept of a Boolean ideal is exactly the same as that of a lattice. Thus a subset H of B is called an **ideal** (*product ideal*) if it satisfies:

(*i*) $a \in H, x \in B$ and $x \leq a \Rightarrow x \in H$;
(*ii*) $a, b \in H \Rightarrow a \cup b \in H$.

A **filter** (union ideal) is defined dually. We note that (*i*) and (*ii*) can be combined into the single condition: $a \cup b \in H \Leftrightarrow a, b \in H$ for an ideal and $a \cap b \in$

$H \Longleftrightarrow a, b \in H$ for a filter. (Exercise.) Furthermore, every ideal is a sub-lattice of $\langle B, \cup, \cap \rangle$, since H is closed under $\cup$ and $\cap$. However, H is not generally a sub-Boolean algebra, since $1 \notin H$. In fact, $1 \in H \Rightarrow H = B$. As an example of an ideal, we may consider the set of all lower bounds to a fixed element a; *i.e.*, $[a]\downarrow\ = \{x | x \leq a\}$. This is called the **principal ideal** generated by a. Thus $[1]\downarrow\ = B$. Dual remarks hold for **principal filters** of the type $[a]\uparrow$. Ideals and filters are related, since, for example, if H is an ideal then the set of complements of the elements of H will form a filter; *i.e.*, $\{x | x = h', h \in H\}$ is the filter associated with the ideal H. For the remainder, we discuss ideals and leave filters to the exercises. If we consider only non-degenerate ideals and filters; *i.e.*, non-empty, then every ideal contains 0, while every filter contains 1. Hence the principal ideals $[0]\downarrow$ and $[1]\downarrow$ are least and greatest elements in the lattice of all ideals of B, and dually for filters. Furthermore, as for lattices or algebras in general, the intersection of any number of ideals is again an ideal, so that the lattice of all ideals $\mathfrak{J}(B)$ is a complete lattice with units. In fact, $\mathfrak{J}(B)$ is a sub-lattice of the lattice $\mathfrak{S}(B)$ of all sub-Boolean algebras of B. Within $\mathfrak{J}(B)$ union is characterized as the smallest ideal containing all the ideals of a given set of ideals, $\{H_\alpha\}_\alpha$. Thus $\bigsqcup_\alpha H_\alpha$ is the intersection of all those ideals which contain all the H_α. Similarly, any subset A of B generates an ideal $[A]$ which is the intersection of all those ideals containing all the elements of A. For example, $\bigsqcup_\alpha H_\alpha$ is the ideal generated by $\mathbf{U}_\alpha H_\alpha$; $[A]$ is also equal to the union of all the principal ideals generated by elements of A; *i.e.*, $[A] = \bigsqcup_{a \in A} [a]\downarrow$. The details are left as exercises and follow the same ideas as for arbitrary lattices. A final characterization of $\bigsqcup_\alpha H_\alpha$ in terms of the elements of the H_α is given by: $\bigsqcup_\alpha H_\alpha = \{x | x = a_1 \cup a_2 \cup \cdots \cup a_n, a_i \in H_i\}$; *i.e.*, the set of all finite unions of elements from the H_α. For example, the union of two principal ideals is given by $[a]\downarrow \sqcup [b]\downarrow\ = \{x \cup y | x \leq a, y \leq b\}$. But this is exactly $[a \cup b]\downarrow$, so that $[a]\downarrow \sqcup [b]\downarrow\ = [a \cup b]\downarrow$. Similarly, $[a]\downarrow \cap [b]\downarrow\ = [a \cap b]\downarrow$. In particular, $[a]\downarrow \sqcup [a']\downarrow\ = [1]\downarrow\ = B$, while $[a]\downarrow \cap [a']\downarrow\ = [0]\downarrow$, so that $[a]\downarrow$ and $[a']\downarrow$ are complementary ideals in the lattice $\mathfrak{J}(B)$. In fact, the mapping $a \rightarrow [a]\downarrow$ is an isomorphism from B into the Boolean algebra $\mathfrak{P}\mathfrak{J}(B)$ within $\mathfrak{J}(B)$, where $\mathfrak{P}\mathfrak{J}(B)$ is the set of all principal ideals of B.

Every homomorphism now determines both an ideal and a filter. Thus if ϕ is a homomorphism from a Boolean algebra B onto an algebra $\bar{B}$, then the sets of inverse images of $\bar{0}$ and $\bar{1}$ are an ideal and a filter respectively; *i.e.*, $H = \phi^{-1}(\bar{0}) = \{x \in B | \phi(x) = \bar{0}\}$ is an ideal of B while $K = \phi^{-1}(\bar{1}) = \{x \in B | \phi(x) = \bar{1}\}$ is a filter. H and K are called the **kernels** of ϕ.

As an example of an ideal which is not principal, we must consider an infinite boolean algebra. For if B is finite, then every ideal is principal (exercise). Thus let X be any infinite set and $\mathfrak{P}(X)$ its power set. Then the set of finite subsets of X is an ideal, since if A is finite, then any subset of A is finite as is the union of two finite subsets. Thus $\mathfrak{F}(X) = \{A \subseteq X | A \text{ finite}\}$ is an ideal.

Dually, the set of subsets of X whose complement is finite, the cofinite subsets of X, is a filter.

A **congruence relation** on a Boolean algbera is defined by specialization from universal algebra as an equivalence relation with the substitution property for the operations of the Boolean algebra. Thus *θ is a congruence relation on B if it is an equivalence relation and $a \equiv c(\theta)$ and $b \equiv d(\theta)$ imply $a \cup b \equiv c \cup d(\theta)$, $a \cap b \equiv c \cap d(\theta)$, $a' \equiv c'(\theta)$.* It is not necessary to consider the nullary operations since they are constants. Note, however, that inequalities do not have the substitution property; *i.e.*, $a \leq b$ does not necessarily imply $c \leq d$. This is because $a \leq b \Rightarrow a \cup b = b \Rightarrow c \cup d \equiv d(\theta)$ which is a congruence, but not an equality. For example, in the four element Boolean algebra $\{0, 1, a, a'\}$ we can write $a \equiv 1$ and $a' \equiv 0$, and verify that this defines a congruence, but $0 \leq 1$ does not imply that $a \leq a'$. Furthermore, a lattice congruence does not necessarily define a Boolean congruence for essentially the same reason. For example, if we define θ by $a \equiv 1$ in $\{0, 1, a, a'\}$, then θ has the substitution property for $\cup$ and $\cap$, but not for $'$.

Every homomorphism ϕ from B to $\bar{B}$ now determines a congruence relation θ_ϕ on B by the definition: $a \equiv b(\theta_\phi) \leftrightarrow \phi(a) = \phi(b)$ (exercise). Conversely, every congruence relation θ determines a homomorphism ϕ_θ which is the natural homomorphism from B onto the quotient algebra $\bar{B}$ where $\bar{B}$ is the set of cosets of B mod θ. Thus if $\bar{a}$ stands for the coset containing the element a, then the definitions $\bar{a} \cup \bar{b} = \overline{a \cup b}$, $\bar{a} \cap \bar{b} = \overline{a \cap b}$, and $\bar{a}' = \overline{a'}$ define a Boolean algebra on $\bar{B}$ where the the definitions are unique because of the substitution property. These facts are simply special cases of the same results already discussed for lattices in general, except for the addition of the results for complementation. Hence $\bar{B} = B$ mod θ is a Boolean algebra and $\phi\colon a \to \bar{a}$ is a Boolean homomorphism from B onto $\bar{B}$. Finally, the correspondences between homomorphisms and congruences are one-to-one and inverses in the sense that $\theta_{\phi_\theta} = \phi$ and $\phi_{\theta_\phi} = \phi$, so that the theory of homomorphisms and the theory of congruences are essentially the same. For example, we can speak either of the lattice of homomorphisms or the lattice of congruences interchangeably. Since the theory is the same as that discussed for lattices, we shall not give the complete details again here. However, it remains to relate the theory of ideals to that of homomorphisms and congruences; *i.e.*, we shall show that the lattice of ideals is essentially the same as that of congruences and homomorphisms. In this case, the result is something better than for arbitrary lattices in that every homomorphism determines a unique congruence.

First, every congruence θ determines an ideal (its kernel) given by the set of elements congruent to 0; *i.e.*, $H_\theta = \{x | x \equiv 0(\theta)\}$. Similarly, θ determines a filter $K_\theta = \{x | x \equiv 1(\theta)\}$. In general for an arbitrary lattice, we saw that a single ideal may determine different congruence relations which have the same kernel, but in the case of Boolean algebra this does not happen as is shown in:

Theorem 6-9. *If H is an ideal of a Boolean algebra B, then the relation* $a \equiv b(\theta_H) \leftrightarrow a \Delta b = (a \cap b') \cup (a' \cap B) \in H$ *is a congruence relation on B. Furthermore, if* θ *is any congruence relation with kernel H, then* $\theta = \theta_H$.

Proof. (*i*) $a \equiv a$ since $a \Delta a \in H$.

(*ii*) $a \equiv b \Rightarrow b \equiv a$ since $a \Delta b = b \Delta a$.

(*iii*) $a \equiv b$ and $b \equiv c$ imply $a \Delta b, b \Delta c \in H$. But H is closed under symmetric difference, since if $a, b \in H$, then $a \cap b', a' \cap b \in H$ and therefore $(a \cap b') \cup (a' \cap b) \in H$. Therefore $a \Delta c = (a \Delta b) \Delta (b \Delta c) \in H$. Thus $a \equiv b$.

(*iv*) Let $a \equiv c$ and $b \in H$. Then $a \Delta c \in H$. From this we obtain $(a \cup b) \Delta (c \cup b) = [(a \cup b) \cap (c \cup b)'] \cup [(a \cup b)' \cap (c \cup b)] = [a \cup b) \cap c' \cap b'] \cup [a' \cap b' \cap (c \cup b)] = (a \cap c' \cap b') \cup (a' \cap b' \cap c) = [(a \cap c') \cup (a' \cap c)] \cap b' = (a \Delta c) \cap b' \in H$, since $(a \Delta c) \cap b' \leq a \Delta c$. Thus $(a \cup b) \Delta (c \Delta b) \in H$ or $a \cup b \equiv c \cup b$. Similarly, if $b \equiv d$, then $a \cup b \equiv c \cup d$.

(*v*) Let $a \equiv c$. Then $a \Delta c \in H$. But $a' \Delta c' = a \Delta c$ so that $a' \equiv c'$. Hence $\equiv$ has the substitution properties for $\cup$ and $'$ and is therefore a congruence.

(*vi*) The kernel of θ_H is $\{x | x \equiv 0(\theta)\}$. But $x \equiv 0(\theta) \leftrightarrow x \Delta 0 = x \in H$. Hence the kernel is H.

(*vii*) Conversely, let θ be any congruence with kernel H. Then $x \equiv 0(\theta) \leftrightarrow x \in H$. But $a \equiv b(\theta) \leftrightarrow a \Delta b \in H \leftrightarrow a \Delta b \equiv 0(\theta) \leftrightarrow a \Delta b \Delta b \equiv a \equiv b(\theta)$. Hence $\theta_H = \theta$.

As an example of the theory of homomorphisms, ideals, and congruences, we can construct new algebras from given ones as homomorphic images by constructing quotient algebras modulo some ideal. Thus let X be any infinite set. Then the set of finite subsets $\mathfrak{F}(X)$ is an ideal in $\mathfrak{P}(X)$. Hence we can construct the quotient algebra $\mathfrak{P}(X)/\mathfrak{F}(X)$. The elements will be the cosets of the congruence relation given by $A \equiv B(\theta)$ if and only if the symmetric difference of A and B is a finite set; *i.e.*, if and only if A and B differ by at most a finite number of elements. The kernel is then exactly $\mathfrak{F}(X)$, while the greatest element of $\mathfrak{P}(X)/\mathfrak{F}(X)$ is the set of cofinite subsets of X. The mapping $A \to \bar{A}$, where $\bar{A}$ is a the set of all subsets which differ from A by at most a finite number of elements, is a homomorphism from $\mathfrak{P}(X)$ onto $\mathfrak{P}(X)/\mathfrak{F}(X)$, so that the resulting algebra is itself Boolean. $\mathfrak{P}(X)$ is a power set algebra, but we can show that the same is not true for $\mathfrak{P}(X)/\mathfrak{F}(X)$, since the latter is not atomic, while the former is. Thus if $\bar{A}$ is any element of $\mathfrak{P}(X)/\mathfrak{F}(X)$, $\bar{A} \neq \emptyset$, then A must be infinite. Hence A will contain a subset which differs from A by an infinite number of elements and is itself infinite. (For example, if $A = \mathbf{N}$ is the set of integers, and $B = \mathbf{E}$ the set of even integers, then B is an infinite subset of A which differs from A by an infinite number of elements.) Hence $\emptyset \subset \bar{B} \subset \bar{A}$, so that $\bar{A}$ is not an atom of $\mathfrak{P}(X)/\mathfrak{F}(X)$. Note also that this same proof shows that $\mathfrak{P}(X)/\mathfrak{F}(X)$ does not satisfy the descending chain condition.

As a second example, let B be any Boolean algebra and let a be fixed in B. Then the mapping ϕ: $x \to x \cap a$ is a Boolean homomorphism (endomorphism) from B onto the Boolean algebra $\bar{B} = [a] \downarrow$, the principal ideal generated by

a. All that needs to be shown is that ϕ preserves $'$, since we have already discussed this homomorphism for distributive lattices. We leave it to the exercises. The (lower) kernel of ϕ is then $H = \{x|x \cap a = 0\} = \{x|x \leq a'\} = [a'] \downarrow$. Dually the (upper) kernel is $K = \{x|x \cap a = a\} = [a] \uparrow$; *i.e.*, the principal filter generated by a. If $\bar{x}$ denotes the coset containing x, then $\bar{x}$ will contain exactly one element y from $[a] \downarrow$. For $y = x \cap a$ will be such an element, while if $y_1, y_2 \in \bar{x}$ and $y_1, y_2 \leq a$, then $y_1 = y_1 \cap a = y_2 \cap a = y_2$. Hence the mapping $\bar{x} \to y$ where $y = x \cap a$ is a one-to-one mapping from $\bar{B}$ onto $[a] \downarrow$. We leave it to the reader to show that it is an isomorphism. Thus $B/[a'] \downarrow \cong [a] \downarrow$. A similar argument shows that $B/[a] \downarrow \cong [a'] \downarrow$. Moreover, we have already seen that the intervals $[a] \downarrow = [0, a]$ and $[a', 1] = [a'] \uparrow$ are isomorphic, so that $B/[a] \downarrow \cong [a] \uparrow$; *i.e.*, B mod any principal ideal is isomorphic to the filter generated by the same element. (Draw a sketch.)

EXERCISES

1. Prove $a \,\Delta\, b = a' \,\Delta\, b'$.
2. Show that if ϕ preserves $\cup$ and $'$, then it preserves $\cap$.
3. Show that a lattice homomorphism on a boolean algebra which preserves 0 and 1 is a Boolean homomorphism.
4. Show that every homomorphic image of a Boolean algebra is a Boolean algebra.
5. Show that $[A] = \bigsqcup_{a \in A} [a] \downarrow$.
6. Show that $\bigsqcup_\alpha H_\alpha = [\bigcup_\alpha H_\alpha]$ = the set of finite unions of elements of the H_α.
7. Show that the mapping $a \to [a] \uparrow$ is a *dual* isomorphism from the Boolean algebra B onto the class of principal filters of B.
8. Show that if ϕ is a homomorphism, then $\phi^{-1}(\bar{0})$ is an ideal and $\phi^{-1}(\bar{1})$ is a filter.
9. Show that the mappings $\phi \to \theta_\phi$ and $\theta \to \phi_\theta$ are one-to-one and inverse mappings between the lattice of homomorphisms and the lattice of congruences of B.
10. Show that if H and K are the two kernels of a homomorphism ϕ, then K is the set of all complements of elements of H and conversely.
11. Show that if $a \in B$, then $x \equiv y[a] \downarrow \leftrightarrow a \cup x = a \cup y$.
12. Show that every ideal H of a Boolean algebra $\langle B, \cup, \cap, 0, 1, ' \rangle$ is a normal subgroup of the group $\langle B, \Delta \rangle$, and a ring ideal in the ring $\langle B, +, \cdot \rangle$ where $a + b = a \,\Delta\, b$.
13. Prove that in any finite Boolean algebra, every coset modulo an ideal contains the same number of elements.
14. Prove directly that $a \equiv c(\theta) \Rightarrow a \cap b \equiv c \cap b(\theta)$ for any Boolean congruence.
15. Prove that the mapping $x \to x \cap a$ preserves $'$.
16. Every homomorphism ϕ determines a kernel H_ϕ which is an ideal and every

ideal determines a congruence θ_H. Further, every homomorphism determines a congruence θ_ϕ. Show that $\theta_{H_\phi} = \theta_\phi$.

17. Use the results of exercise 16 to show that if ϕ is a homomorphism from $B \to \bar{B}$ with kernel H_ϕ, then $\bar{B} \cong B/H_\phi$.
18. Show that $[a \cup b] \downarrow = [a] \downarrow \bigsqcup [b] \downarrow$ and $[a \cap b] \downarrow = [a] \downarrow \cap [b] \downarrow$.
19. Show that a one-to-one mapping ϕ from a Boolean algebra B to a Boolean algebra $\bar{B}$ is an isomorphism if and only if ϕ and ϕ^{-1} are both isotone.

6-6. MAXIMAL IDEALS

Of particular importance amongst the class of all ideals of a Boolean algebra B is the class of maximal ideals. Thus an ideal M is called *maximal* if it is itself a proper ideal of B but is not contained in another proper ideal of B; *i.e.*, $M \neq B$ and $M \subseteq H \subseteq B \Rightarrow$ either $H = M$ or $H = B$, for any ideal H. Hence M is a dual atom in the lattice of all ideals of B. Maximal ideals are characterized by the following theorem:

Theorem 6-10. *An ideal M of a Boolean algebra B is maximal if and only if for any $a \in B$ either $a \in M$ or $a' \in M$ but not both.*

Proof. Clearly, both a and a' cannot be in M, since otherwise $a \cup a' = 1 \in M$, so that $M = B$. If we now assume M is maximal and there exists $a \in B$ such that $a \notin M$, then we let $H = M \bigsqcup [a] \downarrow$ be the union of M and $[a] \downarrow$. Then since $a \notin M$, $H \neq M$ although $M \subseteq H$. Hence by the maximality condition, $H = B$. Therefore, $a' \in H$. But the elements of H are of the form $m \cup x$ where $m \in M$ and $x \in [a] \downarrow$. Hence $a' = m \cup x$ where $m \in M$ and $x \leq a$. Thus $a' = m \cup x \leq m \cup a$; *i.e.*, $a' = a' \cap (m \cup a) = (a' \cap m) \cup (a' \cap a) = a' \cap m$. Hence $a' \leq m$ and therefore $a' \in M$. Thus $a \notin M$ implies $a' \in M$.

Maximal ideals determine homomorphisms as in the last section, but these homomorphisms always determine the same homomorphic image, namely **2**, as in:

Theorem 6-11. *A ideal M is maximal in B if and only if the homomorphism ϕ_M determined by M is two-valued.*

Proof. (*i*) If M is maximal, then $a \equiv 0 \bmod M \Leftrightarrow a \in M$. But for any a, either $a \in M$ or $a' \in M$. But $a' \in M \Rightarrow a' \equiv 0 \Rightarrow a \equiv 1$. Hence for any $a \in B$, either $a \equiv 1$ or $a \equiv 0$. Therefore, B mod M has exactly two cosets, $\bar{1}$ and $\bar{0}$; *i.e.*, $\phi(B) \cong \mathbf{2}$.

(*ii*) Conversely, if ϕ is a two-valued homomorphism from B onto $\mathbf{2} = \{\bar{0}, \bar{1}\}$ with kernel M, then M is maximal. For if $a \in B$, then either $\phi(a) = \bar{0}$ in which case $a \in M$ or $\phi(a) = \bar{1}$, in which case $\phi(a') = \phi(a)' = \bar{0}$, so that

$a' \in M$. Hence either $a \in M$ or $a' \in M$ and M is maximal by the previous theorem.

As examples of maximal ideals, let B be an atomic Boolean algebra. Then B is also dual-atomic. If now a is any dual atom, then the principal ideal $[a]\downarrow$ will be a maximal ideal. For if b is any element of B and $b \notin [a]\downarrow$, then $b \nleq a$. Hence $a < a \cup b$, so that $a \cup b = 1$, whence $b' \leq a$; *i.e.*, $b' \in [a]\downarrow$. Thus by Theorem 6-10 $[a]\downarrow$ is maximal. The converse, however, is not true, and we can exhibit maximal ideals, even in an atomic Boolean algebra, which are not principal. Thus let X be an infinite set and let $\mathfrak{F}(X) \cup \mathfrak{C}\mathfrak{F}(X)$ be the set of finite or cofinite subsets of X. We have already seen that this is a Boolean algebra. Furthermore, $\mathfrak{F}(X)$ is an ideal. If we now consider the quotient algebra, $\mathfrak{F}(X) \cup \mathfrak{C}\mathfrak{F}(X)/\mathfrak{F}(X)$, then there will be exactly two cosets, since any set is either finite or cofinite; *i.e.*, the cosets are $\mathfrak{F}(X)$ and $\mathfrak{C}\mathfrak{F}(X)$. Hence by Theorem 6-11, $\mathfrak{F}(X)$ is a maximal ideal, but it is not principal. Futhermore, the algebra $\mathfrak{F}(X) \cup \mathfrak{C}\mathfrak{F}(X)$ is atomic.

The concept of a maximal ideal within the theory of Boolean algebras coincides with that of a prime ideal. Thus an ideal M is called **prime** if $a \cap b \in M \Rightarrow$ either $a \in M$ or $b \in M$. This is again a corollary of Theorem 6-10. For let M be maximal and $a \cap b \in M$. Then if $a \notin M$, then $a' \in M$. Hence $b = b \cap (a \cup a') = (b \cap a) \cup (b \cap a') \in M$. Conversely, if $a \cap b \in M \Rightarrow$ either $a \in M$ or $b \in M$, then since $a \cap a' = 0 \in M$, either $a \in M$ or $a' \in M$. Hence M is maximal. (The concept of a prime ideal arises from the theory of rings. Thus in the ring of integers, a number p is called prime if $p|ab$ implies either $p|a$ or $p|b$. If $[a]$ designates the principal ring ideal generated by a, then $p|a$ can be written as $a \in [p]$, which in turn is equivalent to $[a] \subseteq [p]$. Thus the condition that p be a prime can be written as $[a] \cap [b] = [ab] \subseteq [p]$ implies either $[a] \subseteq [p]$ or $[b] \subseteq [p]$.)

The principal problem concerning maximal ideals is to show that they always exist in any Boolean algebra. The proof that this is the case rests on the use of the axiom of choice, which we use here in the form of Zorn's lemma. In general, however, the converse is not true, so that the statement that every Boolean algebra contains some maximal ideal is essentially weaker than the axiom of choice. This result has been established only recently, and we shall not attempt to prove it here (*cf:* Cohen). Here we will prove the existence of maximal ideals in a special form that we will need later.

Theorem 6-12. *If B is any Boolean algebra, x is any element of B, and H any ideal not containing x, then there exists a maximal ideal M such that $H \subseteq M$ and $x \notin M$.*

Proof. Let $\mathfrak{M} = \mathfrak{M}_{H,x}$ be the class of proper ideals containing H but not containing x. Let $\langle \mathfrak{M}, \subseteq \rangle$ be partially ordered by set inclusion. We shall show that every chain $\mathfrak{C}$ in $\mathfrak{M}$ has an upper bound in $\mathfrak{M}$. Thus let $\mathfrak{C}$ be a chain of ideals $\{K_\alpha\}_\alpha$ in $\mathfrak{M}$, and $K = \bigsqcup_\alpha K_\alpha$. Then K is the smallest ideal of B containing all the K_α. We must show that K is in $\mathfrak{M}$; *i.e.*, K is a proper ideal, $H \subseteq K$ and $x \notin K$. But $\bigsqcup_\alpha K_\alpha$ is the set of all finite unions of elements from the K_α. Thus if $k \in K$, then $k = k_1 \cup k_2 \cup \cdots \cup k_n$ where each $k_i \in K_i$ for some i. But since $\mathfrak{C}$ is a chain, one of the finite number of K_i's will contain all the others. Let it be K_{i_0}. Then each $K_i \subseteq K_{i_0}$, so that $k_i \in K_{i_0}$. Hence $k \in K_{i_0}$. Thus every $k \in K$ is in some individual K_i so that K is the set union of the K_α; *i.e.*, in this case $K = \bigsqcup_\alpha K_\alpha = \mathbf{U}_\alpha K_\alpha$. From this we can deduce that K is a proper ideal. For if not, $1 \in K$ and therefore $1 \in K_\alpha$ for some α, contrary to our hypothesis. Next $H \subseteq K_\alpha \ \forall_\alpha$ so that $H \subseteq K$. Finally, $x \notin K$. For if $x \in K$, then $x \in K_\alpha$ for some α. Thus every chain in the partially ordered set $\langle \mathfrak{M}, \subseteq \rangle$ is bounded within $\mathfrak{M}$. We may therefore apply Zorn's lemma to establish the existence of a maximal ideal M in $\mathfrak{M}$. M is then the maximal ideal required by the theorem.

Corollary. *Given $x \neq y$ in B, there exists a maximal ideal M containing x but not containing y.*

EXERCISES

1. Prove that every maximal ideal in a Boolean algebra determines a maximal filter. State the results of Theorems 6-11 and 6-12 for filters.
2. Prove the corollary of Theorem 6-12.

6-7. REPRESENTATION THEORY

(a) Atomic Case. In this section, we shall show how every Boolean algebra can be represented by an algebra of sets; *i.e.*, given a Boolean algebra B we must find a set X such that B is isomorphic to some field of subsets of X. Hence the theory of abstract Boolean algebras can be represented within the theory of sets discussed in Chapter 2. We first consider the case in which B is atomic; *i.e.*, every element a contains some atom x. We then let X be the class of all atoms of B. Hence X is a non-empty set. We now let A_x be the class of all atoms of B which are contained in a given $x \in B$. Then A_x is a non-empty subset of X for $x \neq 0$. We let $A_0 = \emptyset$ be the empty set. We then need to show that the mapping $\theta\colon x \to A_x$ is an isomorphism between B and the subsets of X of the form A_x. We begin with three lemmas.

Lemma 1. *If $\langle B, \cup, \cap, 0, 1, ' \rangle$ is an atomic Boolean algebra and $x < y$, then $\exists$ a such that a is an atom and $a \leq y$ but $a \nleq x$.*

Proof. $x < y \Rightarrow \exists\, x'_y = x' \cap y$ satisfying $x \cup x'_y = y$ and $x \cap x'_y = 0$. Since $\langle B, \cup, \cap\rangle$ is a modular lattice, the intervals $[x, y]$ and $[0, x'_y]$ are isomorphic. Hence $x \neq y$ implies $x'_y \neq 0$ so that there exists an atom a satisfying $0 < a \leq x'_y \leq y$. But $x \cap x'_y = 0$ implies $x \cap a = 0$, so that $a \not\leq x$.

Lemma 2. *Under the preceding hypotheses* $x = \bigcup\{a \in A | a \leq x\} = \bigcup_{a \in A_x} a$ *where* A *is the class of atoms of* B *and* A_x *is the subclass of atoms contained in* x.

Proof. By definition $a \in A_x \leftrightarrow a \leq x$. Hence $\bigcup_{a \in A_x} a \leq x$. If now $y = \bigcup_{a \in A_x} a$ and $y < x$, then by lemma 1, there exists an atom a satisfying $a \leq x$; *i.e.*, $a \in A_x$ and $a \not\leq y$. But $a \in A_x$, and $y = \bigcup_{a \in A_x} a$ implies $a \leq y$ contrary to $a \not\leq y$. Thus $x = \bigcup_{a \in A_x} a$; *i.e.*, every element of B is the union of those atoms contained in it.

Lemma 3. *If* a *is an atom and* $a \leq x \cup y$, *then either* $a \leq x$ *or* $a \leq y$.

Proof. If the lemma is false, then $a \not\leq x$ and $a \not\leq y$. But $a \not\leq x$ implies $a \cap x < a$. But since a is an atom, this implies $a \cap x = 0$. Similarly, $a \not\leq y$ implies $a \cap y = 0$. Hence, $a \cap (x \cup y) = (a \cap x) \cup (a \cap y) = 0$ contrary to hypothesis.

Theorem 6-13. *If* $\langle B, \cup, \cap, 0, 1, '\rangle$ *is an atomic Boolean algebra, then* B *is isomorphic to a sub-Boolean algebra of* $\mathfrak{P}(A)$ *where* A *is the set of atoms of* B.

Proof. As before we let θ be the mapping $\theta\colon x \to A_x$. Then

(*i*) θ is one-to-one. For if $A_x = A_y$, then $x = \bigcup_{a \in A_x} a = \bigcup_{a \in A_y} a = y$.

(*ii*) θ preserves $\cup$; *i.e.*, $A_{x \cup y} = A_x \cup A_y$ where the $\cup$ on the left is $\cup$ in B while $\cup$ on the right is set union. For if $a \in A_x$, then $a \leq x \leq x \cup y$, so that $a \in A_{x \cup y}$. Hence $A_x \subseteq A_{x \cup y}$. Hence $A_x \cup A_y \subseteq A_{x \cup y}$. Conversely, if $a \in A_{x \cup y}$, then $a \leq x \cup y$. But by lemma 3, this implies either $a \leq x$; *i.e.*, $a \in A_x$ or $a \leq y$; *i.e.*, $a \in A_y$. Hence $a \in A_x \cup A_y$. Therefore, $A_{x \cup y} = A_x \cup A_y$.

(*iii*) $A_{x \cap y} = \{a | a \leq x \cap y\} = \{a | a \leq x \text{ and } a \leq y\} = \{a | a \leq x\} \cap \{a | a \leq y\} = A_x \cap A_y$.

(*iv*) $A_0 = \{a | a \leq 0\} = \emptyset$.

(*v*) $A_1 = \{a | a \leq 1\} = A$.

(*vi*) $A_{x'} = \{a | a \leq x'\} = \{a | a \not\leq x\} = A'_x$.

Hence θ preserves the operations of B and is therefore an isomorphism.

Theorem 6-13 is called the representation theorem for the case of atomic Boolean algebras. It states that every atomic Boolean algebra is isomorphic to some field of sets, specifically a field of sets of atoms; *i.e.*, a sub-Boolean algebra of $\mathfrak{P}(A)$. The condition that B be isomorphic to all of $\mathfrak{P}(A)$ is now simply the condition that B be complete. This condition is also necessary, since every power set algebra is both atomic and complete. Hence we have:

Theorem 6-14. *A Boolean algebra is isomorphic to some power set algebra if and only if B is both atomic and complete.*

Proof. The only part of the proof remaining is to show that θ is an onto mapping if B is complete. Thus let $X = \{a_\alpha\}_\alpha$ be an arbitrary subset of A; *i.e.*, element of $\mathfrak{P}(A)$. Let $x = \mathbf{U}_\alpha a_\alpha$. Then x exists, since B was complete. We must show that $A_x = X$; *i.e.*, x maps onto X under θ. First, $a_\alpha \in X \Rightarrow a_\alpha \leq x$ and $a_\alpha \in A$; *i.e.*, $X \subseteq A_x$. Conversely, if $a \in A_x$, then $a \in A$ and $a \leq x$. Hence $a \leq \mathbf{U}\, a_\alpha$. But if we extend lemma 3 to arbitrary unions (exercise), then $a \leq a_\alpha$ for some $a_\alpha \in X$; *i.e.*, $a \in X$. Thus $A_x \subseteq X$. Therefore $A_x = X$, so that the proof is complete.

(b) The General Case. In the case where B fails to contain any atoms, then the above proof clearly is inadequate, and we must find a new set to play the role of the set of atoms. For this purpose, we use the set of maximal ideals; *i.e.*, the set of dual atoms in the lattice of ideals of B. Thus let $\mathfrak{M}$ be the class of all maximal ideals of B. Then we shall show that there is an isomorphism from B into the power set of $\mathfrak{P}(\mathfrak{M})$. Using the maximal ideal Theorem 6-12 of the preceding section, the proof is essentially the same as the atomic case.

Theorem 6-15. (Stone's Representation Theorem). *If* $\langle B, \cup, \cap, 0, 1, '\rangle$ *is any Boolean algebra, then B is isomorphic to a field of sets.*

Proof. Let $\mathfrak{M}$ be the class of all maximal ideals of B and $\theta: x \to \mathfrak{M}_x$ where $\mathfrak{M}_x$ is the class of maximal ideals of B which do not contain x; *i.e.*, $M \in \mathfrak{M}_x \leftrightarrow x \notin M$.

(*i*) θ is one-to-one. For if $\mathfrak{M}_x = \mathfrak{M}_y$, then $x = y$. For if $x \neq y$, then by the corollary to Theorem 6-12, there exists a maximal ideal M which contains x but not y; *i.e.*, $M \in \mathfrak{M}_y$ and $M \notin \mathfrak{M}_x$. Thus $\mathfrak{M}_x \neq \mathfrak{M}_y$.

(*ii*) θ preserves $\cup$; *i.e.*, $\mathfrak{M}_{x \cup y} = \mathfrak{M}_x \cup \mathfrak{M}_y$. First, let $M \in \mathfrak{M}_{x \cup y}$. Then $x \cup y \notin M$. Hence either $x \notin M$ or $y \notin M$. For if $x, y \in M$, then $x \cup y \in M$, since M is an ideal. But $x \notin M$ implies $M \in \mathfrak{M}_x$, while $y \notin M$ implies $M \in \mathfrak{M}_y$. In either case $M \in \mathfrak{M}_x \cup \mathfrak{M}_y$. Conversely, if $M \in \mathfrak{M}_x \cup \mathfrak{M}_y$, then either $M \in \mathfrak{M}_x$; *i.e.*, $x \notin M$, or $M \in \mathfrak{M}_y$; *i.e.*, $y \notin M$. In either case, $x \cup y \notin M$, since $x \cup y \in M$, M an ideal, implies $x \in M$ and $y \in M$. Thus $M \in \mathfrak{M}_{x \cup y}$. Therefore, $\mathfrak{M}_x \cup \mathfrak{M}_y = \mathfrak{M}_{x \cup y}$.

(*iii*) The proof that $\mathfrak{M}_x \cap \mathfrak{M}_y = \mathfrak{M}_{x \cap y}$ is left as an exercise.

(*iv*) $\mathfrak{M}_0 = \emptyset$ since $0 \in M \;\forall\; M \in \mathfrak{M}$.

(*v*) $\mathfrak{M}_1 = \mathfrak{M}$ since $1 \notin M$ for all proper ideals.

(*vi*) Finally, $\mathfrak{M}_{x'} = \mathfrak{M}'_x$; *i.e.*, if M is maximal and $x \notin M$, then $x' \in M$ by Theorem 6-10 and conversely.

Thus θ is a Boolean isomorphism, and the proof is complete.

We note that the Stone Theorem shows that every abstract Boolean algebra as defined by the term "complemented distributive lattice" can be represented by a field of sets in the sense that there is a Boolean isomorphism from the elements of the abstract Boolean algebra and subsets of some fixed set. The word "isomorphism" here means that the mapping θ of the theorem preserves all the usual Boolean operations; *i.e.*, $\cup$, $\cap$, 0, 1 and $'$. Thus the Boolean union of any finite set of elements of B is mapped onto the corresponding set union. This does not, however, imply that if B is complete, then arbitrary unions of elements of B will correspond to the set unions of their images under θ; *i.e.*, we have not proved that $\mathbf{U}_\alpha x_\alpha \leftrightarrow \mathbf{U}_\alpha \mathfrak{M}_{x_\alpha}$ for anything more than a finite set of elements. In fact, it is not necessarily true that θ preserves arbitrary unions for collections of infinite sets of sufficiently large cardinality. We shall not discuss this topic here but refer the reader to Sikorski for further details.

EXERCISES

1. If B is a Boolean algebra and $a \neq 0$, show that there exists a two-valued homomorphism ϕ from B onto $\mathbf{2}$ such that $\phi(a) = \bar{1}$.

6-8. REPRESENTATION THEORY, TOPOLOGICAL FORM*

In the preceding section, we showed that every boolean algebra is isomorphic to some Boolean algebra of sets (field of sets). In this section we show how every Boolean algebra is isomorphic to the algebra of closed-open sets of some totally disconnected, compact Hausdorff space.

We begin with an abstract Boolean algebra $\langle B, \cup, \cap, ', 0, 1\rangle$ defined on the carrier set B. We then form the cartesian product $\mathbf{2}^B$ where $\mathbf{2} = \langle 0, 1\rangle$ is the 2 element set consisting of 0 and 1. $\mathbf{2}^B$ is the set of all functions defined on B with values in $\mathbf{2}$. For example, if B is either finite or denumerably infinite, then $\mathbf{2}^B$ is either the set of n-tuples or the set of infinite sequences of 0's and 1's. We can also look at the elements of $\mathbf{2}^B$ as being characteristic functions of subsets of B. For example, if $X \in \mathfrak{P}(B)$ is any subset of B, then its character-

*This section should be read in conjuction with Appendix 2. It may be omitted on first reading.

istic function f_X is given by:

$$f_X(x) = \begin{cases} 1 \text{ if } x \in X \text{ and} \\ 0 \text{ if } x \notin X. \end{cases}$$

Hence there is a bijection between $\mathbf{2}^B$ and $\mathfrak{P}(B)$. Furthermore, since $\langle \mathfrak{P}(B), \cup, \cap, ', \emptyset, B \rangle$ is a Boolean algebra under set union, intersection and complementation, this bijection induces a natural Boolean algebraic structure on $\mathbf{2}^B$. The operations within $\mathbf{2}^B$ are given by:

$$(f_X \cup f_Y)(x) = f_X(x) \cup f_Y(x) = f_{X \cup Y}(x) \ \forall\ x \in B;$$

$$(f_X \cap f_Y)(x) = f_X(x) \cap f_Y(x) = f_{X \cap Y}(x) \ \forall\ x \in B; \text{ and}$$

$$(f_X)'(x) = (f_X(x))' = f_{X'}(x) \ \forall\ x \in B.$$

Finally $\mathbf{2}^B$ is partially ordered by:

$$f_X \leq f_Y \Leftrightarrow f_X(x) \leq f_Y(x) \ \forall\ x \in B.$$

We next note that since $\mathfrak{P}(B)$ is a power set algebra, it is atomic and dual atomic where the atoms are the singleton sets $\{x\}$ and the dual atoms are complements of singleton sets $\{x\}'$. The corresponding atomic functions in $\mathbf{2}^B$ are those functions on B which are 0 for every x except one, say x_0, and 1 on x_0. Similarly, the dual atomic functions are 1 everywhere in B except at one point, x_0, where the value is 0. Within the Boolean algebra $\mathfrak{P}(B)$, a maximal ideal is a principal ideal of the form $[\{x_0\}'] \downarrow$ which consists of all subsets of B which fail to contain x_0. Similarly, a maximal filter is a family of subsets of B which contain x_0 for some fixed x_0 in B; *i.e.*, $[\{x_0\}] \uparrow$. Again in $\mathbf{2}^B$ a maximal ideal is a family of all functions f which take on the value 0 at some fixed point in B. Finally, a maximal filter in $\mathbf{2}^B$ is the family of functions which take on the value 1 at some fixed $x_0 \in B$.

We now introduce topologies into $\mathbf{2}^B$ and $\mathfrak{P}(B)$, respectively. We begin by considering the discrete topology $\mathfrak{T}_0 = \{\emptyset, \{0\}, \{1\}, \mathbf{2}\}$ on the space $\mathbf{2} = \{0, 1\}$. This topology then induces the product topology $\mathfrak{T}$ on the cartesian product $\mathbf{2}^B$. In turn the bijection $X \leftrightarrow f_X$ between $\mathbf{2}^B$ and $\mathfrak{P}(B)$ induces a corresponding topology on $\mathfrak{P}(B)$, which we also denote by $\mathfrak{T}$. Within $\langle \mathbf{2}^B, \mathfrak{T} \rangle$ the subbasic open sets are those sets of functions such that for some fixed x_0 in B, $f(x_0)$ lies in an open set of $\langle \mathbf{2}, \mathfrak{T}_0 \rangle$. There are four cases according as $f(x_0) \in \emptyset$, $f(x_0) = 0$, $f(x_0) = 1$ or $f(x_0) \in \mathbf{2}$. The first and last show that the empty set and the full set are subbasic open sets. The second and third show that the sets $S = \{f \in \mathbf{2}^B | f(x_0) = 0\}$ and $S = \{f \in \mathbf{2}^B | f(x_0) = 1\}$ are subbasic open sets. But these are exactly the maximal ideals and maximal filters of $\mathbf{2}^B$. Furthermore, the bijection between $\mathbf{2}^B$ and $\mathfrak{P}(B)$ induces a family of corresponding subbasic open sets in $\mathfrak{P}(B)$ consisting of the maximal ideals and maximal filters of $\mathfrak{P}(B)$.

The subbasic open sets of either $\mathbf{2}^B$ or $\mathfrak{P}(B)$ now determine the basic open sets of $\mathfrak{T}$ as finite intersections of subbasic open sets. In the case of $\mathbf{2}^B$, a set of functions is a basic open set if there exists a finite set of elements $x_1, x_2, \ldots,$

$x_n \in B$ and $\delta_1, \delta_2, \ldots, \delta_n \in \mathbf{2}$ such that $f(x_i) = \delta_i$; *i.e.*, f is fixed at a finite number of points of B. In $\mathfrak{P}(B)$ the intersection of a finite number of maximal ideals $[\{x_1\}'] \downarrow, [\{x_2\}'] \downarrow, \ldots, [\{x_n\}'] \downarrow$ is the principal ideal generated by the finite set $\{x_1, x_2, \ldots, x_n\}$; *i.e.*, $[\{x_1, x_2, \ldots, x_n\}] \downarrow$. Similarly, the intersection of a finite number of maximal filters is the principal filter $[\{x_1\}] \uparrow \cap [\{x_2\}] \uparrow \cap \cdots \cap [\{x_n\}] \uparrow = [\{x_1\} \cup \{x_2\} \cup \cdots \cup \{x_n\}] \uparrow = [\{x_1, x_2, \ldots, x_n\}] \uparrow$. Finally, the intersection of a maximal ideal and a maximal filter is a lattice subinterval of $\mathfrak{P}(B)$ of the form $[F, CF]$ where F is any finite subset of B and CF is a cofinite set (one whose complement is finite). Roughly speaking, the basic open sets of $\langle \mathfrak{P}(B), \mathfrak{T} \rangle$ are those intervals within $\mathfrak{P}(B)$ stretching from "almost" 0 to "almost" 1 ("almost" means to "within a finite chain of").

We note that the complement of a subbasic open set is also a subbasic open set. Hence the subbasic open sets are simultaneously closed and open. But the intersection of a finite number of closed-open sets are closed-open. Therefore, the spaces $\langle \mathbf{2}^B, \mathfrak{T} \rangle$ and $\langle \mathfrak{P}(B), \mathfrak{T} \rangle$ both have closed-open bases; *i.e.*, they are totally disconnected topological spaces.

The open sets are now arbitrary unions of basic open sets.

We next note that $\langle \mathbf{2}, \mathfrak{T}_\circ \rangle$ being finite is automatically compact. Hence, by the Tychonoff theorem, the product spaces $\langle \mathbf{2}^B, \mathfrak{T} \rangle$ and $\langle \mathfrak{P}(B), \mathfrak{T} \rangle$ are compact spaces.

Finally $\langle \mathbf{2}, \mathfrak{T}_\circ \rangle$ is a Hausdorff space, so that $\langle \mathbf{2}^B, \mathfrak{T} \rangle$ and $\langle \mathfrak{P}(B), \mathfrak{T} \rangle$ are also, since the product of Hausdorff spaces is Hausdorff.

We can summarize the above result by first defining a **Boolean space** to be a **totally disconnected, compact Hausdorff space.** We then have:

Theorem 6-16. *The spaces* $\langle \mathbf{2}^B, \mathfrak{T} \rangle$ *and* $\langle \mathfrak{P}(B), \mathfrak{T} \rangle$ *are Boolean spaces.*

The space $\langle \mathbf{2}^B, \mathfrak{T} \rangle$ is also called the **Cantor space** associated with the set B.

We next consider the subset H of $\mathbf{2}^B$ which consists of all mappings from B into $\mathbf{2}$ which are Boolean homomorphisms; *i.e.*, preserve $\cup$, $\cap$, 0, 1, and $'$. As a subset of $\langle \mathbf{2}^B, \mathfrak{T} \rangle$ H becomes a topological space under the relative topology $\mathfrak{T}_H$ inherited from $\langle \mathbf{2}^B, \mathfrak{T} \rangle$. First, we note that $\langle H, \mathfrak{T}_H \rangle$ being a subspace of a totally disconnected space is also a totally disconnected space. Second, $\langle H, \mathfrak{T}_H \rangle$ is Hausdorff, a property also inherited from $\langle \mathbf{2}^B, \mathfrak{T} \rangle$. The following lemma shows that H is a closed subset of $\langle \mathbf{2}^B, \mathfrak{T} \rangle$. From this it will follow that H is compact, being a closed subspace of a compact Hausdorff space.

Lemma 1. *H is a closed subset of* $\langle \mathbf{2}^B, \mathfrak{T} \rangle$.

Proof. Let $H_\cup = \{f \in \mathbf{2}^B | f(x \cup y) = f(x) \cup f(y)\}$; *i.e.*, $H_\cup$ is the set of mappings from B into $\mathbf{2}$ which preserve unions. For *fixed* $x, y \in B$, let $H_{\cup, x, y} = \{f \in \mathbf{2}^B | f(x \cup y) = f(x) \cup f(y)\}$; *i.e.*, the set of mapping which map $x \cup y$ onto $f(x) \cup f(y)$. Then $H_\cup = \mathbf{U}_{x,y} H_{\cup, x, y}$. We now consider four cases:

(*i*) $f(x \cup y) = f(x) = f(y) = 1$,
(*ii*) $f(x \cup y) = f(x) = 1$ and $f(y) = 0$,
(*iii*) $f(x \cup y) = f(y) = 1$ and $f(x) = 0$ and
(*iv*) $f(x \cup y) = f(x) = f(y) = 0$.

The sets $\{f | f(x \cup y) = 1\}$, $\{f | (f(x) = 1\}$ and $\{f | f(y) = 1\}$ are subbasic sets and therefore closed. Hence their intersection is closed. But this is just the set of functions satisfying the conditions of case (*i*). Similarly, the sets of funtions satisfying the conditions of cases (*ii*), (*iii*) and (*iv*) are closed. But the set $H_{\cup,x,y}$ is the union of these four sets, and therefore also closed. Finally $H_{\cup}$ is closed, since it is an intersection of closed sets.

By similar arguments we see that the set of functions which preserve meet, complement, 0 and 1 are also closed sets. But H is exactly the intersection of these sets, so that it is also a closed set.

Corollary L. *$\langle H, \mathfrak{T}_H \rangle$ is a Boolean space.*

The next lemma gives an interpretation of the set H within space $\langle \mathfrak{P}(B), \mathfrak{T} \rangle$.

Lemma 2. *A mapping f from B into $\mathbf{2}$ is a Boolean homomorphism if and only if it is the characteristic function of a maximal filter in B.*

Proof. (*i*) Let $f \in \mathbf{2}^B$ be a mapping from B into $\mathbf{2}$ which is a Boolean homomorphism. Then $f = f_M$ is the characteristic function of some set M in B such that:

$$f_M(x) = \begin{cases} 1 \text{ if } x \in M \text{ and} \\ 0 \text{ if } x \notin M. \end{cases}$$

Let $a \in M$ and $a \leq x$. Then $f_M(a) = 1$. Furthermore, since f_M is a Boolean homomorphism, it will preserve order, so that $f_M(a) \leq f_M(x)$, so $f_M(x) = 1$. This implies $x \in M$.

Next, let $a, b \in M$. Then $f_M(a) = f_M(b) = 1$, which implies $f_M(a \cap b) = f_M(a) \cap f_M(b) = 1$. Thus $a \cap b \in M$. Therefore, M is a filter in B.

Let $x \in B$ and $x \notin M$. Then $f_M(x) = 0$, so that $f_M(x') = (f_M(x))' = 1$. Therefore, $x' \in M$. Hence, by Theorem 6-10, M is a maximal filter.

(*ii*) Conversely, if M is a maximal filter and f_M is its characteristic function, we must show that f_M is a Boolean homomorphism. First, $f_M(x \cup y) = f_M(x) \cup f_M(y)$. For if $f_M(x) = 1$, then $x \in M$. But since M is a filter, $x \cup y \in M$ for any y, whence $f_M(x \cup y) = 1$. Similarly, if $f_M(y) = 1$, then $f_M(x \cup y) = 1$. Finally, if $f_M(x) = f_M(y) = 0$, then $x, y \notin M$, so that $x', y' \in M$ since M is maximal. Since M is a filter $x' \cap y' = (x \cup y)' \in M$, from which it follows that $f_M(x \cup y) = 0$. In all cases, $f_M(x \cup y) = f_M(x) \cup f_M(y)$.

We leave it as an exercise to show that f_M also preserves meets, complements and the nullary operations. Therefore, f_M is a Boolean homomorphism.

We now consider the family A of closed-open subsets of H. They form a Boolean algebra $\langle A, \cup, \cap, \emptyset, H, ' \rangle$ which is called the **Stone algebra** associated with the Boolean algebra B. The next lemma shows that these two Boolean algebras are isomorphic.

Lemma 3. *Every Boolean algebra is isomorphic to its Stone algebra.*

Proof. Let $x \in B$ and $\phi(x) = \{f \in H | f(x) = 1\}$. Then ϕ is a mapping from B whose value at x is the set of Boolean homomorphisms which map x onto 1. First, we note that $\phi(x)$ is non-empty. This is simply the statement that there exists a two-valued homomorphism on a boolean algebra B which maps a given x onto 1. But a two-valued homomorphism corresponds to a maximal filter (Theorem 6-10 for filters) and there exists a maximal filter containing any given element (Theorem 6-11 for filters, exercise 1, section 6-6). Note that this result required Zorn's lemma.

Next, since the set $\{f \in \mathbf{2}^B | f(x) = 1\}$ is a subbasic closed-open set in $\langle \mathbf{2}^B, \mathfrak{T} \rangle$, its intersection with H will be closed-open in $\langle H, \mathfrak{T}_H \rangle$ under the relative topology. Hence $\phi(x)$ is a closed-open subset of H; *i.e.*, $\phi(x) \in A$.

Next ϕ is one-to-one. For if $x \neq y$, then there exists $f \in \phi(x)$ such that $f(x) = 1$ and $f(y) = 0$. Hence $f \notin \phi(y)$, so that $\phi(x) \neq \phi(y)$.

To show that ϕ preserves $\cup$ note that $\phi(x \cup y) = \{f \in H | f(x \cup y) = 1\}$ $= \{f \in H | f(x) \cup f(y) = 1\}$. But $f(x) \cup f(y) = 1$ implies either $f(x) = 1$ or $f(y) = 1$; *i.e.*, $f \in \phi(x \cup y) \Rightarrow f \in \phi(x)$ or $f \in \phi(y)$. Hence $\phi(x \cup y) \subseteq \phi(x) \cup \phi(y)$. Conversely, $f \in \phi(x) \cup \phi(y)$ implies either $f \in \phi(x)$ or $f \in \phi(y)$. If $f \in \phi(x)$, then $f(x) = 1$, so that $f(x) \cup f(y) = f(x \cup y) = 1$, whence $f \in \phi(x \cup y)$. Similarly, $f \in \phi(y)$ implies $f \in \phi(x \cup y)$. Therefore $\phi(x) \cup \phi(y) \subseteq \phi(x \cup y)$, from which $\phi(x \cup y) = \phi(x) \cup \phi(y)$.

ϕ will preserve the nullary operation 1, since $\phi(1) = \{f \in H | f(1) = 1\} = H$, since every homomorphism f must preserve the greatest element.

ϕ preserves complements, since $\phi(x') = \{f \in H | f(x') = 1\} = \{f \in H | f(x) = 0\} = \{f \in H | f(x) = 1\}'$. ϕ is therefore a Boolean homomorphism from B into A.

It remains to show that ϕ is surjective. Let C be any closed-open subset of H. Then since C is open, it is the union of a family of basic open sets, $C = \bigcup_\alpha G_\alpha$ where the G_α are basic open sets. Since C is a closed subset of a compact space and the G_α form a cover for C, there exists a finite subcover of C by sets $G_1, G_2, \ldots, G_n$. But each G_i is a finite intersection of subbasic open sets; *i.e.*, $G_i = \bigcap_{j=1}^{n_i} S_{i_j}$ where the S_{i_j} are subbasic open sets. The subbasic open sets are of the form $S_{i_j} = \{f \in H | f(x_{i_j}) = 1\}$ or $S_{i_j} = \{f \in H | f(x_{i_j}) = 0\}$ for some fixed $x_{i_j} \in B$. In the second case we can write $S_{i_j} = \{f \in H | f(x'_{i_j}) = 1\}$, so that in either case $G_i = \bigcap_j \{f \in H | f(x_{i_j}) = 1\} = \bigcap_j \phi(x_{i_j}) = \phi(\bigcap_j x_{i_j})$. Finally, $C = \bigcup_i G_i = \bigcup_i \phi(\bigcap_j x_{i_j} = \phi(\bigcup_i \bigcap_j x_{i_j}) = \phi(x)$ where $x = \bigcup_i \bigcap_j x_{i_j} \in B$. Thus $C = \phi(x)$ for some x, whence ϕ is surjective.

The results may now be summarized as the fundamental topological form of the Stone Representation Theorem.

Theorem 6-17. **(Stone Representation Theorem, Topological Form)** *Any Boolean algera is isomorphic to the Boolean algebra of all closed-open subsets of some totally disconnected, compact Hausdorff space.*

The Stone algebra may be interpreted in either of two homomorphic spaces. First, it is the algebra of closed-open subsets of $\langle H, \mathfrak{T}_H \rangle$ where H is the family of Boolean homomorphisms of the Cantor space $\mathbf{2}^B$ topologized by the product topology $\mathfrak{T}$ induced by the discrete topology $\mathfrak{T}_0$ on the space $\mathbf{2}$. Second, it is the Boolean algebra of closed-open subsets of the space $\mathfrak{M}$ of maximal filters M of B. In this case, the topology on $\mathfrak{M}$ is the relative topology $\mathfrak{T}_{\mathfrak{M}}$ inherited from the topology $\mathfrak{T}$ on $\mathfrak{P}(B)$ which is generated by the basic open sets which are finite-cofinite intervals (*i.e.*, of the form $[F, CF]$ where F is finite and CF is cofinite in B).

Finally we note that, although the Stone representation theorem was derived using the axiom of choice (Zorn's lemma) the converse is not true; *i.e.*, the Stone theorem is basically weaker than the axiom of choice. We omit the proof.

EXERCISES

1. Describe the functions f_ϕ and f_B.
2. Prove that the partial order in $\mathbf{2}^B$ is given by $f_X \leq f_Y \Leftrightarrow f_X(x) \leq f_Y(x)\ \forall x \in B$.
3. Prove that the set $H_\cap = \{f \in \mathbf{2}^B | f(x \cap y) = f(x) \cap f(y)\}$ is a closed subset of $\langle \mathbf{2}^B, \mathfrak{T} \rangle$. State and prove the corresponding results for the unary operations and nullary operations.
4. Prove that f_M in lemma 6-2 preserves meets, complements and the nullary operations.
5. Let α be any ordinal, and let B be the set of all ordinals less than or equal to α. Prove that B is a Boolean space under the order topology. The order topology of a chain is the topology generated by the open intervals of the chain.

6-9. DIRECT PRODUCTS

A final concept that is useful in generating new Boolean algebras from given ones is the formation of direct products. We have already introduced the notion of a direct product in Chapter 2 and we apply it here to the case of

Boolean algebras. Thus if $\langle B_1, \cup, \cap, 0, 1, ' \rangle$ and $\langle B_2, \cup, \cap, 0, 1' \rangle$ are two Boolean algebras, we first form the cartesian product of their carrier sets, $B_1 \times B_2$; *i.e.*, the set of ordered pairs $\langle a_1, a_2 \rangle$ where $a_1 \in B_1$ and $a_2 \in B_2$. We now define the operations of the direct product coordinatewise by:

$$\langle a_1, a_2 \rangle \cup \langle b_1, b_2 \rangle = \langle a_1 \cup b_1, a_2 \cup b_2 \rangle,$$
$$\langle a_1, a_2 \rangle \cap \langle b_1, b_2 \rangle = \langle a_1 \cap b_1, a_2 \cap b_2 \rangle,$$
$$0 = \langle 0, 0 \rangle \text{ and } 1 = \langle 1, 1 \rangle,$$
$$\langle a_1, a_2 \rangle' = \langle a_1', a_2' \rangle,$$

where in general we use the same operational symbols for each of B_1, B_2 and $B_1 \times B_2$. The algebra $\langle B_1 \times B_2, \cup, \cap, 0, 1, ' \rangle$ is then called the **direct product** of B_1 and B_2. It remains to show that it is a Boolean algebra. But this is quite simple, since the defining equations for the direct product follow from the corresponding equations for each of B_1 and B_2 separately, and the operations in the direct product are formed on each coordinate independently. This is, of course, not a result of Boolean algebra alone, but is a theorem of universal algebra. Furthermore, any derived concept such as partial order or the symmetric difference operation, for example, can be defined coordinatewise and will satisfy all the usual properties as in any Boolean algebra. For example, $\langle a_1, a_2 \rangle \leq \langle b_1, b_2 \rangle \leftrightarrow a_1 \leq b_1, a_2 \leq b_2$. In general if $B_1 = B_2$, we write B_1^2 for $B_1 \times B_2$ and call it the **direct power** of B_1. Clearly, the concept of direct product and direct power extend to any finite number of factors by induction. Thus $\prod_{i=1}^{n} B_i$ is the set of n-tuples where $a_i \in B_i$ while B^n is the set of n-tuples from B and all operations are performed on each coordinate separately. To generalize to an arbitrary number of factors, we need only review the concept of cartesian product for an arbitrary number of factors. Thus, in the case of n-factors we can view $a_1, a_2, \ldots, a_n$ as a mapping from the set $\mathbf{P}_n$ of integers $1, 2, \ldots, n$ such that $i \rightarrow a_i \in B_i$. If we replace $\mathbf{P}_n$ by an arbitrary index set, then the elements of the cartesian product are the mappings $\alpha \rightarrow a_\alpha \in B_\alpha$. The direct product of the family of Boolean algebras $\{B_\alpha\}_\alpha$ is then given by $\langle \Pi_\alpha B_\alpha, \cup, \cap, 0, 1, ' \rangle$ where $\Pi_\alpha B_\alpha$ is the cartesian product and the operations are again performed coordinatewise. Thus if $a = \langle \ldots, a_\alpha, \ldots \rangle$ and $b = \langle \ldots, b_\alpha, \ldots \rangle$, then $a \cup b = \langle \ldots, a_\alpha \cup b_\alpha, \ldots \rangle$, etc. In particular, if all the $B_\alpha = B$, then the direct power is the set of functions f from the index set into $B, f\colon \alpha \rightarrow a_\alpha \in B$ or using functional notation $a_\alpha = f(\alpha)$. In this notation we use f, g, etc., for elements of the direct power, so that $(f \cup g)(\alpha) = f(\alpha) \cup g(\alpha)$ defines the union $f \cup g$ of f and g in terms of union within B, and similarly for the other operations. For example, the function $f(\alpha) = 0$ identically is the 0 function of the direct product. We therefore write 0 for this function; *i.e.*, $0(\alpha) = 0 \ \forall \ \alpha$. The concept of the partial order within the direct product is then written as $f \leq g \leftrightarrow f(\alpha) \leq g(\alpha) \ \forall \ \alpha$.

The concept of direct product enables us to generate many new examples of Boolean algebras. The most important are those which occur when B is the two element Boolean algebra $\mathbf{2} = \{0, 1\}$. The simplest case is when the index set is $\{1, 2\}$. We then obtain the algebra $\mathbf{2}^2$ consisting of the four elements $\langle 0, 0\rangle$, $\langle 0, 1\rangle$, $\langle 1, 0\rangle$, and $\langle 1, 1\rangle$ which is isomorphic to the Boolean algebra of subsets of a pair set. More generally, $\mathbf{2}^n$ is the set of n-tuples of 0's and 1's; *i.e.*, $\langle a_1, a_2, \ldots, a_n\rangle$ where $a_i = 0$ or 1. Operations on such n-tuples are performed by applying the rules from tables of figure 6-1 to each coordinate. The diagram for $\mathbf{2}^n$ is then exactly the diagram of an n-cube. Thus we consider $\mathbf{2}^n$ as a vector space over the field $\mathbf{2}$ of characteristic 2, where addition of two such vectors is performed by forming the symmetric difference (addition mod 2) on each coordinate.

If X is an infinite set, then $\mathbf{2}^X$ is the set of mappings from the set X considered as an index set onto $\{0, 1\}$. Each function f determines a subset A given by $A = \{x \in X | f(x) = 1\}$, and conversely, each set A determines the function defined by $f(x) = 1$ for $x \in A$ and $f(x) = 0$ for $x \notin A$. This function is then exactly the characteristic function of the corresponding set A. Hence $\mathbf{2}^X$ is isomorphic to the power set algebra $\mathfrak{P}(X)$. Hence we often write $\mathbf{2}^X$ for the power set algebra, and this is exactly the same as the direct power of the Boolean algebra $\mathbf{2}$ with exponent (i.e., index set) X.* But we have already seen that any abstract Boolean algebra B can be represented by a sub-Boolean algebra of a power set algebra. Hence, if X is the set of atoms of an atomic Boolean algebra or the set of maximal ideals in the more general case, and if α is the cardinality of X, then B is isomorphic to a sub-Boolean algebra of $\mathbf{2}^\alpha$. In particular, if B is a complete atomic Boolean algebra, then $B \cong \mathbf{2}^\alpha$ for some cardinal α. Furthermore, every power set algebra $\mathfrak{P}(X)$ is isomorphic to $\mathbf{2}^\alpha$ where $\alpha = \overline{\overline{X}}$.

In the case where B is finite, this theorem shows that the only finite Boolean algebras are of the type $\mathbf{2}^n$ for n finite. Hence, every finite Boolean algebra is a Boolean algebra of n-tuples from $\{0, 1\}$ where the operations are performed coordinatewise. Every finite Boolean algebra determines and is determined by an n-dimensional vector space over the field of integers modulo 2. This fact is the essential reason why we can use Boolean algebra to do arithmetic in a binary system and forms a basis for the design of a digital computer. Every finite Boolean algebra can be coordinatized from the field $\mathbf{Z}/2$. The case of the algebra $\mathbf{2}^3$ is show in figure 6-2. This is the algebra of subsets of three elements. We also show the case of $\mathbf{2}^4$. Hence, finite Boolean algebras are relatively simple objects and have a very rigid and well-defined structure.

The simplest infinite power set algebra is the case when $\alpha = \aleph_0$. In this case $\mathbf{2}^\alpha$ consists of all infinite sequences of 0's and 1's. The cardinality of

*We note here that X carries no structure but is simply any set considered as a cardinal number. This is in contrast to the case where X is itself a Boolean algebra, and the meaning of $\mathbf{2}^X$ is quite different as used by some authors. (*cf:* Birkhoff). We also write $\mathbf{2}^\alpha$ where α is the cardinality of X, *i.e.*, $\overline{\overline{X}} = \alpha$.

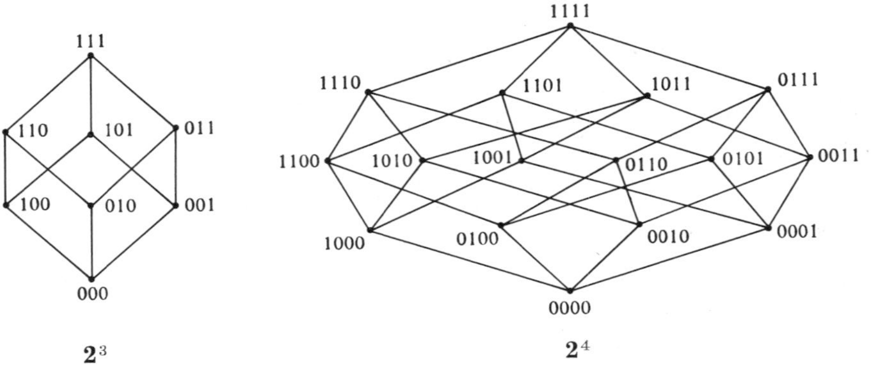

FIGURE 6-2

$B = \mathbf{2}^\alpha$ is then c, the cardinality of the real numbers. We see that there are no power set algebras of cardinality $\aleph_0$. However, we may obtain Boolean algebras which are sub-algebras of direct products of $\mathbf{2}$ and have cardinality $\aleph_0$. For example, if we consider only sequences which have either a finite number of 0's or only a finite number of 1's, then we obtain a denumerably infinite Boolean algebra. If a sequence has all 0's except a finite number of 1's, then it is the characteristic function of a finite set, while if it contains all 1's but a finite number of 0's, it is the characteristic function of a cofinite set. Therefore, the Boolean algebra of all sequences with only a finite number of 0's or a finite number of 1's is exactly the Boolean algebra of all finite subsets or cofinite subsets of a denumerably infinite set; *i.e.*, $\mathfrak{F}(X) \cup \mathfrak{C}\mathfrak{F}(X)$ discussed in Chapter 2 and section 6-6. This algebra is both atomic and dual atomic, but is not complete. It is not representable as a power set algebra.

On the other hand, we can also obtain a second sub-Boolean algebra of $\mathbf{2}^{\aleph_0}$ which is itself denumerable but is not atomic. For example, we let B_p be the set of periodic sequences of 0's and 1's which have period 2^n for some finite n; *i.e.*, $\langle a_1, a_2, \ldots, a_{2n}, a_1, \ldots, a_{2n}, \ldots \rangle$. Clearly the complement of such a sequence is also periodic with the same period and hence in B_p. Also, if a has period 2^n and b has period 2^m, then both the union and meet of a and b have period $2^{\max\{n,m\}}$ and belong to B_p. Therefore B_p is a sub-Boolean algebra of $\mathbf{2}^{\aleph_0}$. Clearly B_p is denumerably infinite (exercise), while if $a \in B_p$ where $a = \langle a_1, \ldots, a_{2n}, a_1, \ldots, a_{2n}, \ldots \rangle$ then $b = \langle a_1, \ldots, a_{2n}, 0, \ldots, 0, a_1, \ldots \rangle$ is also in B_p and $0 < b < a$, so that a could not be an atom. Thus B_p is not atomic. B_p does not satisfy either chain condition and is also not complete as is shown in the exercises.

If now B_1 and B_2 are any two Boolean algebras, and $B = B_1 \times B_2$ is their direct product, then we can define the projection mapping π_1 from B onto B_1

by mapping $b = \langle b_1, b_2 \rangle \in B$ onto $b_1 \in B_1$. π_1 is then a Boolean homomorphism and has the kernel $K = \{b \in B | \langle b_1, b_2 \rangle \to 0 \in B_1\} = \{\langle b_1, b_2 \rangle | b_1 = 0\}$, so that $K \cong B_2$. It follows that $B/B_2 \cong B_1$.

EXERCISES

1. Prove that the set of all sequences of 0's and 1's for which either all except a finite number of terms are 0 or are 1 is a Boolean algebra.
2. Show that the Boolean algebra of exercise 1 is atomic but not complete. Describe its atoms.
3. Show that the Boolean algebra of exercise 1 contains both infinite ascending and descending chains.
4. Show that the direct product of $\mathbf{2}^n$ and $\mathbf{2}^m$ is isomorphic to $\mathbf{2}^{n+m}$ for n and m finite.
5. Show that the Boolean algebra of periodic sequences described in the text is denumerably infinite, but does not satisfy either chain condition.
6. Show that the algebra of exercise 5 is not complete.
7. Show that a diagram can be constructed for the Boolean algebra of exercise 5 by letting $x_a = 0.\, a_1 a_2 \cdots a_{2n}, \ldots$ be the real number in binary form corresponding to $a = \langle a_1, a_2, \ldots, a_{2n}, \ldots \rangle$ and by letting $y_a = N_a/2^n$ where N_a is the number of 1's in a single period of a and 2^n is the period of a. Then the set of points $\langle x_a, y_a \rangle$ forms a graph of B_p. Show that this graph is an extension of the concept of a lattice diagram, but that it has no convering relations. Show that the function $d_a = y_a$ is a generalization of the dimension concept and satisfies the law $d(a \cup b) + d(a \cap b) = d(a) + d(b)$.
8. Define the direct product of two arbitrary lattices, and show that it is itself a lattice.
9. If C_1 and C_2 are both chains, show that their direct product may not be a chain.
10. Define the direct product for rings and show that the correspondence between Boolean algebras and Boolean rings carries over into direct products.

6-10. BOOLEAN POLYNOMIALS

Another topic of universal algebra that can be applied to Boolean algebra is the study of polynomials and their associated functions, and the algebras generated by them. Thus we begin with a set of "variables," $X = \{x_1, x_2, \ldots, x_n\}$, and form formal expressions from them by combining them with the formal operations of Boolean algebra. We then identify expressions in accordance with the laws of Boolean algebra and obtain Boolean polynomials in n variables in a fashion similar to that in forming ordinary polynomials in n real variables over the field of real numbers. Each polynomial then determines a Boolean function by assigning the variables "values" in a given Boolean algebra. The set of all such functions itself then forms an algebra which is the goal of our study. Thus we begin with the formal definition of a Boolean expression.

Definition 6-2. *A Boolean expression $e(x_1, x_2, \ldots, x_n)$ in the n variables $x_1, x_2, \ldots, x_n$ is any finite string of symbols formed in the following way:*

1. 0 and 1 are Boolean expressions;

2. $x_1, x_2, \ldots, x_n$ are Boolean expressions;

3. If e_1 and e_2 are Boolean expressions, then $(e_1) \cup (e_2)$ and $(e_1) \cap (e_2)$ are Boolean expressions;

4. If e is a Boolean expression, then $(e)'$ is a Boolean expression;

5. No string of symbols except those formed in accordance with rules 1–4 is a Boolean expression.

Thus a Boolean expression is any string of symbols that can be formed from expressions already formed by sandwiching a symbol $\cup$ or $\cap$ between two expressions, or adding a symbol $'$ to one of them. We also agree to drop surplus parentheses. Thus x_1, $x_1 \cup 0$, $x_1 \cap (x_2' \cup x_1)'$, $(x_1 \cap x_2)'$, $x_1' \cup x_2'$, etc. are Boolean expressions in the two variables x_1 and x_2. Note that as formal expressions, the last two mentioned expressions are not the same. Every Boolean expression now determines a Boolean function. For if $e = e(x_1, x_2, \ldots, x_n)$ is a Boolean expression in n variables and B is a given Boolean algebra, then for every n-tuple $\langle a_1, a_2, \ldots, a_n\rangle$, e determines an element of B determined by replacing x_1 by $a_1, \ldots, x_n$ by a_n everywhere $x_1, \ldots, x_n$ occur in e. Thus e determines a mapping $f_{e,B}$ from B^n into B; *i.e.*, $f_{e,B} = \{\langle\langle a_1, \ldots, a_n\rangle, a\rangle | a = e(a_1, \ldots, a_n)\}$. We call $f_{e,B}$ the Boolean function on B associated with e. For example, the expression $e(x_1, x_2) = x_1 \cup x_2$ determines the function $f_{e,B} = \{\langle\langle a_1, a_2\rangle, a_1 \cup a_2\rangle | a_1, a_2 \in B\}$, which is the same as union operation. We note that, although the expressions $x_1 \cup (x_1 \cap x_2)$ and $x_1 \cap (x_1 \cup x_2)$ are different formal expressions, they both determine the same function, $f_{x_1,B}$, since by the absorption law $a_1 \cup (a_1 \cap a_2) = a_1 = a_1 \cap (a_1 \cup a_2)$ for all $a_1, a_2 \in B$; *i.e.*, as sets of ordered pairs, they are equal for any B. As a second example, the expressions 0 and $x_2 \cap x_2'$ both determine the same function from B^2 into B which maps every ordered pair $\langle a_1, a_2\rangle$ onto 0. Hence this function is called a constant function.

We now let E_n designate the set of all Boolean expressions in n variables. Clearly E_n is denumerably infinite, since there are at most a finite number of different expressions of a given length (number of symbols). We can introduce operations on E_n itself by defining $\cup$, $\cap$ and $'$ as $e_1 \cup e_2$, $e_1 \cap e_2$, e' in accordance with 1–5 above. However, since we have not introduced a notion of equality of expressions, we cannot as yet claim that E_n is a Boolean algebra as we would like. However, if we introduce an equivalence relation into E_n by writing $e_1 \equiv e_2$ whenever e_1 and e_2 determine the same Boolean function on any

B, then we can convert the set $P_n = E_n/\equiv$ of equivalence classes within E_n into a Boolean algebra. Thus we write $e_1 \equiv e_2 \Longleftrightarrow f_{e_{1,B}} = f_{e_{2,B}} \; \forall \; B$ and must prove that $\equiv$ is an equivalence relation. We then extend the operations $\cup$, $\cap$ and $'$ from E_n to P_n by letting $p_1 \cup p_2$ be the equivalence class containing $e_1 \cup e_2$ where e_1 and e_2 are arbitrary elements of the classes p_1 and p_2. We need, of course, to show that this definition is independent of the particular elements e_1 and e_2 chosen. We leave the proof to the exercises as well as the corresponding theorems for $\cap$ and $'$. We call the elements of P_n **Boolean polynomials.** Hence Boolean polynomials are Boolean expressions with a notion of equality introduced, so that each polynomial determines a unique function and conversely. Thus in the future, we shall write $p(x_1, x_2)$ to stand for the expression $e(x_1, x_2)$ or any other equivalent expression. P_n is then a Boolean algebra itself under the definition of $\cup$, $\cap$, 0, 1, $'$ given here. The postulates for Boolean algebra for P_n now follow directly from the same laws within the original Boolean algebra B.

Using this meaning for equality of polynomials, we can now reduce any given polynomial to a canonical form, so that equations between polynomials can be determined by reducing both sides to this canonical form. We can first use the law $p'' = p$ to drop any two successive symbols $'$. Next if $'$ occurs applied to either a union or meet of two other polynomials, then we can apply the de Morgan laws until no prime occurs, except as applied to one of the original variables $x_1, \ldots, x_n$. Next we can apply the the distributive laws until p is reduced to a union of expressions which contain only meets and primes; *i.e.*, $p = q_1 \cup q_2 \cup \cdots \cup q_m$ where each q_i is of the form of a meet of either x_k's or x_k''s. For convenience we write x_k^0 for x_k' and x_k^1 for x_k. Then q_i has the form $x_1^{i_1} \cup x_2^{i_2} \cup \cdots \cup x_n^{i_n}$ where $i_1, i_2, \ldots, i_n = 0$ or 1. We may also assume that each x_k occurs exactly once in each q_i. For if a given x_k occurs more than once, then we may apply the idempotent law for meet to delete all but one occurrence. Furthermore, if a given x_k fails to appear in q_i, then we may write $q_i = q_i \cap 1 = q_i \cap (x_k \cup x_k')$, which by the distributive law reduces to a union of two terms which both contain x_k. Finally, if q_i contains both x_k and x_k', then it may be dropped entirely, since $x_k \cap x_k' = 0$ and $a \cup 0 = a$. Thus every polynomial has a canonical form $p = \bigcup_{i=1}^{m} \bigcap_{k=1}^{n} x_k^{i_k}$ where i_k is either 0 or 1. This form is called the **disjunctive normal form.** Similarly, if p is reduced to a meet of unions, then it is said to be in **conjunctive normal form.** The number m of terms occurring in a given p may be only one, as for example in $p(x_1, x_2) = x_1 \cap x_2'$, but by the use of coefficients we may consider that each polynomial contains terms corresponding to each combination of exponents $i_1, i_2, \ldots, i_n$. Thus we write $0 \cap q_i$ for the Boolean 0 if a particular q_i fails to appear in p and $1 \cap q_i$ if it appears. We can then write

$$p = \bigcup_{<i_1, \ldots, i_n>} a_{i_1, \ldots, i_n} x_1^{i_1} \cap \cdots \cap x_n^{i_n}$$

where the union is taken over all possible sequences $\langle i_1, \ldots, i_n \rangle$ and the coefficients $a_{i_1 \cdots i_n}$ are either 0 or 1. But there are 2^n different sequences $\langle i_1, \ldots, i_n \rangle$ and 2^{2^n} different sets of coefficients; *i.e.*, 2^{2^n} different polynomials in n variables. For example if $n = 2$, then every polynomial in two variables has the form $p(x_1, x_2) = a_{00}(x_1^0 \cap x_2^0) \cup a_{01}(x_1^0 \cap x_2^1) \cup a_{10}(x_1^1 \cap x_2^0) \cup a_{11}(x_1^1 \cap x_2^1)$ where each a_{ij} is either 0 or 1. Hence there are $2^{2^2} = 16$ different polynomials in two variables. For example, $p(x_1, x_2) = x_1 \cup x_2 = (x_1 \cap 1) \cup (1 \cap x_2) = [x_1 \cap (x_2 \cup x_2')] \cup [(x_1 \cup x_1') \cap x_2] = (x_1 \cap x_2) \cup (x_1 \cap x_2') \cup (x_1' \cap x_2)$ which corresponds to the case where $a_{11} = a_{01} = a_{10} = 1$ and $a_{00} = 0$. Thus each p determines a mapping given by the a's from $\mathbf{2}^n$ into $\mathbf{2}$. Thus P_n is isomorphic to $\mathbf{2}^{2^n}$.

Furthermore, we can obtain an explicit evaluation for the coefficients in terms of the Boolean function $f_{p,2}$ associated with p on the two element Boolean algebra $\mathbf{2}$. For if $x_1 = a_1, \ldots, x_n = a_n$, then $f(a_1, \ldots, a_n) = \bigcup_{<i_1,\ldots,i_n>} a_{i_1 \cdots i_n} x_1^{i_1} \cap \cdots \cap x_n^{i_n}$. But every term will vanish, except when $a_1^{i_1} = a_2^{i_2} = \cdots = a_n^{i_n} = 1$. Again, $a_k^{i_k} = 1$ if and only if $a_k = i_k =$ (exercise). Thus $f(a_1, \ldots, a_n)$ reduces to the single term $a_{i_1 \cdots i_n} 1 \cap \cdots \cap 1$; *i.e.*, $f(i_1, \ldots, i_n) = a_{i_1 \cdots i_n}$. Hence we may summarize:

Theorem 6-18. *If p is a Boolean polynomial in n variables, then p has a canonical form:*
$p(x_1, \ldots, x_n) = \bigcup_{<i_1,\ldots,i_n>} f(i_1, \ldots, i_n) x_1^{i_1} \cap \cdots \cap x_n^{i_n}$ *where* $f = f_{p,2}$ *is the Boolean function associated with p on* $\mathbf{2}$.

Corollary 1. *The set of polynomials* P_n *in n variables is isomorphic to* $\mathbf{2}^{2^n}$.

Corollary 2. *The values of any Boolean function f are completely determined by the values on the Boolean algebra* $\mathbf{2}$.

Thus if we have a Boolean function defined on a Boolean algebra B, then we can completely determine all of its values as soon as we know the values corresponding to 0's and 1's for $x_1, \ldots, x_n$. As a further result, we can decide when two expressions are equivalent as soon as we know that substitution of 0's and 1's produces the same results. For example, if $n = 2$, then a Boolean function f from $B \times B$ into B is completely known when we know the values of f corresponding to the sequences $\langle 00 \rangle, \langle 01 \rangle, \langle 10 \rangle$ and $\langle 11 \rangle$; *i.e.*, if we construct a table of values of f for these four sequences, then we know f for all of B. As a further example, let $p(x_1, x_2, x_3) = x_1 \cup x_2$, be a function in three variables. Then p has the canonical form

$$\begin{aligned} p(x_1, x_2, x_3) &= (x_1 \cap 1 \cap 1) \cup (x_2 \cap 1 \cap 1) \\ &= (x_1 \cap (x_2 \cup x_2') \cap (x_3 \cup x_3')) \cup (x_2 \cap (x_1 \cup x_1') \cap (x_3 \cup x_3')) \\ &= (x_1 \cap x_2 \cap x_3) \cup (x_1 \cap x_2 \cap x_3') \cup (x_1 \cap x_2' \cap x_3) \cup \\ &\quad\ (x_1 \cap x_2' \cap x_3') \cup (x_1' \cap x_2 \cap x_3) \cup (x_1' \cap x_2 \cap x_3'). \end{aligned}$$

The associated Boolean function on **2** is a mapping from $\mathbf{2}^3$ into **2**. This function is shown in figure 6-3 which shows $\mathbf{2}^3$ coordinatized by triples of 0's

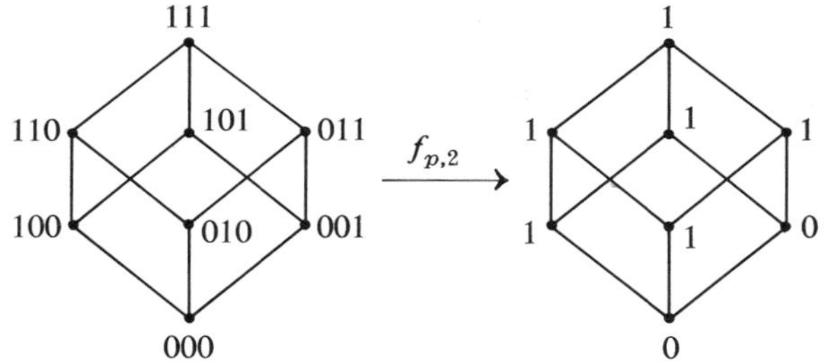

FIGURE 6-3

and 1's and the associated coefficients which are also 0's and 1's. Thus the canonical polynomial has six terms corresponding to the six values 1 in the second diagram. The total number of polynomials in three variables is therefore the total number of ways of assigning 0's and 1's to the first diagram of the figure *i.e.*, there are $2^{2^3} = 256$ such functions. If now B is any other Boolean algebra, finite or infinite, then the function associated with p on B is still determined by its values on the subalgebra **2**. Thus p is independent of B so that there are no possible Boolean equalities except those that hold on **2**; *i.e.*, if two Boolean expressions are equal for values in **2**, then they are equal for all values in B. We therefore have:

Theorem 6-19. *Every Boolean identity which holds on any Boolean algebra holds for every Boolean algebra.*

Corollary. *There are no Boolean identities which are not derivable from the Huntington postulates.*

We also say that Boolean algebra is **equationally complete** in the sense that there are no proper subclasses of Boolean algebras determined by special identities. The situation for Boolean algebras is therefore different from that of general lattice theory where, for example, the class of distributive lattices is a subclass of the class of all lattices as determined by the two equalities *D1* and *D2; i.e.*, the distributive laws.

We have discussed the Boolean algebra P_n of all polynomials in n variables for any finite n. If now P_m is the set of polynomials in m variables where $n \leq m$, then we may consider P_n as a subset of P_m, since every polynomial in n variables is also a polynomial in m variables for any larger m. Thus we have a chain of Boolean algebras $\{P_n\}_n$. We can now let $P = \bigcup_{n=1}^{\infty} P_n$ be the union (point set) of all P_n for finite n. Then P is the set of all polynomials and is itself a Boolean algebra. We leave it to the exercises to extend the results for P_n to P.

6-11. FREE BOOLEAN ALGEBRAS

In the last section we defined the Boolean algebra P_n of all Boolean polynomials in n variables. Each p in P_n determines a function on any Boolean algebra B whose values are obtained by replacing each x_i by an element a_i in B. We can consider this process as a mapping ϕ from the set $X = \{x_1, \ldots, x_n\}$ into B where ϕ: $x_1 \to a_1, \ldots, x_n \to a_n$. This mapping ϕ can then be extended to a mapping θ from all of P_n into B by mapping each $p = p(x_1, \ldots, x_n)$ in P_n into $a = p(a_1, \ldots, a_n) \in B$. Furthermore, this extended mapping is a homomorphism from P_n into B. For if $p \to a$ and $q \to b$, then $p \cup q = p(x_1, \ldots, x_n) \cup q(x_1, \ldots, x_n) \to p(a_1, \ldots, a_n) \cup q(a_1, \ldots, a_n) = a \cup b$ and similarly for $p \cap q$ and p'. For example, if P_1 is the set of all polynomials in one variable x, then P_n consist of the four polynomials $x, x', x \cap x' = 0$, and $x \cup x' = 1$. If now B is any Boolean algebra and we let ϕ be defined by $x \to a \in B$, then ϕ can be extended to θ: $x \to a$, $x' \to a'$, $0 \to 0$ and $1 \to 1$, which is a homomorphism from P_1 into B. In particular, if $a = 0$, then θ becomes $x \to 0$, $x' \to 1$, $0 \to 0$ and $1 \to 1$.

We call the elementary polynomials $x_1, \ldots, x_n$ *generators* for P_n since every polynomial can be generated by them by applying the Boolean operations to them. Our result thus shows that any mapping from the generators of P_n can be extended to a homomorphism on all of P_n. P_n is then called the **free Boolean algebra** with n generators. As we saw in Theorem 6-17, it has no identities except those derivable from the definition of a Boolean algebra. We can extend this notion to arbitrary sets of generators for any Boolean algebra. Thus a set of elements of a Boolean algebra B is called a set of generators if the smallest subalgebra of B which contains all the generators is B itself. Furthermore, the set of generators is called independent if no (proper) subset is a set of generators; *i.e.*, it contains no superfluous elements. A Boolean algebra is then called **free** if any mapping from a set of independent generators can be extended to a homomorphism on all of B. The notion is taken from universal algebra, but we are only concerned with the case of a Boolean algebra here. Theorem 6-18 now states that the free Boolean algebra with n generators is $\mathbf{2}^{2^n}$. Hence, any other Boolean algebra of the form $\mathbf{2}^n$ where n is not of the form of a power of $\mathbf{2}$ will not be free. For example, $\mathbf{2}^3$ is not free. For if $x_1 = 100$ and $x_2 = 010$ (figure 6-2), then $x_1 \cap x_2 = 0$. Any mapping ϕ from $\mathbf{2}^3$ into a boolean algebra B which is extended to a homomorphism on all of $\mathbf{2}^3$ must map $x_1 \cap x_2$ into 0. For example, ϕ might map $x_1 \to a_1 = 10$ of $\mathbf{2}^2$ and $x_2 \to a_2 = 11$. Then $x_1 \cap x_2 \to a_1 \cap a_2 = a_1 \neq 0$. Thus ϕ cannot be extended to a homomorphism, and the condition $x_1 \cap x_2 = 0$ is an equation in $\mathbf{2}^3$ which is not derivable from the axioms. Thus $\mathbf{2}^3$ is not a free Boolean algebra.

The situation for free algebras with an infinite number of generators is not as simple as that for that finite case. Thus we would expect that the simplest infinite free algebra would have to contain $2^{2^{\aleph_0}} = 2^c$ elements. However, it is known that there are no free Boolean algebras with a denumerable number of free generators. We shall not attempt to give a proof here (*cf:* Halperin).*

EXERCISES

1. Show that the definition of equivalence for expressions is an equivalence relation. Show that if $e_1 \equiv e_3$ and $e_2 \equiv e_4$, $e_1 \cup e_2 \equiv e_3 \cup e_4$, $e_1 \cap e_2 \equiv e_3 \cap e_4$, and $e_1' \equiv e_3'$.
2. Show that $E_n/\equiv$ is a Boolean algebra under the definitions given in the text.
3. Express the following expressions in three variables in conjunctive and disjunctive normal forms: (*a*) x_2, (*b*) $x_1 \cap x_2$, (*c*) $x_1 \cup x_2$, (*d*) $x_1 \cup (x_2 \cap x_3')'$, (*e*) $x_1 \Delta x_2 \Delta x_3$.
4. Determine all polynomials in two variables and express each as a four-digit binary number.
5. Show that the mapping $p(x_1, \ldots, x_n) \to f_{p,B}$ is a Boolean homomorphism.
6. Show that the polynomials of the form $e(x_1, \ldots, x_n) = x_1^{i_1} \cap x_2^{i_2} \cap \cdots \cap x_n^{i_n}$ which fail to contain the symbol $\cup$ are atoms of the Boolean algebra P_n.
7. Show that $a_k^{i_k} = 1$ if and only if $a_k = i_k$.
8. Using the diagram of figure 6-2 for $\mathbf{2}^4$, construct the Boolean function corresponding to the expression $e(x_1, x_2, x_3, x_4) = (x_1 \cap x_2') \cup x_4$. Write the normal form for e.
9. Verify the following Boolean equations by reducing both sides to conjunctive normal form (disjunctive normal form):

   (*a*) $(A \cap (B' \cup C))' \cap (B' \cup (A \cap C')')' = A \cap B \cap C'$
   (*b*) $A \cap [(B' \cup C)' \cup (B \cap C)] \cup [(A \cup B')' \cap C] = (A' \cap C) \cap B$
10. Show that if $P = \mathbf{U}_n P_n$, then P is a Boolean algebra. Show that its elements are all polynomials in a finite number of variables.
11. Let P_3 be the Boolean algebra of all polynomials in x_1, x_2, x_3. Let B be the Boolean algebra $\mathbf{2}^4$. Extend the mapping $x_1 \to 0010$, $x_3 \to 0001$ and $x_4 \to 1111$ to a homomorphism of P_3 into $\mathbf{2}^4$.

*For further discussion of Boolean polynomials and their applications, see any of the references in the bibliography on Boolean algebra, in particular, Arnold, Whitesitt, Hohn, or Flegg.

7

SEMI-BOOLEAN ALGEBRAS AND IMPLICATION ALGEBRA

7-1. PSEUDO-COMPLEMENTED LATTICES

We begin this chapter with a brief discussion of lattices which are similar to Boolean algebras in that they are distributive, but only satisfy a weakened form of the complementation laws. Thus we have seen that the lattice $\langle \mathbf{P}, | \rangle$ of divisors of an integer n is distributive, but that if n is not square free, then it will not be complemented. For example, figure 7-1 shows the lattice of divisors of 12 in which the element 4 has no complement; *i.e.*, there is no integer which satisfies the two equations (*i*) LCM $\{4, x\} = 12$ and (*ii*) GCF $\{4, x\} = 1$. However, if we consider only the first equation, both 6 and 12 satisfy it. Of these, 6 is a smallest element; *i.e.*, 6 is the least element satisfying (*i*). In general, if L is a lattice with unit 0 and 1, then any element a' which satisfies (*i*) $a \cup a' = 1$ is called an **upper semi-complement** of a and dually an element which satisfies (*ii*) $a \cap a' = 0$ is called a **lower semi-complement**. If furthermore, a^* is a *least* element which satisfies (*i*), then a^* is called an **upper pseudo-complement** (union complement) of a in $\langle L, \cup, \cap, 0, 1 \rangle$, while dually a_* is called a **lower pseudo-complement** (meet complement) if it is a greatest element satisfying (*ii*). Thus an upper pseudo-complement a^* is characterized by the two conditions:

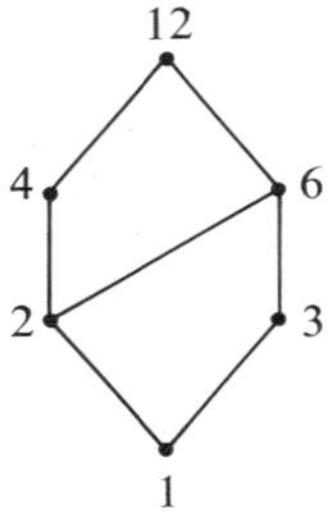

FIGURE 7-1

$$(ia)\ a \cup a^* = 1,$$

and:

$$(ib)\ a \cup x = 1 \Rightarrow a^* \leq x,$$

while a lower pseudo-complement satisfies:

$$(iia)\ a \cap a_* = 0$$

and:

$$(iib)\ a \cap x = 0 \Rightarrow x \leq a_*$$

These two conditions can be combined into one if we write (*i*) $a \cup x^* = 1 \Leftrightarrow a^* \leq x$ and (*ii*) $a \cap x = 0 \Leftrightarrow x \leq a_*$ (exercise). Thus a^* and a_* represent the "best" solutions of (*i*) and (*ii*) respectively. Note that if a' is both an upper and lower pseudo-complement of a simultaneously, then it is, in fact, a complement. We call a lattice **upper (lower) pseudo-complemented** if every element has an upper (lower) pseudo-complement. If L is also distributive, then we can characterize a^* in the following way. We let $A^* = \{x \mid a \cup x = 1\}$ be the set of all solutions of (*i*). Then A^* is a filter in L. For if $x \in A^*$ and $x \leq y$, then $y \in A^*$, since if $a \cup x = 1$, then $a \cup y = 1$. Furthermore, if $x, y \in A^*$, then $a \cup (x \cap y) = (a \cup x) \cap (a \cup y) = 1$, so that $x \cap y \in A^*$. We now let $a^* = \bigcap A^*$ be the greatest lower bound of A^*. If a^* exists and lies in A^*, then a^* will be an upper pseudo-complement of a. In this case, A^* is a principal filter and $A^* = [a^*]\uparrow$. Dual remarks of course hold for a_*. It is clear that if L is complete and completely distributive, then it will be pseudo-complemented (upper and lower), for if L is complete, then $a^* = \bigcap A^*$ will exist and by the distributive laws $a \cup a^* = a \cup \bigcap \{x \mid x \in A^*\} = \bigcap \{a \cup x \mid x \in A^*\} = 1$. We will discuss the converse situation in the next section.

The basic properties of pseudo-complementation are given by:

Theorem 7-1. *In a pseudo-complemented lattice* $\langle L, \cup, \cap, 0, 1\rangle$ *the correspondences* $a \to a^*$, $a \to a_*$ *are unary operations which satisfy:*

(*i*) $a \leq b \Rightarrow b^* \leq a^*$ and $b_* \leq a_*$;
(*ii*) $a^{**} \leq a \leq a_{**}$;
(*iii*) $a^{***} = a^*$; $a_{***} = a_*$;
(*iv*) $(a \cup b)^* \leq a^* \cap b^*$; $(a \cup b)_* = a_* \cap b_*$;
(*v*) $(a \cap b)^* = a^* \cup b^*$; $a_* \cup b_* \leq (a \cap b)_*$;
(*vi*) $0^* = 0_* = 1$ and $1^* = 1_* = 0$.

Proof. We shall prove the results for * and leave those for $_*$ to the reader.

(*i*) $a \leq b$ and $a \cup a^* = 1 \Rightarrow b \cup a^* = 1$. Hence, $b^* \leq a^*$.
(*ii*) $a^* \cup a = 1 \Rightarrow a^{**} \leq a$.
(*iii*) First $a^{***} \leq a^*$ by (*ii*). But $a^{**} \leq a \Rightarrow a^* \leq a^{***}$ by (*i*). Hence $a^{***} = a^*$.
(*iv*) $a, b \leq a \cup b \Rightarrow (a \cup b)^* \leq a^*, b^*$, so that $(a \cup b)^* \leq a^* \cap b^*$.
(*v*) The first half follows similar to (*iv*); *i.e.*, $a^* \cup b^* \leq (a \cap b)^*$. To prove the converse, note that $a \cup a^* = 1$ implies $a \cup a^* \cup b^* = 1$. Hence $(a^* \cup b^*)^* \leq a$. Similarly, $(a^* \cup b^*)^* \leq b$, so that $(a^* \cup b^*)^* \leq a \cap b$. Hence $(a \cap b)^* \leq (a^* \cup b^*)^{**} \leq a^* \cup b^*$. Therefore $(a \cap b)^* = a^* \cup b^*$.
(*vi*) is left to the exercises.

We note that (*vi*) shows that every upper pseudo-complemented lattice has a least element; *i.e.*, we needed to assume the existence of a 1 in the definition, but the existence of a 0 follows without additional axioms. We also note from the lattice of figure 7-2 that the inequalities of (*iv*) and (*v*) cannot be strength-

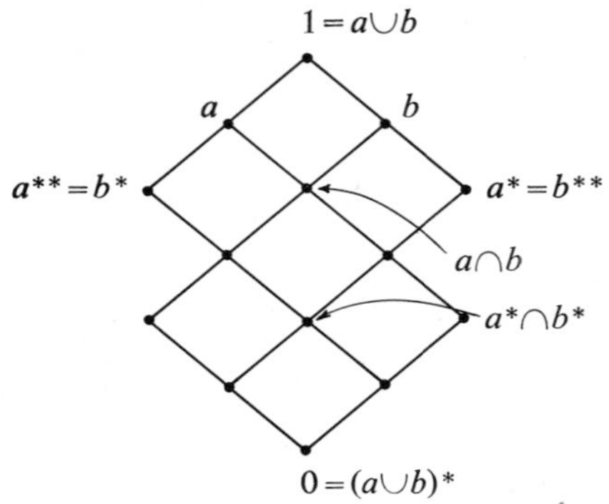

FIGURE 7-2

ened to equations. However, the following lemma due to Frink does give better results (*cf:* Frink).

Lemma 7-1. $(a \cup b)^* = (a^{**} \cup b^{**})^* = (a^* \cap b^*)^{**}$;
$(a \cap b)_* = (a_{**} \cap b_{**})_* = (a_* \cup b_*)_{**}$.

Proof. (*i*) $a^{**} \leq a$ and $b^{**} \leq b \Rightarrow a^{**} \cup b^{**} \leq a \cup b$, so that $(a \cup b)^* \leq (a^{**} \cup b^{**})^*$.

(*ii*) Let $x = (a \cup b)^* \cup a^{**} \cup b^{**}$. Then $(a \cup b)^* \leq x$. Therefore $x \cup a \cup b = 1$. From this it follows that $b^* \leq x \cup a$. However, we also have $b^{**} \leq x \leq x \cup a$, so that $b^{**} \cup b^* \leq x \cup a$. But $b^{**} \cup b^* = 1$, so that $x \cup a = 1$; *i.e.*, $a^* \leq x$. Finally, $a^{**} \leq x$, so that $a^{**} \cup a^* = 1 \leq x$, or $x = 1$. Thus $(a \cup b)^* \cup a^{**} \cup b^{**} = 1$ which implies $(a^{**} \cup b^{**})^* \leq (a \cup b)^*$. The first equality of the lemma now follows. The second follows from Theorem 7-1 (*v*). The second set of equalities follow by duality.

We now note that the mappings $a \rightarrow a^*$, $a \rightarrow a^*$ form a Galois connection within L, so that it follows that the mapping $a \rightarrow a^{**}$ is an interior mapping. Similarly $a \rightarrow a_{**}$ is a closure mapping. Hence we call $a^\circ = a^{**}$ the **interior** of a and $a^- = a_{**}$ the **closure** of a. The lemma can now be rewritten in the following form:

Corollary. $(a \cup b)^* = (a^\circ \cup b^\circ)^* = (a^* \cap b^*)^\circ$;
$(a \cap b)_* = (a^- \cap b^-)_* = (a_* \cup b_*)^-$.

The properties for the interior and closure operations, $a \to a^\circ$ and $a \to a^-$, are given by:

Theorem 7-2. *If L is a pseudo-complemented lattice, then the operation* $a \to a^\circ = a^{**}$ *is an interior operation while* $a \to a^- = a_{**}$ *is a closure operation and these operations satisfy:*

(*i*) $a \leq b \Rightarrow a^\circ \leq b^\circ$ *and* $a^- \leq b^-$;

(*ii*) $a^\circ \leq a \leq a^-$;

(*iii*) $a^{\circ\circ} = a^{--} = a$;

(*iv*) $(a \cup b)^\circ = a^\circ \cup b^\circ$; $a^- \cup b^- \leq (a \cup b)^-$;

(*v*) $(a \cap b)^\circ \leq a^\circ \cap b^\circ$; $(a \cap b)^- = a^- \cap b^-$.

(*vi*) $0^\circ = 0^- = 0$ *and* $1^\circ = 1^- = 1$.

Proof. The only parts that remains to be proven are the equalities of (*iv*) and (*v*), since the rest follow from Theorem 7-1. But from the lemma we have $(a \cup b)^\circ = (a^\circ \cup b^\circ)^\circ$ by applying * to both sides. But by (*ii*) $(a^\circ \cup b^\circ)^\circ \leq a^\circ \cup b^\circ$. On the other hand $a, b \leq a \cup b \Rightarrow a^\circ, b^\circ \leq (a \cup b)^\circ$ from which $a^\circ \cup b^\circ \leq (a \cup b)^\circ$. Thus $(a \cup b)^\circ \leq a^\circ \cup b^\circ \leq (a \cup b)^\circ$, so that $(a \cup b)^\circ = a^\circ \cup b^\circ$. (*v*) is similar.

If we now consider the set G of open elements; *i.e.*, the elements satisfying $a^\circ = a$, then we obtain a Boolean algebra, although not under the same operations as in L. Thus if a and b are open, then $(a \cup b)^\circ = a^\circ \cup b^\circ = a \cup b$, so that $a \cup b$ is also open. However, the same is not generally true for $a \cap b$; *i.e.*, $a \cap b$ may not be open, even though a and b are. But if we take the interior of $a \cap b$, then we obtain an open element which is also a greatest lower bound for a and b within G considered as a sub-partially ordered set of L; *i.e.*, $(a \cap b)^\circ$ is the largest open set contained in both a and b. Hence we are led to define $a \wedge b = (a \cap b)^\circ$, which we call the **normalized meet** of a and b. It will then follow that G is a boolean algebra under union, normalized meet and upper pseudo-complementation as in:

Theorem 7-3. *If G is the set of open elements of a pseudo-complemented distributive*† *lattice,* $\langle L, \cup, \cap, 0, 1, *, _* \rangle$, *then* $\langle G, \cup, \wedge, 0, 1, * \rangle$ *is a Boolean algebra where* $a \wedge b = (a \cap b)^\circ$. *Dually the set F of closed elements* ($a^- = a$) *is a Boolean algebra* $\langle F, \vee, \cap, 0, 1, _* \rangle$ *under* $a \vee b = (a \cup b)^-$.

Proof. We leave it as an exercise to show that $a \wedge b$ is a greatest lower bound of a and b in $\langle G, \leq \rangle$. From this it follows that $\langle G, \cup, \wedge \rangle$ is a lattice. We therefore next need to prove the distributive laws. We first note that an element a is open if and only if $a = b^*$. For if $a = b^*$, then $a^\circ = b^{***} = b^* = a$. Conversely, if a is open, then $a = a^{**} = b^*$ where $b = a^*$. For distributivity, $a \wedge (b \cup c) = [a \cap (b \cup c)]^\circ = [(a \cap b) \cup (a \cap c)]^\circ = (a \cap b)^\circ$

†The condition for distributivity may be dropped. See exercise 26 of section 7-5.

$\cup (a \cap c)^\circ = (a \wedge b) \cup (a \wedge c)$. Finally, to show that a^* is a complement, we already know that $a \cup a^* = 1$. But also $a \wedge a^* = (a \cap a^*)^\circ = (b^* \cap b^{**})^{**} = (b^{**} \cup b^{***})^* = (a^* \cup a)^* = 1^* = 0$ where $b^* = a$. Hence, G is a boolean algebra. The similar result for F is an exercise.

We can now consider the map ϕ: $a \to a^\circ$ which maps each element onto its interior. Then, since $(a \cup b)^\circ = a^\circ \cup b^\circ$ and $(a \wedge b)^\circ = (a \cap b)^{**} = (a^* \cup b^*)^* = (a^{***} \cup b^{***})^* = (a^{**} \cap b^{**})^{**} = (a^\circ \cap b^\circ)^\circ = a^\circ \vee b^\circ$, ϕ will preserve $\cup$ and $\wedge$. But $a^{*\circ} = a^{\circ *}$, so that ϕ also preserve complements, while it is clear that it preserves 0 and 1. Hence it is a homomorphism from L onto the boolean algebra G. Finally, if an element satisfying $a^\circ = 0$ is called **co-dense** while one satisfying $a^- = 1$ is called **dense**, then the kernel of ϕ is the set of co-dense elements while the kernel of the dual map is the set of dense elements. We have therefore shown that:

Theorem 7-4. *If $\langle L, \cup, \cap, 0, 1, {}^*, {}_*\rangle$ is a pseudo-complemented lattice, then the mapping ϕ: $a \to a^\circ$ ($a \to a^-$) is a homomorphism from L onto the boolean algebra $\langle G, \cup, \wedge, 0, 1^*\rangle$ ($\langle F, \vee, \cap, 0, 1_*\rangle$) whose lower (upper) kernel is the set of co-dense (dense) of L.*

In general, we saw that a chain was not a complemented lattice. However, if G is a chain with least and greatest elements, then C is a pseudo-complemented lattice. More specifically, if $a \neq 1$, then $a^* = 1$ and $1^* = 0$. But if C has no least element, then it is no longer pseudo-complemented, since 1 has no pseudo-complement. In the lattice of divisors of 12, shown in figure 7-1, 3 is a lower pseudo-complement of 2 while 1 is its upper pseudo-complement. In the non-modular lattice M_5 of figure 5-1, $b_* = c$ while $b^* = a$. Furthermore $a_* = a^* = c_* = c^* = b$, so that this non-modular lattice is both upper and lower pseudo-complemented. On the other hand, the non-distributive lattice D_5 of figure 5-2 is not pseudo-complemented, since the set $A^* = \{x | x \cup a = 1\} = \{b, c\}$ has no least element. These examples show that a pseudo-complemented lattice need not be distributive.

The lattice of divisors of 12 can be generalized to the lattice of divisors of any integer $\langle \mathbf{P}_n, |\rangle$. Thus if $a \in \mathbf{P}_n$, then a_* is the greatest divisor of n which is relatively prime to a. Thus if n has a prime factorization $n = p_1^{k_1} \cdots p_r^{k_r}$, and if $a = p_1^{j_1} \cdots p_s^{j_s}$ where $1 \leq j_i < k_i$ for $i = 1, 2, \ldots, s \leq r$, then $a_* = p_{s+1}^{k+1} \cdots p_r^{k_r}$; *i.e.*, a_* contains all prime factors which do not divide a with exponents equal to their exponents in n. On the other hand, a^* contains each prime factor $p_i^{k_i}$ of n whose exponent in a is less than its exponent in n. In particular, if n is square free, then $a_* = a^* = a'$ is a complement of a. Hence in this case $\langle \mathbf{P}_n, |\rangle$ is Boolean.

A further generalization of this example can be obtained by considering the set of all real functions defined on the real unit interval [0, 1] into itself. The class

L of all such functions is partially ordered by $f \leq g \leftrightarrow f(x) \leq g(x) \;\forall\; x \in [0, 1]$ and has greatest and least elements given by $f_1(x) = 1$ and $f_0(x) = 0 \;\forall\; x$. Furthermore, L is a lattice under this partial order, and is also a pseudo-complemented lattice. Thus we let $f^*(x) = 1$ if $f(x) \neq 1$ and $f^*(x) = 0$ if $f(x) = 1$. Then it is an exercise to show that f^* is an upper pseudo-complement of f.

EXERCISES

1. Prove that a_* is a lower pseudo-complement of a if and only if $a \cap x = 0 \Longleftrightarrow x \leq a_*$.
2. Prove (*vi*) of Theorem 6-1.
3. Prove the duals of Theorems 6-1 and 6-2.
4. Show directly that the co-dense elements of a pseudo-complemented lattice form an ideal and that the dense elements form a filter.
5. Show that $(a \cap b)^\circ$ is the greatest lower bound of a, b in $\langle G, \leq \rangle$.
6. Show that the set of closed elements of a pseudo-complemented lattice is a boolean algebra.
7. Show that $\phi: a \rightarrow a^\circ$ preserves 0 and 1.
8. Draw a lattice diagram of the lattice of divisors of 36 and determine the mappings $a \rightarrow a^*$, $a \rightarrow a_*$, $a \rightarrow a^\circ$ and $a \rightarrow a^-$.
9. Determine the co-dense and dense elements of the lattice of exercise 8. What is the quotient algebra of this lattice, modulo its co-dense elements?
10. Let X^X be the lattice of all functions defined from $X = [0, 1]$ into itself; *i.e.*, real functions defined on the unit interval $[0, 1]$ with values between 0 and 1, where the partial order is defined by $f \leq g \Longleftrightarrow f(x) \leq g(x) \;\forall\; x$. Show that this lattice is pseudo-complemented and determine the nature of the functions f^*, f_*, f° and f^- for any f.
11. Show that the lattice of divisors of an integer n can be treated as a lattice of functions defined over the set of prime divisors of n with values which are integers. Show, therefore, that the lattice of exercise 10 gives the same meaning to f^*, f_*, f° and f^- to $\langle \mathbf{P}_n, | \rangle$ as in exercise 10.

7-2. RELATIVELY PSEUDO-COMPLEMENTED LATTICES, BROUWERIAN LATTICES

In a Boolean algebra, every element a has a complement a' which is characterized as an element which satisfies the simultaneous equations (*i*) $a \cup a' = 1$ and (*ii*) $a \cap a' = 0$. Using one of these equations alone, we can still characterize a complement either as $a' = \text{glb}\,\{x \mid a \cup x = 1\}$ or as $a' = \text{lub}\,\{x \mid a \cap x = 0\}$. For example, in a power set algebra, $\mathfrak{P}(U)$, if A is any subset of U, then A' is either the smallest set whose union with A is all of U, or the largest set disjoint from A. Using either of these characterizations alone leads to the concepts of upper and lower pseudo-elements in any lattice $\langle L, \cup, \cap, 0, 1\rangle$ with units. On the other hand, we also found it useful to generalize the notion of complement to that of relative complement in a Boolean algebra. Hence it is natural to generalize the concept of relative complement to that of relative pseudo-complement. In this section we shall assume that $\langle L, \cup, \cap, 0, 1\rangle$ is a distributive lattice with units and obtain various generalizations of Boolean algebra by replacing the concept of complement with that of relative pseudo-complement. In fact, however, we do not need to assume quite as much about L, and the theories of this section can also be further generalized to either semi-lattices or lattices with one but not necessarily two units. Finally, we shall show that in the most important case distributivity need not be assumed, but will follow as a theorem; however, we shall leave such further generalizations to the literature.

There are four different types of pseudo-complementation possible, depending on whether we use equation (*i*) or (*ii*) and upper or lower pseudo-complementation. We shall define all four types and then study one in detail which is of value in logic. Once again we may use set theory as a model and first characterize the difference set $B - A = A'_B$; *i.e.*, the complement of A relative to B, by either $B - A = \text{glb}\,\{X \mid B \subseteq X \cup A\}$ or $B - A = \text{lub}\,\{X \mid X \subseteq B$ and $X \cap A = \emptyset\}$. Thus $B - A$ is either the smallest set whose union with A covers B or it is the largest subset of B which is disjoint from A. In general, we therefore define:

$$b -^* a = \text{glb}\,\{x \mid b \leq x \cup a\}$$

and

$$b -_* a = \text{lub}\,\{x \mid x \leq b \text{ and } a \cap x = 0\}$$

in any lattice. We call these the **upper** and **lower pseudo-differences** respectively, or upper and lower pseudo-complements of a relative to 0 and b. Thus we also write $b - {}^*a = a^*_{0,b}$ and $b - {}_*a = a_{*0.b}$. Thus they are both pseudo-complements within the interval sub-lattice $[0, b]$; *i.e.*, the principal ideal generated by b. In particular, if we now let $b = 1$, then we obtain the upper and lower pseudo-complements of a as defined in the last section; *i.e.*, $1 - {}^*a = \text{glb}\,\{x \mid x \cup a = 1\} = a^*$ while $1 - {}_*a = \text{lub}\,\{x \mid a \cap x = 0\} = a_*$.

We can now dualize these concepts to obtain two other relative pseudo-complements. Thus in set theory the dual of $B - A = A' \cap B$ is the set $A \to B = A' \cup B$; *i.e.*, the set implication product of A and B. By dualizing the characterizations of the pseudo-differences, we therefore obtain two pseudo-implication products. These are given by

$$a \to {}^*b = \text{glb}\,\{x \mid b \leq x \text{ and } a \cup x = 1\}$$

and

$$a \rightarrow {}_*b = \text{lub}\,\{x \mid x \cap a \leq b\}$$

Again they can be written as relative pseudo-complements as $a \rightarrow {}^*b = a^*_{b,1}$ and $a \rightarrow {}_*b = a_{*b,1}$; *i.e.*, pseudo-complements are now taken in the interval sub-lattice $[b, 1]$, or the principal filter generated by b instead of the ideal generated by b. Again using $b = 0$ gives the definitions of peeudo-complements of section 7-1; *i.e.*,

$$a \rightarrow {}^*0 = \text{glb}\,\{x \mid x \cup a = 1\} = a^*$$

and

$$a \rightarrow {}_*0 = \text{lub}\,\{x \mid x \cap a = 0\} = a_*.$$

Finally we note that the difference set $B - A$ can be written purely in terms of complements within the boolean algebra $\mathfrak{P}(B)$ by writing $B - A = B - (A \cap B)$, since $A \cap B \in \mathfrak{P}(B)$. Similarly, we can express the pseudo-differences and implication products entirely within the ideal $[0, 1]$ or the filter $[b, 1]$ by replacing a either by $a \cap b$ or $a \cup b$. Thus we obtain the alternate characterizations of our four operations as

$$(1)\ a \rightarrow {}^*b = (a \cup b)^*_{b,1},$$

$$(2)\ a \rightarrow {}_*b = (a \cup b)_{*b,1},$$

$$(3)\ b - {}^*a = (a \cap b)^*_{0,b},$$

and

$$(4)\ b - {}_*a = (a \cap b)_{*0,b}.$$

They are illustrated in figure 7-3. Lattices within which any of the four operations 1–4 are defined are called by the respective terms involving relative pseudo-difference or implication products.

Of the four operations defined here, the most important is $a \rightarrow_* b$ and is called Brouwerian implication. It has particular significance both in applications to logic and topology. Hence we shall concentrate on this one operation and write it simply as $a * b$, omitting further discussion of the other three. Thus we define a **Brouwerian lattice** as a lattice with 0 and 1 in which every pair of elements determine an element $a * b$ satisfying $a \cap x \leq b \Leftrightarrow x \leq a * b$. Alternatively, L is Brouwerian if $X_{a,b} = \{x \mid a \cap x \leq b\}$ has a least upper bound and this least

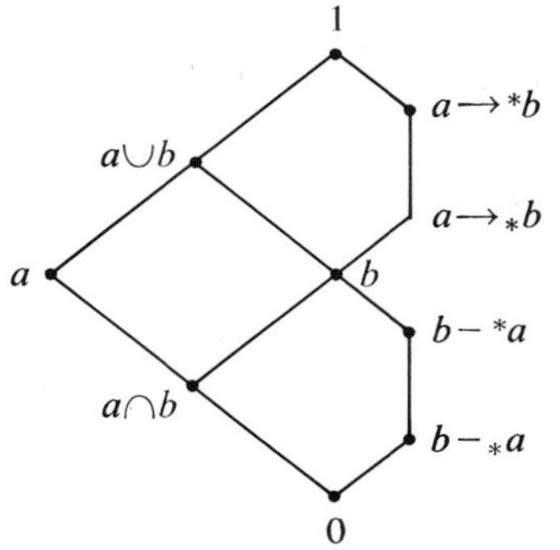

FIGURE 7-3

upper bound lies in $X_{a,b}$. The definition does not require that L be distributive, since we can now show that distributivity follows from the very existence of $a*b$ for all a and b. This is contrary to the case of pseudo-complemented lattices which do not have to be distributive. However, it is not surprising, since we know that in lattices in general the uniqueness of relative complements is equivalent to the distributive laws, and the uniqueness of $a * b$ necessarily follows from its definition.

Theorem 7-5. *If $\langle L, \cup, \cap, 0, 1, *\rangle$ is a Brouwerian lattice, then L is distributive.*

Proof. We need to prove that $a \cap (b \cup c) \leq r = (a \cap b) \cup (a \cap c)$, since we already know the reverse inequality holds in any lattice and that one distributive law implies the other. But $a \cap b \leq r$ implies $b \leq a * r$. Similarly, $c \leq a * r$, so that $b \cup c \leq a * r$. Therefore $a \cap (b \cup c) \leq r$.

In the special case that L is finite, the converse is also true, so the finite Brouwerian lattices are exactly the same as finite distributive lattices; *i.e.*,:

Corollary 1. *A finite lattice is Brouwerian if and only if it is distributive.*

Proof. If L is finite, then $X_{a,b} = \{x_1, \ldots, x_n\}$ is also finite. Hence $c = \bigcup_{i=1}^{n} x_i$ exists in L. But $a \cap c = a \cap \bigcup_{i=1}^{n} x_i = \bigcup_{i=1}^{n} (a \cap x_i) \leq b$, so that $c \in X_{a,b}$. Hence $c = a * b$ and L is Brouwerian.

For complete lattices, the condition that L be Brouwerian is equivalent to the infinite distributive law for meet onto arbitrary unions; *i.e.*,

Corollary 2. *A complete lattice is Brouwerian if and only if the distributive law $a \cap \bigcup_\alpha a_\alpha = \bigcup_\alpha (a \cap a_\alpha)$ holds.*

The proof is an extension of that of the theorem and corollary 1 and is therefore left to the exercises. Other than distributivity, the most important algebraic properties for Brouwerian lattices are given in the following theorem:

Theorem 7-6. *If $\langle L, \cup, \cap, 0, 1, *\rangle$ is a Brouwerian lattice, then:*

(1) $a * a = 1$, $1 * a = a$, *and* $a * 1 = 1 \;\forall\, a \in L$;
(2) $a \leq b \Leftrightarrow a * b = 1$;
(3) $a \leq b \Rightarrow c * a \leq c * b$ *and* $b * c \leq a * c$;
(4) $b \leq a * b = (a \cup b) * b$;
(5) $(a \cup b) * c = a * c \cap b * c$ *and* $a * c \cup b * c \leq (a \cap b) * c$;
(6) $a * (b \cup c) \leq a * b \cup a * c$ *and* $a * (b \cap c) = a * b \cap a * c$;
(7) $a \leq (a * b) * a$;

(8) $a \cup b \leq (a * b) * b$;

(9) $a * (b * c) = b * (a * c) = (a * b) * (a * c) = (a \cap b) * c$.

Proof. (1) First $a * a = \bigcup \{x \mid x \cap a \leq a\} = \bigcup \{x \mid x \in L\} = 1$. Secondly, $1 * a = \bigcup \{x \mid x \cap 1 \leq a\} = a$. Finally $a * 1 = \bigcup \{x \mid x \cap a \leq 1\} = 1$.

(2) $a \leq b \Rightarrow x \cap a \leq a \leq b \ \forall\ x$. Hence $a * b = \bigcup \{x \mid x \in L\} = 1$. Conversely, $a * b = 1$ implies $1 \cap a \leq b$; *i.e.*, $a \leq b$.

(3) First, $a \leq b \Rightarrow X_{c,a} = \{x \mid c \cap x \leq a\} \subseteq \{x \mid c \cap x \leq b\} = X_{b,c}$. Hence $\bigcup X_{c,a} \leq \bigcup X_{c,b}$; *i.e.*, $c * a \leq c * b$. Secondly, $a \leq b \Rightarrow X_{b,c} = \{x \mid x \cap b \leq c\} \subseteq X_{a,c} = \{x \mid x \cap a \leq c\}$, since $x \cap a \leq x \cap b$. Hence $b * c \leq a * c$.

(4) $a, b \leq a \cup b \Rightarrow (a \cup b) * c \leq a * c \cap b * c$ by the antitone law of (3). To prove the converse, $a * c \cap a \leq c$ and $b * c \cap b \leq c$ imply $(a * c \cap a) \cup (b * c \cap b) \leq c$, so that $a * c \cap b * c \cap (a \cup b) \leq c$. Hence $a * c \cap b * c \leq (a \cup b) * c$.

We leave the second half of (4) as well as (5)–(8) to the exercises.

(9) First $[a * (b * c)] \cap a \leq b * c$. Hence $[a * (b * c)] \cap (a \cap b) \leq b * c \cap b \leq c$, so that $a * (b * c) \leq (a \cap b) * c$. Conversely, $(a \cap b) * c \cap a \cap b \leq c$, so that $[(a \cap b) * c] \cap a \leq b * c$. Hence $(a \cap b) * c \leq a * (b * c)$. Therefore, $a * (b * c) = (a \cap b) * c$. The commutativity of $\cap$ now gives the second statement: $a * (b * c) = b * (a * c)$. We leave it as an exercise to prove that $a * (b * c) = (a * b) * (a * c) = (a \cap b) * c$.

The prime examples of Brouwerian lattices other than the usual power set algebra and arbitrary Boolean algebras are the lattices of divisors of an integer n. They are, of course, Brouwerian since they are finite and distributive. We leave the interpretation of $a * b$ to the reader. We can also generalize many of the concepts of this section to systems which have weaker hypotheses. For example, we do not need to assume the existence of a greatest element 1, since we can define 1 as $a * a$ for any a. We can also develop a theory of semilattices by requiring only that L be closed under meet. We may also drop the requirement that L have a zero, in which case we obtain a system known as a generalized Brouwerian algebra similar to generalized Boolean algebras. We refer the reader to the literature for further discussion of these topics (*cf:* Rasiowa).

EXERCISES

1. Prove that in a distributive lattice $a * b = (a \cup b)_{*b,1}$ where $a * b$ is defined by $x \leq a * b \Longleftrightarrow x \cap a \leq b$. Use the non-distributive lattice M_5 of figure 5-1 to show that this result need not hold without the assumption of distributivity.
2. Prove corollary 2 of Theorem 7-5.
3. Prove the second half of Theorem 7-5, (4).

4. Prove 5—8 of Theorem 7-5.

5. Show that in a Brouwerian lattice:
(*a*) $a * b \cup c \leq (a \cup c) * (b \cup c)$;
(*b*) $(a \cup b) \cap (a * b) = b$;
(*c*) $(a * b) \cap (b * a) = (a \cup b) * (a \cap b)$;
(*d*) $a \cap (a * b) = a \cap b$.

6. Prove that in a Brouwerian lattice $a * b = b * a \Longleftrightarrow a = b$.

7. Show that in a Brouwerian lattice $a * 0 \cup b \leq a * b$.

8. Show that in a Brouwerian lattice $[(a * b) * b] * b = a * b$. Interpret for the case $b = 0$.

9. Interpret the laws 5 and 8 of Theorem 7-5 for the case $b = 0$.

10. Show that $\langle \mathbf{P}_n, | \rangle$ is a Brouwerian lattice and determine the meaning of $a * b$.

11. Show that the set of real functions f defined on $X = [0, 1]$ into X is a Brouwerian lattice and interpret $f * g$.

12. Show by examples that the inequalities of Theorem 7-5 cannot be strengthened.

13. Show that the open sets of a topological space form a Brouwerian lattice and determine the nature of the operation $a * b$.

7-3. SEMI-BOOLEAN ALGEBRAS

In the last chapter we discussed Boolean algebras from the point of view of an abstract characterization of a power set algebra. However, we also saw earlier that the algebra of set theory as a whole cannot be characterized completely by means of Boolean algebra. Every Boolean algebra must have a greatest element, whereas there cannot be a greatest set. Furthermore, complements of sets cannot be defined in any absolute sense. The advantages of Boolean algebra within set theory lie in its applicability as a model for the algebra of subsets *of some fixed universal set*. It also has the additional advantage of being self-dual, so that the principle of duality may be used. In fact, in most of our discussions of the more general lattice theory, we have preserved this duality and discussed systems closed under both union and meet. But there are many branches of mathematics where duality plays no essential role, and is in fact a limitation rather than an advantage. For example, in most theories of limits we need only be concerned with a partial order which is directed in only one direction; *i.e.*, we may need either upper bounds or lower bounds, but not necessarily both. Again in theories of integration, the set of partitions involved needs to form a partially ordered system such that every pair of partitions have a common refinement, but we make no essential use of the dual property. Hence in such theories duality is not important, and there is some need to concentrate more on semi-lattices than lattices. In this section we wish to find generalizations of Boolean algebra of this same character; *i.e.*, to define a semi-Boolean algebra in which we require neither closure under both union and meet nor both a greatest and least element, but only one or the other. However, we shall preserve the requirements of distributivity and relative complementation, so that we still have the essential properties of Boolean algebra. There are therefore two cases, neither of which is a self-dual theory, but the two theories are dual to each other. In the first, we assume a union semi-lattice with a greatest element which has the further property that every principal filter of the form $[a, 1]$ is a Boolean algebra, while in the second we assume meet closure and a least element such that every principal ideal $[0, 1]$ is Boolean. We use the general term semi-Boolean algebra to cover both cases, and union or meet semi-Boolean algebra when it is necessary to distinguish between them. We then establish a common axiomatic system which will include both, and shall discuss this system in detail in the next section. We thus begin with the formal definition:

Definition 7-1. *A union (meet) semi-lattice* $\langle L, \cup\rangle$ $(\langle L, \cap\rangle)$ *in which every principal filter (ideal) is a Boolean algebra is called a* **union (meet) semi-Boolean algebra.**

Here, of course, the term principal filter is meant in the sense of partially ordered set theory as the set $[a]\uparrow = \{x \mid a \leq x\}$, while an ideal is defined dually as $[a]\downarrow = \{x \mid x \leq a\}$. No mention is made of the existence of a greatest (or least) element, since we can now show the existence of such an element from the stated conditions. Since $[a]\uparrow$ is a Boolean algebra, it tacitly has a greatest element, 1_a. If now b is any other element, then $[b]\uparrow$ also has a greatest element, 1_b. But since L is a union semi-lattice, there is a union $1_a \cup 1_b$ in L. But the fact that 1_a is the greatest element containing a and $1_a \leq 1_a \cup 1_b$ implies $1_a = 1_b \cup 1_a$; *i.e.*, $1_b \leq 1_a$. Similarly, $1_a \leq 1_b$, so that $1_a = 1_b = 1$ is a greatest element for all of L.

In general, a union semi-Boolean algebra need not be closed under meet. If, however, it does have this additional property, then it is called a **generalized Boolean algebra** (union-generalized Boolean algebra). The terminology is due to Stone, who uses it in the meet sense. In fact, we have already discussed such algebras in section 6-3, where we showed that the theory of Boolean rings (without identities) coincides with the theory of generalized Boolean algebras. Thus a generalized Boolean algebra is a lattice in which every principal filter (ideal) is Boolean. In fact, however, we do not have to postulate that L be meet closed, but merely that every pair of elements a and b have some lower bound. For if p is a lower bound for a and b, then we can define $a \cap b$ by $a \cap b = (a'_p \cup b'_p)'_p$ using the de Morgan laws within the Boolean algebra $[p]\uparrow$. Thus we can characterize a generalized Boolean algebra as a union (meet) semi-Boolean algebra in which every pair of elements has a lower (upper) bound. The theory of sets, for example, is such an algebra. We first generalize the notion of an algebraic system so that the carrier B is a class in the sense of von Neumann-Gödel set theory (see Appendix 1) instead of a set. B is then the class of all sets, although it is not itself a set. The complement of a set within B is also not a set, but the elements of B are sets. The meet of two sets is then a set using the axiom of abstraction. Finally, using the axiom of upper bounds, every pair of sets are subsets of some larger set. Hence we have a semi-Boolean algebra in which the set of subsets of a fixed set U; *i.e.*, the principal ideal generated by U, is a Boolean algebra and in which every pair of sets have an upper bound. Hence we have a generalized Boolean algebra as the natural model for axiomatic set theory, whereas Boolean algebra serves only as a model for the algebra of subsets of some fixed set. Since the main goal of this book is to discuss abstract algebras which arise in a natural way as models for set theory, we achieve this goal by the discussion of semi-Boolean algebras. We devote the rest of this chapter to a discussion of these algebras from a simpler algebraic point of view. This simpler view will unify the theories of both union and meet semi-Boolean algebras under a common algebraic system which uses only a single binary operation, and which gives Boolean algebras as a special case.

Since every ideal $[b]\downarrow$; *i.e.*, interval sub-lattice $[0, 1]$, is a Boolean algebra, it is complemented. Hence if $a \leq b$, then there exists an element $a'_{0,b}$ which is a complement of a relative to 0 and b. But this is exactly the difference $b - a$ defined in the last section. Furthermore, using the same technique established there, we can also define the difference $b - a$ even when $a \notin [b]\downarrow$; *i.e.*, $b - a = (a \cap b)'_{0,b}$ where $a \cap b \leq b$. Hence every meet semi-Boolean algebra is closed under the difference operation $b - a$. Dually, every union semi-Boolean algebra is closed under the implication operation $a \to b = (a \cup b)'_{b,1}$. In either case, we can now show that both operations satisfy the same set of laws as given in:

Theorem 7-7. *Every union (meet) semi-Boolean algebra* $\langle I, \cup, 1\rangle(\langle I, \cap, 0\rangle)$ *is closed under the implication product* $a \to b = (a \cup b)'_{b,1}$ *(difference* $b - a = (a \cap b)'_{0,b}$*) which satisfies:*

I1: $(a \to b) \to a = a, \qquad (a - (b - a) = a);$

I2: $(a \to b) \to b = (b \to a) \to a, \ (b - (b - a) = a - (a - b));$

I3: $a \to (b \to c) = b \to (a \to c), \ ((c - b) - a = (c - a) - b).$

Proof. We shall use the notation x'_a for the complement of x within the Boolean algebra $[a]\uparrow$.

I1: $(a \to b) \to a = [(a \to b) \cup a]'_a$. But $a \to b = (a \cup b)'_b$, so that $(a \to b) \cup a \cup b = 1$. However, $b \leq (a \to b)$, so that $b \cup (a \to b) = a \to b$. Hence, $(a \to b) \cup a = 1$. Therefore, $(a \to b) \to a = 1'_a = a$.

I2: $(a \to b) \to b = [(a \to b) \cup b]'_b$. But as in *I1* $(a \to b) \cup b = a \to b$, so that $[(a \to b) \cup b]'_b = (a \to b)'_b = (a \cup b)''_b = a \cup b$. Hence by the commutativity of $a \cup b$, $(a \to b) \to b = (b \to a) \to a$.

I3: $a \to (b \to c) = [a \cup (b \to c)]'_{b \to c} = [a \cup (b \to c)]'_c \cup (b \to c) = [a \cup c \cup (b \to c)]'_c \cup (b \to c) = [(a \cup c)'_c \cap (b \to c)'_c] \cup (b \to c) = [(a \to c) \cap (b \to c)'_c] \cup (b \to c) = [(a \to c) \cup (b \to c)] \cap [(b \to c)'_c \cup (b \to c)] = (a \to c) \cup (b \to c)$. But the final expression is symmetric in a and b, so that $a \to (b \to c) = b \to (a \to c)$.

The laws for differences are duals.

Our goal is now to prove the converse; *i.e.*, that any system defined by equations *I1–I3* determines a semi-Boolean algebra. We call such systems either implication algebras or subtraction algebras, depending on whether we write the operation as $a \to b$ or $b - a$. But since the same postulates hold for both operations, there is no real need to distinguish between the two. Hence we shall merely write ab for the operation, and only use $a \to b$ or $b - a$ when we feel the need to distinguish one case from the other. We shall use the term "implication algebra" for convenience in discussing either type; *i.e.*, implication or subtraction. The theory of implication algebras will therefore replace the theory of semi-Boolean algebras, and we can drop the cumbersome terminology union semi-Boolean algebra or union generalized Boolean algebra and discuss only systems $\langle I, \cdot \rangle$ which have a single binary operation; *i.e.*, are of type $\langle 2 \rangle$. The theory of Boolean algebras will then appear as a special case.

7-4. IMPLICATION ALGEBRA

We begin with:

Definition 7-2. *An* **implication algebra** *is a system* $\langle I, \cdot \rangle$ *defined on a carrier set I with a single binary operation ab satisfying:*

$$I1: \ (ab)a = a;$$

$$I2: \ (ab)b = (ba)a;$$

$$I3: \ a(bc) = b(ac).$$

Before relating implication algebra to the theory of semi-lattices and Boolean algebras, we first develop some of the elementary arithmetic based on postulates *I1–I3*. In particular, we can determine the free algebra with two generators a and b. We first show that every implication algebra contains a distinguished element which we denote by 1 and which is the square of every other element. Hence, even though an implication algebra is initially defined as an algebra of type $\langle 2 \rangle$; *i.e.*, with a single binary operation, we can always introduce the nullary operation or constant 1, so that it becomes of type $\langle 2, 0 \rangle$. We first prove two lemmas:

Lemma 7-2. $a(ab) = ab$.

Proof. $a(ab) = [(ab)a](ab) = ab$ by *I1* used twice.

Lemma 7-3. $aa = (ab)(ab)$.

Proof. $aa = [(ab)a]a = [a(ab)](ab) = (ab)(ab)$ by *I1*, *I2* and lemma 7-2.

Theorem 7-8. *Every implication algebra contains a constant* 1 *satisfying:*

(*i*) $aa = 1$;
(*ii*) $1a = a$;
(*iii*) $a1 = 1$.

Proof. (*i*) $aa = (ab)(ab) = [(ab)b][(ab)b] = [(ba)a][(ba)a] = (ba)(ba) = bb$. Hence we write $aa = 1 \ \forall\ a$.

(*ii*) $1a = (aa)a = a$ by *I1*.
(*iii*) $a1 = a(aa) = aa = 1$ by lemma 7-1.

We now leave it to the exercises to develop the remaining properties for implications involving a and b as given by Table 7-1. Thus the only elements generated by a and b using the implication operation and postulates *I1–I3* are the six elements $1, a, b, ab, ba, (ab)b$. The free implication algebra with two generators therefore contains only these six elements and is completely defined by Table 7-1. Thus we note that the column for the element 1 consists of 1 alone since 1 is a right zero; *i.e.*, $a1 = 1$. On the other hand, the row corresponding to 1 is identical to the column headings since 1 is a left identity; *i.e.*, $1a = a$. Finally, the main diagonal consists of 1 alone, since $aa = 1 \ \forall\ a$.

·	1	a	b	ab	ba	$(ab)b$
1	1	a	b	ab	ba	$(ab)b$
a	1	1	ab	ab	1	1
b	1	ba	1	1	ba	1
ab	1	a	$(ab)b$	1	ba	$(ab)b$
ba	1	$(ab)b$	b	ab	1	$(ab)b$
$(ab)b$	1	ba	ab	ab	ba	1

TABLE 7-1

We also may note from this table that ab and ba are always distinct unless $a = b$. This result in general is given in the following:

Lemma 7-4. *Every implication algebra is anti-commutative in that* $ab = ba \leftrightarrow a = b$.

Proof. If $ab = ba$, then $a = (ab)a = (ba)a = (ab)b = (ba)b = b$. The converse is obvious.

We can now show that every implication algebra determines a partially ordered set under the definition $a \leq b \leftrightarrow ab = 1$ as contained in:

Theorem 7-9. *Every implication algebra* $\langle I, \cdot \rangle$ *determines a partially ordered set* $\langle I, \leq \rangle$ *with greatest element 1 under* $a \leq b \leftrightarrow ab = 1$.

Proof. (*i*) $aa = 1$ implies $a \leq a \ \forall \ a$; *i.e.*, $\leq$ is reflexive.

(*ii*) $a \leq b$ and $b \leq a$ are equivalent to $ab = 1$ and $ba = 1$; *i.e.*, $ab = ba$. Hence, by lemma 7-4, $a = b$. Therefore $\leq$ is anti-symmetric.

(*iii*) To prove transitivity, note that $a \leq b$ and $b \leq c$ imply $ab = bc = 1$. Hence $ac = a(1c) = a[(bc)c] = a[(cb)b] = (cb)(ab) = (cb)1 = 1$; *i.e.*, $a \leq c$.

(*iv*) Finally, $a1 = 1$ implies $a \leq 1 \ \forall \ a$; *i.e.*, 1 is a greatest element.

Since $\langle I, \leq \rangle$ is a partially ordered set, we can construct a partial order diagram for any implication algebra. For example, the partial order diagram for the free algebra of Table 7-1 is given in figure 7-4. The next lemma gives an alternate characterization for the partial order in terms of implication; *i.e.*, $a \leq b$ if and only if b is a left (implication) multiple of a.

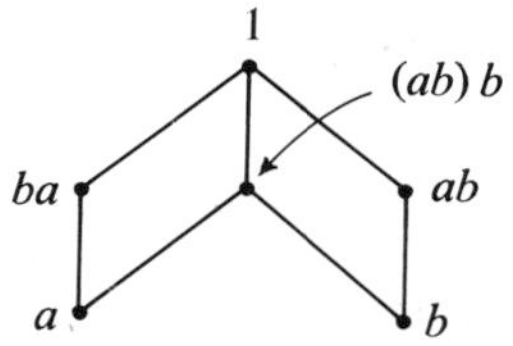

FIGURE 7-4

Lemma 7-5. $a \leq b \leftrightarrow b = xa$ *for some* $x \in I$.

Proof. (*i*) If $b = xa$, then $ab = a(xa) = x(aa) = x1 = 1$.

(*ii*) Conversely, if $ab = 1$, then $b = 1b = (ab)b = (ba)a = xa$ where $x = ba$.

We can now show that every implication algebra determines not only a partially ordered set, but with respect to this partial order I is also a union semi-lattice where the element $(ab)b$ is the union of a and b; *i.e.*, their least upper bound.

Theorem 7-10. *Every implication algebra* $\langle I, \cdot \rangle$ *determines a union semi-lattice* $\langle I, \leq, \cup, 1 \rangle$ *under* $a \cup b = (ab)b$.

Proof. (*i*) $a[(ab)b] = 1 \Rightarrow a \leq (ab)b$ and similarly $b \leq (ba)a = (ab)b$, so that $(ab)b$ is an upper bound for a and b.

(*ii*) Next if $a, b \leq c$, by lemma 7-5, $c = xa$ for some x, while by the definition of the partial order $bc = 1$. Hence $[(ab)b]c = [(ab)b](xa) = x\{[(ab)b]a\} = x(ba) = b(xa) = bc = 1$. Hence $(ab)b \leq c$ and therefore $(ab)b$ is a least upper bound for a and b. Therefore $(ab)b = a \cup b$ in $\langle I, \leq \rangle$.

Since $\langle I, \leq \rangle$ is a partially ordered set, we can use the terminology of principal filters generated by elements. Furthermore, we can characterize the elements of the filter $[a]\uparrow$ as the set of left multiples of a using lemma 7-5; *i.e.*,

Lemma 7-6. *In any implication algebra $\langle I, \cdot, \leq \rangle$, the principal filter generated by a is the set of left multiples of a; i.e.,* $[a]\uparrow = \{x | a \leq x\} = \{x | \exists t \in I \text{ and } x = ta\}$.

It remains to show that every such principal filter is a Boolean algebra. We first show that the partial order is preserved under left multiplication but inverted by right multiplication.

Theorem 7-11.
(*i*) $a \leq b \Rightarrow ca \leq cb$ (*isotone*);
(*ii*) $a \leq b \Rightarrow bc \leq ac$ (*antitone*).

Proof. (*i*) $a \leq b \Rightarrow b = xa$ for some x. Hence $cb = c(xa) = x(ca)$ which implies $ca \leq cb$.
(*ii*) $a \leq b \Rightarrow ab = 1$. Hence $(bc)(ac) = a[(bc)c] = a[(cb)b] = (cb)(ab) = (cb)1 = 1$, so that $bc \leq ac$.

Lemma 7-7. *In any implication algebra $\langle I, \cdot \rangle$, if any pair of elements a, b have a lower bound p, then they have a greatest lower bound given by* $a \cap b = (ap \cup bp)p$.

Proof. (*i*) Let $p \leq a, b$. Then $a \cup p = a$. Furthermore, $ap \leq ap \cup bp \Rightarrow (ap \cup bp)p \leq (ap)p = a \cup p = a$. Similarly, $(ap \cup bp)p \leq b$; *i.e.*, $(ap \cup bp)p$ is also a lower bound for a and b.
(*ii*) Now let $q \leq a, b$. Then $ap, bp \leq qp$ and hence $ap \cup bp \leq qp$. Thus $q \leq q \cup p = (qp)p \leq (ap \cup bp)p$; *i.e.*, $(ap \cup bp)p$ is a greatest lower bound for a and b.

This theorem also shows that $a \cap b$, although originally defined in terms of the parameter p is, in fact, independent of p. As a second result, it follows that every principal filter is closed under meet as well as union and hence is a lattice; *i.e.*,

Corollary. *If p is any element of an implication algebra I, then* $[p]\uparrow$ *is a lattice.*

It next follows that a and ap are complements within this lattice; *i.e.*,

Lemma 7-8. *If I is an implication algebra, and $p \leq a$, then (i) $a \cup ap = 1$ and (ii) $a \cap ap = p$.*

Proof. (*i*) $a \cup ap = [a(ap)](ap) = (ap)(ap) = 1$.
(*ii*) $a \cap ap = [(ap) \cup (ap)p]p = (ap \cup a)p = 1p = p$.

Thus ap is a complement of a relative to p and 1; *i.e.*, we can write $ap = a'_{p,1} = a'_p$.

Corollary. *For any $a, b \in I$, $ab = (a \cup b)'_b$.*

For $(a \cup b)'_b = (a \cup b)b = [(ab)b]b = ab$. See Table 7-1.

Lemma 7-9. *Complements within any principal filter are unique.*

Proof. We already know that if $p \leq a$, then ap is a complement of a within $[p]\uparrow$. Now let x be a second complement of a; *i.e.*, let $a \cup x = 1$ and $a \cap x = p$. Then (*i*) $p \leq x \Rightarrow ap \leq ax = [(ax)x]x = (a \cup x)x = 1x = x$. Also (*ii*) $xp \leq a(xp) \Rightarrow [a(xp)]p \leq (xp)p = x$. Similarly, $[a(xp)]p = [x(ap)]p \leq a$. Hence $[a(xp)]p \leq a \cap x = p$. But $p \leq [a(xp)]p$, so that $[a(xp)]p = p$. Therefore $ap = a\{[a(xp)]p\} = [a(xp)](ap) = [x(ap)](ap) = x$; *i.e.*, $x = ap$ and ap is a unique complement of a within $[p]\uparrow$.

Corollary 1. $p \leq b \Rightarrow ab = ap \cup b = a'_p \cup b$ *for any* a.

Proof. Since $p \leq b$, then $ap \leq ab$, so that $ap \cup b \leq ab \cup b = ab$. Hence $b \leq (a \cup b) \cap (ap \cup b) \leq (a \cup b) \cap ab = b$. Thus $(a \cup b) \cap (ap \cup b) = b$. On the other hand, $(a \cup b) \cup (ap \cup b) = 1$, so that the result follows from the uniqueness of complements.

Corollary 2. $p \leq a, b \Rightarrow a \cap b = [a(bp)]p = (ab'_p)'_p$.

Lemma 7-10. *In any implication algebra, every principal filter $[p]\uparrow$ is a distributive lattice.*

Proof. Let $r = (a \cap b) \cup (a \cap c)$ and $s = a \cap (b \cup c)$. Then $a \cap b \leq r$, so that $a(a \cap b) \leq ar$. But if $q = a \cap b$, then $a(a \cap b) = a\{[a(bq)]q\} = [a(bq)](aq) = [b(aq)](aq) = b \cup aq = ab$. Hence $b \leq ab = a(a \cap b) \leq ar$. Similarly, $c \leq ar$, so that $b \cup c \leq ar$; *i.e.*, $(b \cup c)(ar) = 1$. Thus, since $r \leq a, b \cup c$, using corollary 2 of lemma 7–9, we have $s = a \cap (b \cup c) = [(b \cup c)(ar)]r = 1r = r$. Thus $a \cap (b \cup c) = (a \cap b) \cup (a \cap c)$; *i.e.*, $[p]\uparrow$ is distributive.

We can now summarize these results in the general theorem:

Theorem 7-12. *Every implication algebra $\langle I, \cdot\rangle$ determines a union semi-lattice $\langle I, \cup\rangle$ in which every principal filter $[p]\uparrow$ is a Boolean algebra. Furthermore implication in I is given by $ab = (a \cup b)'_b$.*

This theorem completes the proof that the theory of semi-Boolean algebras is completely determined by the theory of implication algebras. This characterization has the advantage that implication algebras are essentially simpler in nature than semi-Boolean algebras in that they are systems with only a single binary operation completely defined by the postulates *I1–I3*. Furthermore, the theory of Boolean algebras is obtained as a special case. Thus if I contains a least element 0, then I is exactly equal to the principal filter generated by this zero; *i.e.*, $I = [0]\uparrow$. Therefore, since $[0]\uparrow$ is a Boolean algebra, I is also. Therefore we have the following characterization of Boolean algebra:

Corollary. *The theory of Boolean algebras is completely determined by the theory of implication algebras which satisfy:*

$$I4\colon\ \exists\, 0 \text{ such that } 0a = 1\ \forall\, a.$$

Hence a Boolean algebra is the same as the system $\langle I, \cdot, 0\rangle$; *i.e.*, is an algebra of type $\langle 2, 0\rangle$ with one binary and one nullary operation (constant), satisfying *I1–I4*. This theorem means that we can treat the theory of Boolean algebras in a fashion entirely similar to the theory of monoids which also have type $\langle 2, 0\rangle$ since they are defined by a binary operation plus a constant, the identity.

We now complete this section with some examples of implication algebras. First of all we note that every Boolean algebra $\langle B, \cup, \cap, 0, 1, '\rangle$ determines two implication algebras under the two operations $ab = a \to b = a' \cup b$ and $ab = b - a = a' \cap b$. We leave it to the exercises to show that these two, $\langle B, \to\rangle$ and $\langle B, -\rangle$, are implication algebras which are dual to each other. Moreover, whether we call an implication algebra in general an implication or a subtraction algebra is purely a matter of terminology. Thus in Theorem 7-8 we arbitrarily denoted the element aa by 1 and then wrote the partial order $a \leq b$ whenever $ab = 1$. We could just as easily have written $aa = 0$ and designated the partial order by $a \geq b \leftrightarrow ab = 0$. In the latter case, the name "subtraction algebra" is perhaps more appropriate, but from the purely algebraic standpoint it makes no difference which notation we use. Hence the theory of implication algebras unifies the two theories of upper and lower semi-Boolean algebras. Thus, for example, if X is any set, then the power set algebra $\mathfrak{P}(X)$ determines two implication algebras $\langle \mathfrak{P}(X), A \to B\rangle$ and $\langle \mathfrak{P}(X), B - A\rangle$.

Next we can apply the general concept of sub-algebra to implication algebras. Thus a system $\langle S, \cdot \rangle$ is a sub-implication algebra of $\langle I, \cdot \rangle$ if S is a subset of I and S is closed under implication; *i.e.*, $a, b \in S \Rightarrow ab \in S$. This means that any subset of a Boolean algebra $\langle B, \cup, \cap, 0, 1, ' \rangle$ determines a sub-implication algebra if it is closed under either $a' \cup b$ or $a' \cap b$. In particular, a subset S of a Boolean algebra is called an **upper section** of a Boolean algebra if $a \in S$ and $a \leq x \Rightarrow x \in S$. Then every upper section determines an implication algebra. For if $a, b \in S$, then $b \leq a' \cup b$, so that $a' \cup b \in S$; *i.e.*, S is closed under $a' \cup b$. Thus every upper section of any Boolean algebra is an implication algebra, and dually every lower section is a subtraction algebra under $a' \cap b$.

For example, if $\mathfrak{J}$ is any family of subsets of a set X which contains $A' \cup B$ whenever it contains A and B, then it defines an implication algebra called a *set implication algebra.* Dually whenever it contains $A' \cap B \ \forall \ A, B \in \mathfrak{J}$, it is called a *subtraction algebra of sets.* In particular, any lower or upper section of a power set algebra is an implication algebra. For example, the set $\mathfrak{P}^{-}(X)$ of non-empty subsets of X is an implication algebra under $A' \cup B$, while the family of proper subsets is a subtraction algebra. Neither of these is Boolean, since the first contains no least element and the second no greatest. More generally, if α is any cardinal number, then the family of subsets of X whose cardinality is $\geq \alpha$ is an implication algebra. For if A and B contain at least α elements, then certainly $A' \cup B$ does. The case above is obtained by using $\alpha = 1$. If $\alpha = 2$ (or any finite n), then we obtain the implication algebra of all subsets which contain at least 2 (n) elements. If $\alpha = \aleph_0$, then we obtain the implication algebra of all infinite subsets of X. Again this is not a Boolean algebra nor even a lattice, since the intersection of two infinite sets is not necessarily infinite. We could just as easily have used $> \alpha$ instead of $\geq \alpha$ and obtained further examples. Dually, the family of subsets of X which have cardinality $\leq \alpha$ (or $< \alpha$) is a subtraction algebra. For example, the set of finite subsets of X is a subtraction algebra. Finally we could have used complements; *i.e.*, the set of subsets of X whose complements have cardinality $\leq \alpha$ ($< \alpha$, $\geq \alpha$, or $> \alpha$) form an implication algebra. For if A and B have complements with cardinality $\leq \alpha$, for example, then so does $A' \cap B$. Thus the set of subsets of X with finite complements is a subtraction algebra. This is the well known finite complement topology of a topological space.

As a further example from topology, we may consider the family $\mathfrak{N}$ of all neighborhoods of a topological space $\langle X, \mathfrak{T} \rangle$. Here by a neighborhood we mean any set which has a non-empty interior; *i.e.*, contains a non-empty open set. For if A and B each contain some non-empty open set, then so does $A' \cup B$. In fact, the concept of a topological space can be characterized entirely in terms of implication algebras using the approach through neighborhoods instead of the more usual approach through open sets (*cf:* Abbott 1).

EXERCISES

1. Using only *I1–I3* prove that in implication algebra (*i*) $a(ba) = 1$, (*ii*) $a[(ab)b] = 1$, (*iii*) $(ab)(ba) = ba$, (*iv*) $[(ab)b]a = ba$, (*v*) $[(ab)b]b = ab$, and (*vi*) $[(ab)b](ba) = ba$.
2. Using the results given in exercise 1 verify the entries of Table 7-1.
3. Verify the diagram of figure 7-4, using Table 7-1.
4. Prove that $ab = a \Longleftrightarrow a = 1$.
5. Prove that $ab = b \Longleftrightarrow ba = a$.
6. Prove that $ab \cup ba = 1$.
7. Show that the law $[(ab)b]b = ab$ is a generalization of the law $a''' = a'$ for Boolean algebra.
8. Show that $(ab)b = a \cup b$ is a generalization of $a'' = a$ in Boolean algebra.
9. Show directly that if we define $a \cup b = (ab)b$, then $\cup$ is idempotent, commutative and associative, so that $\langle I, \cup \rangle$ is a semi-lattice. Hence show that this definition *imposes* the definition $a \leq b \Longleftrightarrow ab = 1$ for partial order in I.
10. Show that if $pa = pb = 1$, then $a \cup b = (ap \cap bp)p$, but that this law is false without these hypotheses.
11. Show that if for any $a, b \in I$ there exists $p = p_{a,b}$ satisfying $pa = pb = 1$, then $\langle I, \rightarrow \rangle$ is an idempotent, commutative group under $a \longleftrightarrow b = ab \cap ba$.
12. Show that every boolean ring $\langle I, +, \cdot \rangle$ becomes an implication algebra under $ab = a \cdot b + b$.
13. Show that the ring of exercise 12 is a ring with identity if and only if the corresponding implication algebra has a zero. Thus show that the theory of implication algebras closed under meet is determined by and determines the theory of Boolean rings and that those rings with identities correspond to Boolean algebras.
14. Prove the distributive laws: (*i*) if $a \cap b$ and $a \cap c$ exist, then $a \cap (b \cup c)$ exists and $a \cap (b \cup c) = (a \cap b) \cup (a \cap c)$; (*ii*) If $b \cap c$ exists, then $a \cup (b \cap c) = (a \cup b) \cap (a \cup c)$. Show that the proof of one distributive law from the other given in Chapter 5 does not hold for general implication algebras.
15. Prove the distributive laws (*i*) $a(a \cup c) = ab \cup ac$; (*ii*) If $b \cap c$ exists, then $a(b \cap c) = ab \cap ac$.
16. Prove the de Morgan laws; (*i*) $(a \cup b)c = ac \cap bc$; (*ii*) If $a \cap b$ exists, then $(a \cap b)c = ac \cup bc$. Show that these laws generalize the de Morgan laws for Boolean algebra.
17. Show that $a(b \cup c) = ab \cup c$.
18. Prove the quasi-associative law: $a[(bc)c] = [(ab)c]c$.
19. Prove the auto-distributive $a(bc) = (ab)(ac)$.
20. Determine all implication algebras with two generators, not necessarily independent. Construct their diagrams, and implication tables.
21. Write the implication table for the Boolean algebra **2**.
22. Prove by examples that the postulates *I1–I3* are independent.

23. Show that the diagram of figure 7-5 determines an implication algebra and write its implication table.

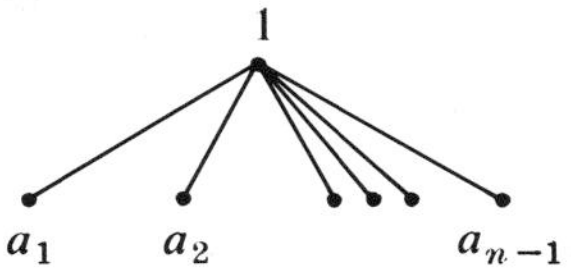

FIGURE 7-5

24. Let $\langle I, *\rangle$ and $\langle J, \circ\rangle$ be two implication algebras and let K be the set of elements of I together with the elements of J but with the units 1_I and 1_J identified, $1_I = 1_J = 1$. Show that K becomes an implication algebra under the definition

$$ab = \begin{cases} a * b \text{ if } a, b \in I, \\ a \circ b \text{ if } a, b \in J, \\ b \text{ if either } a \in I, \text{ and } b \in J, \text{ or } b \in I \text{ and } a \in J, a, b \neq 1 \\ \text{and } ab \text{ has the meaning of Theorem 7-8 if } a \text{ or } b = 1. \end{cases}$$

25. Generalize the process of exercise 24 to an arbitrary finite number of implication algebras.

26. Let $\mathfrak{F}$ be any family of fixed subsets of a set X and let $\mathfrak{J}$ be the set of all subsets which contain some member of $\mathfrak{F}$. Show that $\mathfrak{J}$ is an implication algebra Dualize.

27. Show that the set of dual atoms of any atomic Boolean algebra together with the greatest element forms an implication algebra and describe the implication product.

28. Show that implication algebra can be characterized by the following two postulates:
(*i*) $(ab)a = a$
(*ii*) $(ab)(cb) = (ba)(ca)$.

29. Prove: (*i*) $\{[(ab)b]c\}c = \{[ac)c]b\}b$;
(*ii*) $\{[c(ba)a\}\{[(ab)b]c\} = ac$.

30. Prove: (*i*) $db = dc = 1 \Rightarrow b(ca) = \{[b(cd)]d\}a$.

31. Prove that every Boolean ring with identity, $\langle I, +, 0, 1\rangle$, determines an implication algebra with last element 0 under $ab = 1 + a + a \cdot b$.

7-5. FILTER THEORY

We can now apply the structural theories from universal algebra to the special case of an implication algebra and thereby obtain a structure theory for implication algebra. We have already defined the concept of sub-implication algebra and can now define the concept of homomorphism. This is particularly simple in the case of an implication algebra, since there is only a single binary operation involved. Thus a **homomorphism** from an implication algebra $\langle I, \cdot\rangle$ onto an implication algebra $\langle \bar{I}, \cdot\rangle$ is a mapping ϕ from I onto $\bar{I}$ which preserves implication; *i.e.*, satisfies $\phi(ab) = \phi(a)\phi(b)$. Since the nullary operation, 1, the binary operation $\cup$, and the partial order $\leq$ are all defined in terms of implication, it follows that every implication homomorphism is also a union semi-lattice homomorphism which will preserve 1 and the partial order. Furthermore, if $a \cap b$ exists for a pair of elements a and b, then $\phi(a) \cap \phi(b)$ will also exist and ϕ will preserve $\cap$. Finally, if I contains a 0; *i.e.*, is a Boolean algebra, then $\bar{I}$ will also and ϕ will be a Boolean homomorphism. Hence the theory of implication homomorphisms is quite straightforward; the details can safely be left to the reader as a test of his understanding of the similar theory of homomorphisms for general lattice theory and universal algebra.

The next problem is to investigate the kernel of a homomorphism, $K_\phi = \{x | \phi(x) = 1\}$. Since ϕ is a union semi-lattice homomorphism, it is natural to expect that the kernel will be a lattice filter. Hence we are led to define a filter in an arbitrary implication algebra by analogy with filters in lattice theory. A **filter** K in an implication algebra I is a subset K satisfying:

$$(i)\ a \in K, a \leq x \Rightarrow x \in K:$$

and

$$(ii)\ a, b \in K \text{ and } \exists\, a \cap b \Rightarrow a \cap b \in K.$$

Here the only new point is that we have had to add the hypothesis that $\exists\, a \cap b$, since not every implication algebra is closed under meet. This definition can be expressed purely in terms of implication as: K is a **filter** if and only if

(*i*) $a \in K \Rightarrow xa \in K$ and

(*ii*) $a, b \in K$, $\exists\, p$ such that $pa = pb = 1 \Rightarrow [a(bp)]p \in K$.

We now again leave it to the exercises to show that the kernel K_ϕ of a homomorphism is a filter.

The next problem is to prove the converse; *i.e.*, that every filter K determines a homomorphism ϕ_K in a unique way such that the kernel of ϕ_K will be precisely K. As usual, we define an **implication congruence relation** as an equivalence relation with the substitution property for implication; *i.e.*, satisfying $a \equiv b$ and $c \equiv d \Rightarrow ac \equiv bd$. Then, starting with a filter K, we define the relation $a \equiv b \bmod K \longleftrightarrow ab, ba \in K$.* It now remains to prove that $\equiv$ so defined is an implication congruence relation.

Theorem 7-13. *If K is a filter in an implication algebra I, then the relation $a \equiv b \bmod K \longleftrightarrow ab, ba \in K$ is an implication congruence relation.*

Proof. (*i*) $a \leq a$ follows from $aa = 1$.

(*ii*) The symmetry of $\equiv$ follows from the symmetry within the definition.

*The motivation for this definition becomes a little more clear if we think of I in terms of group theory. In the case that I is meet closed, we have seen that I determines the commutative group $\langle I, \longleftrightarrow \rangle$ where $a \longleftrightarrow b = ab \cap ba$. But in group theory, the kernel of homomorphism ϕ is a normal subgroup K and two elements a and b are congruent mod $K \Longleftrightarrow ab^{-1} \in K$; *i.e.*, $a \longleftrightarrow b \in K$ (note that in $\langle I, \longleftrightarrow \rangle, b^{-1} = b$, since I is idempotent). Therefore, in the general case where I may not be meet closed, it is natural to write $a \equiv b \Longleftrightarrow ab, ba \in K$.

(*iii*) To prove transitivity, first note that $(a \cup b) \cap ab = b$, since ab is the relative complement of $a \cup b$ within $[b]\uparrow$. Next, $ac \cup ab = a(c \cup b) = ac \cup b$, while $ac \cup bc = a(c \cup bc) = a(bc) = b(ac)$. Hence $(ac \cup ab) \cap (ac \cup bc) = (b \cup ac) \cap b(ac) = ac$. Now let $a \equiv b$ and $b \equiv c$. Then ab, ba, bc, and $cb \in K$. Hence $ac \cup ab, ac \cup bc \in K$. Therefore $ac = (ac \cup ab) \cap (ac \cup bc) \in K$ where the existence of this meet follows, since ac is a lower bound for the required elements. Similarly, $ca \in K$, so that $a \equiv c$.

(*iv*) To establish the substitution property, we first note that $ab \leq (ca)(cb)$. For $(ab)[(ca)(cb)] = (ca)[(ab)(cb)] = (ca)\{c[(ab)b]\} = (ca)\{[(ca)b]b\} = [(ca)b][(ca)b] = 1$. (see exercise 18 of section7-4). Now let $a \equiv b$ and $c \equiv d$. Then $ab, ba \in K$. Hence $(ac)(bc) = b[(ac)c] = b[(ca)a] = (ca)(ba) \in K$. Similarly, $(bc)(ac) \in K$, so that $ac \equiv bc$. Finally, $c \equiv d$ implies $cd, dc \in K$. Therefore $(bc)(bd) \in K$, since $cd \leq (bc)(bd) = b(cd)$. Similarly, $(bd)(bc) \in K$, so that $bc \equiv bd$. Therefore, $ac \equiv bd$.

It follows from this theorem that every filter K determines a congruence relation $\equiv_K$. The kernel of this congruence relation is then the set $K = \{x|x \equiv 1\}$. But $x \equiv 1 \leftrightarrow x1, 1x = x \in K$. Hence $K = K$, so that the correspondence between filters and congruences is one-to-one. But every congruence relation $\equiv$ defines a quotient algebra which consists of the cosets $\bar{a} = \{x|x \equiv a\}$ with implication defined by $\bar{a}\bar{b} = \overline{ab}$. This definition is unique, since $\equiv$ has the substitution property under implication. The natural homomorphism $\phi : a \to \bar{a}$ is then a homomorphism from I onto $\bar{I} = I \bmod \equiv$ whose kernel is precisely the kernel K of the congruence relation. Hence the cycle between filters, congruences and homomorphisms is now complete. We can also state the fundamental isomorphism theorem for implication algebras in the following form:

Theorem 7-14. *If ϕ is a homomorphism from an implication algebra I onto an implication algebra $\bar{I}$, then the kernel of ϕ is a filter K and $I/K \cong \bar{I}$.*

The next theorem shows that the definition of congruence relation modulo a filter agrees with our earlier definition given for general lattice theory in the case that I is meet closed; *i.e.*, a lattice.

Theorem 7-15. *If I is meet closed, then $a \equiv b \bmod K \leftrightarrow \exists\, k \in K$ such that $a \cap k = b \cap k$.*

Proof. (*i*) Let $a, b \in I$ and $a \equiv b \bmod K$. Then $k = ab \cap ba \in K$. Let $p = a \cap b$. Then $ab = ap \cup b$ and $ba = bp \cup a$. Hence $a \cap ab = a \cap (ap \cup b) = (a \cap ap) \cup (a \cap b) = p$. Therefore $a \cap k = a \cap ab \cap ba = p \cap ba = p$, and similarly $a \cap k = p$. Hence a $\cap\, k = b \cap k$.

(*ii*) Conversely, let $a \cap k = b \cap k$ for some $k \in K$. Then $p = a \cap k$ implies $k \leq ap \leq ab$, so that $ab \in K$. Similarly, $ba \in K$, so that $a \equiv b \bmod K$.

Hence we have shown that the lattice of homomorphisms $\mathfrak{H}(I)$, the lattice of filters $\mathfrak{F}(I)$ and the lattice of congruence relations $\Theta(I)$ are essentially the same. In the future we shall concentrate on the lattice of filters, but the reader should keep in mind that we could equally well be talking of the lattice of homomorphisms or the lattice of congruences. Furthermore, by using subtraction algebras instead of implication algebras, this is the same as the theory of ideals or, more properly, dual to this theory. Thus $\mathfrak{F}(I)$ is partially ordered by set inclusion and the meet of two filters is their point set intersection. Furthermore, the union $H \sqcup K$ of two filters H and K is the smallest filter containing them both; *i.e.*, the intersection of all filters which contain them both. We can also carry over the concept of the filter generated by an arbitrary subset A of I to the case of implication algebra by defining $[A]$ as the intersection of all filters which contain A.

We can now consider the set $\mathfrak{P}(I)$ of all principal filters of I as a subset of $\mathfrak{F}(I)$. There is then a natural dual isomorphism between $\mathfrak{P}(I)$ and I itself given by $a \to [a]\uparrow$. Thus $a \leq b$ implies $[b] \subseteq [a]$ (we write $[a]$ for $[a]\uparrow$.) while $[a \cup b] = [a] \cap [b]$ and $[a \cap b] = [a] \sqcup [b]$ as long as $a \cap b$ exists. Again the verification is an exercise. Hence the diagram for $\mathfrak{P}(I)$ may be obtained from that of I by inverting the latter. However, since I is an implication algebra under the operation ab it is natural to investigate the meaning of the filter generated by the product ab in terms of the two filters $[a]$ and $[b]$. The following lemma gives a motivation for the general definition of the implication product of two filters in general.

Lemma 7-11. $[ab] = \{x \in [b] | ax = x\}$.

Proof. First, since $b \leq ab$, $[ab] \subseteq [b]$, so that $x \in [ab]$ implies $x \in [b]$. Furthermore, $x \in [ab]$ implies $x = y(ab) = a(yb) = a[a(yb)] = ax$. Conversely, $x \in [b]$ and $ax = x$ imply $x = yb$ and $x = ax = a(yb) = y(ab)$; *i.e.*, $x \in [ab]$.

We are therefore led to generalize this lemma and define the **implication pseudo-product** $H \circ K$ of two filters by:

$$H \circ K = \{x \in K | hk = k \ \forall\ h \in H\}$$

Alternatively, $hk = k \leftrightarrow kh = h$ (exercise 5, section 7-4), so that we also have $H \circ K = \{x \in K | kh = h \ \forall\ h \in H\}$. Furthermore, we obtain a characterization more in keeping with lattice theory if we note that $hk = k \leftrightarrow h \cup k = (kh)h = hh = 1$. Thus:

$$H \circ K = \{x \in K | h \cup k = 1 \ \forall\ h \in H\}.$$

The reader may then verify that this definition applied to principal filters gives $[a] \circ [b] = [ab]$ using lemma 7-11, thus justifying our definition. We next note that $H \circ K$ is indeed a filter if H and K are. First, from the definition, $H \circ K \subseteq K$. Hence $k \in H \circ K \Rightarrow k \in K$. Thus $k \leq x \Rightarrow x \in K$, since

K was a filter. Also $1 = h \cup k \leq h \cup x$ implies $h \cup x = 1 \ \forall \ h \in H$, so that $x \in H \circ K$. Secondly, if $k_1, k_2 \in H \circ K$, and $\exists \ k_1 \cap k_2$, then $k_1 \cap k_2 \in K$. Finally, $(k_1 \cap k_2)h = k_1 h \cup k_2 h = h \cup h = h \ \forall \ h \in H$, so that $k_1 \cap k_2 \in H \circ K$. Hence $H \circ K$ is a filter.

If we now consider the special case where $K = I$, then we obtain $HI = \{x | x \cup h = 1 \ \forall \ h \in H\}$. HI is then characterized as the maximal ideal whose intersection with H is the zero ideal; *i.e.*, the ideal $[1]$ whose only element is 1. For first, if $x \in H \cap HI$, then $x \cup x = x = 1$. Second, if K is any other ideal satisfying $H \cap K = [1]$, and if $k \in K, h \in H$, then $h \cup k \in H \cap K = [1]$. Therefore $h \cup k = 1$, so that $k \in HI$. Thus $K \subseteq HI$. Therefore $HI = H_*$ is a lower pseudo-complement of H within the lattice $\mathfrak{F}(I)$. Thus $\mathfrak{F}(I)$ is a lower pseudo-complemented distributive lattice (the distributivity follows exactly as in the lattice of filters of any general lattice or Boolean algebra.). As a corollary, we may apply Theorems 7-1 and 7-2 to obtain the principal properties of the mappings $H \to H_*$, and $H \to H^- = H_{**}$, the latter being a closure operation. Furthermore, recalling the duality between I and $\mathfrak{P}(I)$, we can characterize the implication product $H \circ K$ between two filters in terms of lower pseudo-complementation and meet by $H \circ K = H_* \cap K = HI \cap K$. This result follows directly from the definition since $H \circ K = \{k \in K | h \cup k = 1 \ \forall \ h \in H\}$, whereas $H_* = \{x \in I | h \cup x = 1 \ \forall \ h \in H\}$. Hence $H \circ K$ is characterized by (*i*) $H \cap H \circ K = [1]$ and (*ii*) $L \leq K$ and $H \cap L = [1]$ imply $L \subseteq H \circ K$. Thus the operation $H \circ K$ within the lattice $\mathfrak{F}(I)$ is exactly the same as the operation $K - {}_*H$, introduced in section 7-1. It is to be noted that this is not a Brouwerian operation or its dual as introduced there. From our point of view, its principal properties are given by:

Theorem 7-16. *If H, K and L are any filters in an implication algebra I, then*

I1: $(H \circ K) \circ H = H$;
I2a: $H \cap K \subseteq (H \circ K) \circ K$;
I3: $H \circ (K \circ L) = K \circ (H \circ L)$;
I4: $I \circ H = [1] \ \forall \ H$.

Proof. *I1:* $(H \circ K) \circ H = (H_* \cap K)_* \cap H \subseteq H$. But $H_{**} \sqcup K_* \subseteq (H_* \cap K)_*$ and $H \subseteq H_{**} = H^-$. Hence $H \sqcup K_* \subseteq H_{**} \sqcup K_* \subseteq (H_* \cap K)_*$. Therefore, $(H \sqcup K_*) \cap H \subseteq (H_* \cap K)_* \cap H = (H \circ K) \circ H$, so that $H \subseteq (H \cap H) \sqcup (K_* \cap H) = (H \sqcup K_*) \cap H \subseteq (H \circ K) \circ H$. *I1* therefore follows.

I2a: $(H \circ K) \circ K = (H_* \cap K)_* \cap K \supseteq (H_{**} \sqcup K_*) \cap K \supseteq (H \sqcup K_*) \cap K = (H \cap K) \sqcup (K_* \cap K) \supseteq H \cap K$.

I3: $H \circ (K \circ L) = H_* \cap (K_* \cap L) = K_* \cap (H_* \cap L) = K \circ (H \circ L)$.

I4: $I \circ H = I_* \cap H = [1] \cap H = [1]$.

Theorem 7-16 shows that the lattice of filters of an implication algebra satisfies the conditions for a Boolean algebra, with the exception of *I2*. Furthermore, an example (exercise) will show that the inequality *I2a* cannot generally be strengthened for arbitrary filters. However, if we consider only those filters which are closed in the sense that $H = H^-$, then we obtain a sub-lattice $\mathfrak{C}(I)$ of $\mathfrak{F}(I)$ which will satisfy *I2*, and hence form a Boolean algebra.

Lemma 7-12. *If H and K are closed filters, then* $(H \circ K) \circ K = H \cap K$.

Proof. We already know from Theorem 7-2 that the closed elements of a lower pseudo-complemented lattice satisfy $(H \cap K)_* = H_* \sqcup K_*$. Hence if $H = H_{**}$, then $(H \circ K) \circ K = (H_* \cap K)_* \cap K = (H_{**} \sqcup K_*) \cap K = (H \cap K) \sqcup (K_* \cap K) \subseteq H \cap K$.

Our main result for implication algebras is now available.

Theorem 7-17. *Every implication algebra can be embedded in a Boolean algebra.*

Proof. We simply have to put together the preceding results. We first note that every principal filter $[a]$ is closed (exercise). Hence the class $\mathfrak{P}(I)$ or principal filters is a subset of the class of closed filters $\mathfrak{C}(I)$. But since the closed filters satisfy *I2* and, by Theorem 7-2, form a sub-lattice of the class of all filters, $\mathfrak{F}(I)$, they form a boolean algebra. But I itself is dually isomorphic to $\mathfrak{P}(I)$, so that the dual of $\mathfrak{C}(I)$ (it is self-dual) is a Boolean algebra which contains a sub-algebra which is isomorphic to I. Thus, to within isomorphism, we have embedded I in a boolean algebra.

We can now conclude our discussion of implication algebras with a few comments on the significance of Theorem 7-17. We first remark that the Boolean algebra $\mathfrak{C}(I)$ is not necessarily the most efficient extension of I to a Boolean algebra in the sense that it is the minimum Boolean algebra which contains I isomorphically. Thus in the exercises we give a second sub-Boolean algebra of $\mathfrak{C}(I)$, which is also a Boolean extension of I. Other extensions are also known, but since this is only an introduction to the subject, we omit them here. Clearly the minimum Boolean extension can be found by taking the intersection of all extensions, but we shall not attempt to characterize it here.

As a second remark, we note that since every implication algebra is a sub-algebra of some Boolean algebra, the theory of implication algebras cannot be expected to give any essential theorems of Boolean algebra not obtainable by classical methods. Furthermore, we can obtain results for implication algebras directly from those of Boolean algebras by use of Theorem 7-17. For example, we now have a simple proof that the distributive laws for $\cup$ and $\cap$ onto each other hold whenever the proper meets exist in I. Secondly, we can extend the representation theorem of Chapter 6 to implication algebra. Thus if I is any implication algebra, then we can embed I in a Boolean algebra and then represent this Boolean algebra by an algebra of sets, so that the original implication algebra I is also representable as an implication algebra of sets. We remark, however, that we could just as easily have developed the theory of representations for implication algebras directly using maximum filters in $\mathfrak{F}(I)$. By this approach the theory of representations for Boolean algebras would follow, since every Boolean algebra is simply a special type of implication algebra.

Finally, the very simplicity of the definition of implication algebras as systems with a single binary operation makes them attractive. The theory of Boolean algebras may be obtained as a special case; furthermore, the theory of Boolean algebras takes on a closer analogy with the theory of groups as basically requiring only a single binary operation. For example, the Jordan-Hölder theory for subgroups can be repeated for implication algebras with even some extensions not available in group theory (see exercises). Similarly, many other theorems from group theory can be carried over into implication algebras. Finally, the existence of many implication algebras which are not Boolean suggests that further study of implication algebra is desirable. In particular, implication algebra is useful as a tool within topology, foundations and model theory for sets.

EXERCISES

1. Show directly that an implication homomorphism preserves 1, $\cup$, $\leq$, $\cap$, and 0 whenever the latter two exist.
2. Prove that if $a \cap b$ exists in I, then $\phi(a) \cap \phi(b)$ exists in $\bar{I}$. Prove that if I is Boolean, then $\bar{I}$ is.
3. Show that for principal filters: (*a*) $a \leq b \Rightarrow [b] \subseteq [a]$; (*b*) $[a \cup b] = [a] \cap [b]$; (*c*) if $\exists\, a \cap b$, then $[a \cap b] = [a] \sqcup [b]$.
4. Prove that $[a] \circ [b] = [ab]$.
5. Show that every principal ideal is closed.
6. Determine the lattice of filters $\mathfrak{F}(I)$ for the implication algebra I of Table 7-1. Draw its diagram.
7. Show that in a finite Boolean algebra, every filter is principal, but that this is not true for implication algebras.
8. Show that every implication homomorphic image of a generalized Boolean algebra is a generalized Boolean algebra.
9. Show that the set $[a]_r = \{ax \mid x \in I\}$ of all right multiples of a fixed element a is a filter, the principal right filter generated by a. Show further that $[a]_r = [a] \circ I = [a]_*$ where $[a]$ is the principal left ideal generated by a. Finally, show that $[a]_r \sqcup [a] = I$.
10. Show that if I is Boolean, then $[a]_r = [a']$.

11. Show that if ϕ is an implication homomorphism on a meet-closed implication algebra $\langle I, \cdot \rangle$, then ϕ is also a group homomorphism on the group $\langle I, \leftrightarrow \rangle$. Show, furthermore, that ϕ is a ring homomorphism on the Boolean ring $\langle I, \leftrightarrow, \cup \rangle$.

12. Show that the kernel of an implication homomorphism is an implication filter.

13. Verify the equivalence of the two definitions of a filter given in the text.

14. Determine the quotient algebra I/K if I is the implication algebra of Table 7-1 and (*a*) $K = [a]$; (*b*) $K = [(ab)b]$; (*c*) $K = \{ab, ba, 1\}$.

15. Verify the following laws for the implication product of filters, $H \circ K$:
(*a*) $H \subseteq K \Rightarrow L \circ H \subseteq L \circ K, K \circ L \subseteq H \circ L$;
(*b*) $(H \sqcup K) \circ L = (H \circ L) \cap (K \circ L)$;
(*c*) $(H \circ L) \sqcup (K \circ L) \subseteq (H \cap K) \circ L$;
(*d*) $(H \circ K) \sqcup (H \circ L) \subseteq H \circ (K \sqcup L)$;
(*e*) $H \circ (K \cap L) = (H \circ K) \cap (H \circ L)$;
(*f*) $[(H \circ K) \circ K] \circ K = H \circ K$.

16. Let $\langle X, \mathfrak{T} \rangle$ be a topological space, and let $I = \mathfrak{N}$ be the set of all neighborhoods of X. Let x be a fixed point of X and let $K = \mathfrak{N}_x$ be the family of all neighborhoods of x. Show that K is a filter in I. Determine the filters $K_* = K \circ I$ and $K^- = K_{**} = (K \circ I) \circ I$. Show that $K^- \supset K = K \cap I$. Hence verify that the inequality of *I2a* cannot be strengthened.

17. If $\langle X, \mathfrak{T} \rangle$ is the space of exercise 16, determines the meaning of $A \equiv B \bmod \mathfrak{N}_x$ where A and B are arbitrary neighborhoods. What is the meaning of $\mathfrak{N}/\mathfrak{N}_x$? If X is a topological group, show that for any $x, y \in X$, $\mathfrak{N}/\mathfrak{N}_x \cong \mathfrak{N}/\mathfrak{N}_y$.

18. Let $\mathfrak{C}_0(I)$ be the set of all filters of I which satisfy $K \sqcup K_* = I$. An element of $\mathfrak{C}_0(I)$ is called a *complemented filter*. Show that the set of complemented filters satisfies *I2* and hence forms a Boolean algebra. Show that every principal filter is complemented, and that every complemented filter is closed; *i.e.*, $\mathfrak{P}(I) \subseteq \mathfrak{C}_0(I) \subseteq \mathfrak{C}(I)$. Thus $\mathfrak{C}_0(I)$ is also an embedding algebra for I and is more efficient than $\mathfrak{C}(I)$.

19. Prove the basic isomorphism theorem for filters in an implication algebra: $H \sqcup K/H \cong H \circ K \cong K/H \cap K$.

20. Define the concept of direct product for implication algebras.

21. Let $a = 1010$ and $b = 1100$ and let x be any four bit binary number obtained from a or b by converting 0's to 1's. Show that the set of all such x's forms an implication algebra which is isomorphic to the algebra of Table 7-1. Show that this is a sub-implication algebra of the boolean algebra $\mathbf{2}^{2^2}$.

22. Show that the free implication algebra with three generators can be obtained by generalizing exercise 21, using as generators $a = 10101010$, $b = 11001100$ and $c = 11110000$. Generalize to n free generators.

23. Determine the number of elements in a free implication algebra with n generators.

24. Show that the implication algebras of exercises 21 and 22 can be generalized to the infinite case with $\aleph_0$ generators by considering infinite repeating sequences of 0's and 1's with periods of the form 2^n for some n.

25. Set up a computer program for determining the complete implication table for the free implication algebra with three free generators.

26. Show that Theorem 7-3 holds without distributivity by showing that G is an implication algebra with 0 under $ab = a^* \cup b$. Hence $a \cap b = [a(b0)]0 = (a \cup b)^\circ$.

APPENDIX 1

REMARKS ON THE AXIOMATICS OF SET THEORY

A 1-1. THE VON NEUMANN-GÖDEL-BERNAYS AXIOMS

In Chapter 1 we discussed the Zermelo-Fraenkel-Skolem approach to set theory and mentioned the alternative viewpoint of von Neumann as modified by Gödel and Bernays. In this appendix, we shall examine the difference in these two theories in more detail and outline parts of the latter at the points where the differences are most significant. In both theories, we assume an underlying logic to start with, which consists of certain symbols denoting either variables or logical constants designating various connectives, quantifiers, etc. These logical symbols may, for example, include $\vee$, $\wedge$, $\sim$, $\Rightarrow$, $\Leftrightarrow$, denoting "or," "and," "not," "implies," "if and only if," and parentheses, (,), [, etc., as well as $\forall$ and $\exists$ for the quantifiers "for all" and "there exists." We can also include the symbol $=$ as a symbol of the basic logic, thus meaning logical identity, or include it in the formal part of axiomatic set theory as was done in Chapter 1. We then form statements and formulas in accordance with the rules of logic. These statements will consist of strings of symbols involving the logical constants as well as symbols for variables such as x, y, t, etc. Thus when we write $p(t)$, we mean some such statement or formula involving the variable t which is a true statement within the theory.

In axiomatic set theory we have, in addition to the symbols of logic, symbols $x, y, t, \cdots$ denoting the objects specific to set theory, plus an additional constant symbol $\in$ which denotes the elementhood relation. The principal difference between the two developments of axiomatic set theory of Zermelo and von Neumann is in the use and meaning of these object symbols. In the von Neumann approach all symbols denote classes, whereas the term "set" has a more restricted role. Specifically, x is a set if and only if there exists a y such that $x \in y$. Thus a set is a special type of class, one that bears the elementhood relation to some other set or class. On the other hand, it is recognized that there may exist classes which are not sets in that they do not bear the elementhood relation to any other class. The existence of such classes or non-sets is the distinguishing feature of the von Neumann theory. Every set is a class, but not every class is a set. Hence mathematics is the study of the theory of classes, or more specifically, sets within the theory of classes.

The formal von Neumann theory thus consists of a collection of class variables $x, y, z, t \cdots$, the symbol $\in$, and a string of statements of the form $x \in y$ or other statements compounded from such statements by means of the logical constants. For example, statements of the form $\sim (x \in y)$ (abbreviated $x \notin y$) or $(\exists\ x) \wedge (x \in y)$ may be included in this theory. The definition of a set may then be formalized by:

Definition A 1-1. *x is a set if "$(\exists\ y) \wedge (x \in y)$" is a statement within the theory.*

We can now introduce equality among classes in terms of the membership relation. Two classes x and y will be called equal if every time the statement $(t \in x)$ occurs in the theory, then the statement $(t \in y)$ also occurs, and conversely. Formalized, this reads:

Definition A 1-2. $(x = y) \leftrightarrow [(t \in x) \leftrightarrow (t \in y)]$.

The reflexive, symmetric and transitive laws follow for equality from the corresponding laws for $\leftrightarrow$ in logic. This definition of equality is similar to the axiom of extension in the Zermelo theory. However, it does not imply the substitution properties necessary for a satisfactory concept of equality. We therefore introduce an axiom of equality from which the substitution properties follow. It states that if x and y are equal according to definition A1-2, and $p(t)$ is any property such that $p(x)$ is a true statement of the theory, then $p(y)$ will also be a true statement of the theory; *i. e.:*

Axiom 1. $x = y \Rightarrow \forall\ p(t), [p(x) \leftrightarrow p(y)]$.

For example, if $p(t)$ means $(t \in x)$, we obtain the first half of Zermelo's substitution axiom, while the second half is obtained by using $p(t) = (x \in t)$. Definition 1 and axiom 1 are stated for classes, but they also include sets as special cases. In the Zermelo theory, we apply them only to sets. Axiom 1 states that if two sets are equal, then they have the same properties. The next axiom is a sort of converse and states that every property determines some class. This is stronger than Zermelo's axiom of abstraction in that it does not require a fixed set to begin with. It states:

Axiom 2. $\forall\ p(t)\ \exists\ x \ni (t \in x) \leftrightarrow p(t)$.*

We designate this class by the classification symbol $x = \{t \mid p(t)\}$. Hence $\{\ \mid\ \}$

*For $\ni$ read "such that."

is a class builder, but not necessarily a set builder, since we have no guarantee that x is a set; *i.e.*, a member of some larger class. However, if we write $y \in \{t \mid p(t)\}$, we mean that y is a set and y has the property $p(t)$, since in this case there is a class x such that $y \in x$. Some properties $p(t)$ determine sets by their very nature. Thus if $p(t)$ is the statement (x is a set) $\wedge$ $(t \in x)$, then the class determined by $p(t)$ is precisely the set x itself. If the property $p(t)$ does determine a set as in this example, then we say that $p(t)$ is *collectivizing* (the term is due to Gödel). As an example of a property that is not collectivizing, consider $p(t) = (t \notin x)$. This not collectivizing, even if x is a set (see the discussion of complements below).

We can now use axiom 2 to define a number of classes similar to concepts of the Zermelo theory, except that they apply to arbitrary classes. In general, if we are dealing with classes, these notions are defined and are classes by axiom 2 without recourse to further axioms. However, if we are dealing with sets, then the concepts do not lead to new sets unless additional postulates are added to this effect. We shall add such postulates below after we have defined the concepts themselves for classes.

The first concept is that of *subclass*, which is defined as expected by:

Definition A 1-3. $x \subseteq y \longleftrightarrow (t \in x) \Rightarrow (t \in y)$.

This definition is as defined for classes, but, since sets are themselves classes, it includes the concept of subset when x and y are both sets. Note, however, that even if y is a set, there is no guarantee that a subclass x will be a subset unless we add a postulate to this effect (axiom 3 below). The properties of class inclusion now follow from definition A1-3 exactly as in the Zermelo theory. Thus $\subseteq$ is reflexive, anti-symmetric and transitive.

The next concept is that of the *null class* given by:

Definition A 1-4. $\phi = \{t \mid t \neq t)\}$.

Again ϕ is not guaranteed to be a set. However, the properties of ϕ considered as a class parallel those of the null set in the Zermelo theory. Thus ϕ is unique, is a subclass of every other class (or set), and has no members. Hence it follows that in the von Neumann theory there is only one memberless class or individual.

At the opposite extreme, the von Neumann theory recognizes a *universal class* given by:

Definition A 1-5. $u = \{t \mid t = t\}$.

Again u is a class, but later we shall see that it cannot be a set. However, every set is a member of u; in fact, we can characterize sets by the property of being members of u. Hence u is the class of all sets as given by the theorem:

Theorem A 1-1. $x \in u \Leftrightarrow x$ is a set.

Proof. (*i*) If $x \in u$, then by definition 1, x is a set. (*ii*) Conversely, every member of u is a set since it bears the membership relation to u. But in addition $x = x$ implies that x has the defining property required to be a member of the class u.

We next introduce the concepts of class union and intersection in:

Definition A 1-6. $x \cup y = \{t \mid (t \in x) \vee (t \in y)\}$;

$$x \cap y = \{t \mid (t \in x) \wedge (t \in y)\}.$$

The usual properties for $\cup$ and $\cap$ follow exactly as in the Zermelo theory. Hence both are commutative, associative, and idempotent, and each distributes with respect to the other. Furthermore, $\cup$ and $\cap$ relate to ϕ and u by $x \cap \phi = \phi$, $x \cup \phi = x$, $x \cap u = x$, and $x \cup u = u$. Finally, if we extend the concepts of union and intersection to any class of classes we also have $\bigcup_{x \in \phi} x = \phi$, $\bigcap_{x \in \phi} x = u$, $\bigcup_{x \in u} x = u$ and $\bigcap_{x \in u} x = \phi$.

The next definition defines the complement of any class:

Definition A 1-7. $x' = \{t \mid t \notin x\}$.

Every class x therefore has a complement, but again it is not known that x' is a set if x is. In fact, we shall show that both x and x' cannot be sets simultaneously. The properties of complements can be derived from the properties of $\sim$ in logic combined with the properties of $\vee$ and $\wedge$, Thus $\phi' = u$, $u' = \phi$, $x'' = x$, $x \cup x' = u$, $x \cap x' = \phi$, $(x \cup y)' = x' \cap y'$ and $(x \cap y)' = x' \cup y'$. Hence we have an algebra of classes similar to the algebra of sets requiring only axioms 1 and 2. The algebra of sets is derived from this algebra after the proper axioms are introduced.

The first axiom specifically concerned with sets is similar to Zermelo's axiom of abstraction. It is obtained by adding the condition $(t \in x)$ to the class builder whenever x is a set. It states that if x is a set and $p(t)$ is any property, then the combined property $(t \in x) \wedge p(t)$ is a collectivizing property.

Axiom 3. *$\forall$ x and $p(t)$ the class $\{t \mid (t \in x) \wedge p(t)\}$ is a set.*

This axiom permits us to conclude that if y is any set and x is any sub*class*, then x is a sub*set*. For x can be defined by $x = \{t \mid (t \in y) \wedge (t \in x)\}$. Hence, by axiom 3 applied to the set y with $p(t) = (t \in x)$, x is a set. Note that it is not necessary that both x and y be sets. In fact, axiom 3 can be formulated in the alternative form: if x is a set and y is any class, then $x \cap y$ is a set. Simply, let $y = \{t \mid p(t)\}$. Hence axiom 3 also guarantees that the intersection of two sets is again a set. Furthermore, we can also deduce that the difference set of two sets is again a set. Thus define $x - y$ by $x - y = x \cap y' = \{t \mid (t \in x) \wedge (t \notin y)\}$. Hence complements relative to sets are always sets. Finally, the null class must be a set since it can be defined by $x - x$ for any set x.

At this point we can now reëxamine the Russell paradox from the point of view of the von Neumann theory. In this theory, every property does determine a class, so that we can define the class of all normal sets by $n = \{t \mid t \notin t\}$. But $x \in n = \{t \mid t \notin t\}$ if and only if x is a set and $x \notin x$. If now $x = n$, then the only conclusion is that n is not a set. Hence the class of all normal sets is not itself a set. Thus we avoid a contradiction by denying the existence of a class y of which n is a member. Therefore, the real difference between the Zermelo and von Neumann approaches to axiomatic set theory is that in the former the term "property" is limited, so that every property does not determine a set, whereas in the latter, the relation of membership is limited so that not every class is a member of some other class. In the von Neumann theory, we have a universal class, whereas there is no universal set in the Zermelo theory. However, even in the von Neumann theory, the universal class cannot be a set. For if u is a set, then since n is contained in u, n would be a set contrary to what we have just proven.

The next step is to introduce an axiom which will guarantee that the union of two sets is again a set. We use the same technique used in Chapter 1 and introduce an axiom of upper bounds for any family of sets, and then apply abstraction to obtain the union of two (or any family of) sets.

Axiom 4. $\forall\, x \in u\ \exists\, z \ni (z \in u) \wedge (y \in x) \Rightarrow (y \subseteq z)$.

Thus for any family x of sets, there exists a set z such that z contains every set y in the family x. Note that the statements $(x \in u)$, $(z \in u)$ are to be read "x is a set", "z is a set" in view of Theorem A1-1. Therefore, z is an upper bound for the family x. By abstraction from z we can now assert that $x \cup y$ is a a sets whenever x and y are both sets. Using this result it now follows that if x is a set, x' cannot be. For if both x and x' are sets, then $x \cup x' = u$ would be a set. *For every set x there exists some class x' which is not a set.*

Corresponding to the pair set axiom of Zermelo, we have a similar axiom in the von Neumann theory.

Axiom 5. *If x and y are sets, then the class $\{x, y\} = \{t \mid (t = x) \vee (t = y)\}$ is a set.*

From this axiom it also follows that if x is a set, then singleton $\{x\}$ is also a set where $\{x\} = \{x, x\}$. Using axiom 5 we can now define ordered pairs in such a way that if x and y are sets, then the ordered pair $\langle x, y\rangle$ is also a set. The definitions are the same as in the Zermelo theory. Finally, cartesian products can be defined for classes, and again the cartesian product of two sets turns out to be a set exactly as in Zermelo. Hence we can define relations between classes as subclasses of the cartesian product. In particular, the membership relation $x \in y$ is a class relation. We denote it by $e = \{\langle x, y\rangle | x \in y\}$. However, e is not a set even if x and y are. Specializing relations to the case of single-valued relations, we can next define functions similarly to the definition in Chapter 1. However, at this point we add an extra axiom not present in the Zermelo theory. It states that if x is a set and f is a function defined over x, then the range class of f must also be a set.

Axiom 6. *If x is a set and f is a function such that dom $f = x$, then ran f is a set.*

The final three axioms of the von Neumann theory are similar to those of Zermelo, corresponding to the axiom of infinity, the power set axiom and the axiom of regularity. The required definitions of power class and successor class are the same as in Zermelo.

Axiom 7. *If x is a set, then $\mathfrak{P}(x)$ is a set.*

Axiom 8. *There exists a set z such that $\phi \in z$ and $x \in z$ implies $x \cup \{x\} \in z$.*

Axiom 9. *If x is a set, then $\exists\, y \in x$ such that x and y are disjoint.*

If now x is a set, then $x \subseteq x$ and hence $x \in \mathfrak{P}(x)$. This in turn implies that $x \neq \mathfrak{P}(x)$, since by regularity $x \notin x$. Hence the power set of any set is distinct from the set. In contrast, if we examine the power class $\mathfrak{P}(u)$ for the universal class u, then $\mathfrak{P}(u) = u$. For let $x \in \mathfrak{P}(u)$. Then by definition A1-1, x is a set, and hence $x \in u$. Thus $\mathfrak{P}(u) \subseteq u$. But conversely, let $x \in u$. Then x is a set. Now let $t \in x$. Then t is also a set and hence $t \in u$. Thus by definition A1-3, $x \subseteq u$. By axiom 8 we then have $x \in \mathfrak{P}(u)$ so that $u \subseteq \mathfrak{P}(u)$. Hence $u = \mathfrak{P}(u)$. Thus in general we find a parallel usage of the term *set* in the Zermelo theory and the von Neumann theory, but in contrast the von Neumann theory permits non-sets which combine similar to sets, but in general behave quite differently with respect to the properties of these combinations. The remainder of the von Neumann theory is concerned with the axiom of choice or whatever alternatives are adopted, but is similar to the theory developed in Chapter 1. If we now consider the algebra of all classes, then we have both a least and greatest element, the empty set and the universal class. Furthermore, unions and meets are defined for classes, as are complements, so that the algebra of classes is a Boolean algebra, the Boolean class algebra. In contrast the algebra of sets is a sub-implication algebra, but it is not Boolean.

APPENDIX 2

LATTICES AND TOPOLOGICAL SPACES

One of the most important sources for applications of lattice theory is in topology. In fact, the most commonly used definition of a topological space is purely lattice theoretic in nature.* In this appendix we consider how the concepts of lattice theory apply within the general field of topology. Clearly, since topology is a major branch of mathematics by itself, we can do no more than give a brief introduction to the central concepts insofar as they relate to lattice theory.† Our secondary purpose in the present section is to prepare the ground for a representation theory of Boolean algebra which is topological in nature.

A 2-1. TOPOLOGICAL SPACES, OPEN SETS

We begin with a definition of a topological space as seen from the lattice theoretic point of view. We first have an abstract carrier set X which we now call the space and whose elements we call points. A topology $\mathfrak{T}$ on X is then any sub-lattice of the power set lattice $\mathfrak{P}(X)$ which is complete under union. Formally, we have:

Definition A 2-1. *A* **topological space** $\langle X, \mathfrak{T} \rangle$ *is an ordered pair in which* X *is any set and* $\mathfrak{T}$ *is a collection of subsets of* X *satisfying:*

G1: $G_\alpha \in \mathfrak{T}$ *for an arbitrary index set* $\Rightarrow \bigcup_\alpha G_\alpha \in \mathfrak{T}$;

G2: $G_\alpha \in \mathfrak{T}$ *for a finite index set* $\Rightarrow \bigcap_\alpha G_\alpha \in \mathfrak{T}$.

We call the elements of $\mathfrak{T}$ **open sets**.

*For a general treatment of topology, see either Kelley or Bourbaki.

†For a more complete treatment of topological space from a lattice theoretic point of view, see the bibligraphy, especially Kowalski, Thron, and Vaidyanathaswami.

Thus the family of open sets is closed under finite intersections and arbitrary unions. In particular, if we apply our definition of intersection and union over the empty index set (see Chapter 1), then we obtain the two additional conditions:

G3: $\emptyset \in \mathfrak{T}$;
G4: $X \in \mathfrak{T}$.

G3 follows, since the union over the empty set is itself empty, while the intersection over the empty set is the universal set X. *G3* and *G4* show that every topology on any (non-empty) space contains at least two distinct open sets.

The simplest examples of a topology on X are obtained by considering the lattice $\mathfrak{T}_0 = \{\emptyset, X\}$, in which the only open sets are $\emptyset$ and X, and the lattice $\mathfrak{T}_1 = \mathfrak{P}(X)$, in which every set is open. The first of these is called the **trivial topology**, while the second is called the **discrete topology**. As a further example, somewhere in between these two extremes, we consider an infinite set X and let $\mathfrak{T}$ consist of the empty set, together with all subsets of X whose complements are finite. It is an exercise to verify *G1* and *G2* in this case. This topology is called the **cofinite** topology X.

As a more familiar example, we consider the real numbers $\mathbf{R}$ and let $\mathfrak{T}$ consist of all subsets G of $\mathbf{R}$ such that $x \in G$, if and only if G contains an open interval (a, b) such that $x \in (a, b)$. We leave the verification of *G1* and *G2* to the exercises. This topology is called the **usual topology** on $\mathbf{R}$.

The last example generalizes to any metric space $\langle X, \rho \rangle$. Here X is any space and $\rho = \rho(x, y)$ is the "distance" between x and y for any $x, y \in X$. The set $S_{X,\epsilon} = \{t \in X \mid \rho(t, x) < \epsilon\}$ is called the **open sphere** (ball) about x with radius ϵ. A set G is called **open** if $x \in G \Rightarrow$ there exists $\epsilon > 0$ such that $S_{X,\epsilon} \subseteq G$. The family of open sets forms a topology $\mathfrak{T}_\rho$ on X which is called the **topology induced by the metric** ρ. We may note in passing that two distinct metrics on the same space will generate the same topology if their lattices of open sets are identical. We call two such metrics **topologically equivalent**.

A 2-2. INTERIORS

Since the topology $\mathfrak{T}$ on a space X is a lattice $\langle \mathfrak{T}, \cup, \cap, \emptyset, X \rangle$ with least and greatest elements which is complete under union, we may apply the corollary to Theorem 6-9 to assert that $\mathfrak{T}$ is a complete lattice. However, an example will show that the point set intersection of an arbitrary family of open sets need not be open, so that infinite meets in $\mathfrak{T}$ treated as a complete lattice may not agree with set intersection. Thus, in the usual topology on the real line, the sets $(0, 1 + 1/n)$ are all open, while their intersection is the half-closed interval

(0, 1] which is not open (in $\mathfrak{T}$). Using the technique of the proof of Theorem 6-9, we see that infinite meets in $\mathfrak{T}$ are defined as greatest lower bounds with respect to the partial order of set inclusion *among members of* $\mathfrak{T}$; *i.e.*, open sets. Thus the infinite meet $\sqcap_\alpha G_\alpha$ of an arbitrary family of open sets is the largest open set contained in all of the G_α. Under this definition, $\langle \mathfrak{T}, \mathbf{U}, \sqcap \rangle$ is a complete lattice.

More generally, if A is any subset of X, then the largest open set contained in A is called the **interior** of A; and designated by A°. It is the union of all the open sets contained in A; *i.e.*, $A^\circ = \mathbf{U}\{G \in \mathfrak{T} \mid G \subseteq A\}$. Every set has an interior, since $\emptyset \subseteq A$ and $\emptyset$ is always open. Using this terminology, we can now write $\sqcap_\alpha G_\alpha = (\mathbf{\cap}_\alpha G_\alpha)^\circ$. Of course for finite intersections $\sqcap_\alpha^n G_\alpha = \mathbf{\cap}_\alpha^n G_\alpha$, since finite intersections of open sets are open. We leave it as an exercise to show that a set is open if and only if $A = A^\circ$.

We now consider the unary operation $A \to A^\circ$ which maps each element of $A \in \mathfrak{P}(X)$ into the largest member of $\mathfrak{T}$ contained in A. The principal properties of this operation are given in the following theorem:

Theorem A 2-1. *The operation $A \to A^\circ$ is a mapping from $\mathfrak{P}(x)$ into $\mathfrak{T}$ satisfying:*

(*i*) $A \subseteq B \Rightarrow A^\circ \subseteq B^\circ$ (*isotonic*);
(*ii*) $A^\circ \subseteq A$ (*decreasing*);
(*iii*) $A^{\circ\circ} = A^\circ$ (*idempotent*);
(*iv*) $(A \cap B)^\circ = A^\circ \cap B^\circ$ (*meet-homomorphic*);
(*v*) $\emptyset^\circ = \emptyset$, $X^\circ = X$.

Proof. (*i*) and (*ii*) follow directly from the definition. (*iii*) follows from the fact that A° is open, and the interior of an open set is the set itself. The first half of (*iv*) follows by applying the isotonic law to $A \cap B \subseteq A, B$; *i.e.*, $(A \cap B)^\circ \subseteq A^\circ, B^\circ$ whence $(A \cap B)^\circ \subseteq A^\circ \cap B^\circ$. To prove the converse inequality, note that since A° and B° are open, $A^\circ \cap B^\circ$ will be open. But since $A^\circ \subseteq A$ and $B^\circ \subseteq B$, it follows that $A^\circ \cap B^\circ \subseteq A \cap B$. Therefore, $A^\circ \cap B^\circ \subseteq (A \cap B)^\circ$. (*v*) follows since both $\emptyset$ and X are open.

This theorem states that the interior operator $^\circ\colon A \to A^\circ$ is a meet semi-lattice homomorphism of $\mathfrak{P}(X)$ into itself, which leaves every element of $\mathfrak{T}$ fixed and is decreasing. It is not generally a lattice homomorphism, since it may not preserve unions; *i.e.*, it is not necessary that $A^\circ \cup B^\circ = (A \cup B)^\circ$. For example, if $A = (0, 1]$ and $B = [1, 2)$ are half open intervals on the real line, then $A^\circ = (0, 1)$ while $B^\circ = (1, 2)$ so that $A^\circ \cup B^\circ = (0, 1) \cup (1, 2)$. On the other hand, $A \cup B = (0, 2) = (A \cup B)^\circ$. Thus $A^\circ \cup B^\circ \neq (A \cup B)^\circ$.

We can now reverse the procedure in Theorem A 2-1 to characterize a topological space in terms of an interior operator satisfying the conditions (*ii*)-(*iv*). We begin by defining an *interior space* as a pair $\langle X, ^\circ \rangle$ where X is the space and $^\circ$ is a unary operator $A \to A^\circ$ from $\mathfrak{P}(X)$ into $\mathfrak{P}(X)$ such that:

O1: $A \subseteq A^\circ$,
O2: $A^{\circ\circ} = A^\circ$,
O3: $(A \cap B)^\circ = A^\circ \cap B^\circ$,
O4: $X^\circ = X$.

We then call a set G $^\circ$*-open* if and only if $G^\circ = G$; *i.e.*, G is fixed under $^\circ$. It remains to prove that the family of $^\circ$-open sets in X forms a topology on X. This result is contained in the next theorem:

Theorem A 2-2. *If X is any set and $^\circ$ is an interior operator on X satisfying O1-O4, then the family $\mathfrak{T}^\circ$ of $^\circ$-open sets is a topology on X.*

Proof. We first note that *O3* implies the monotonic law (*i*) above, since any meet semi-lattice homomorphism is order-preserving. Now let $\{G_\alpha\}_\alpha$ be an arbitrary family of $^\circ$-open sets; *i.e.*, $G_\alpha{}^\circ = G_\alpha$. Then $G_\alpha \subseteq \mathbf{U}_\alpha G_\alpha$ implies $G_\alpha{}^\circ \subseteq (\mathbf{U}_\alpha G_\alpha)^\circ\ \forall_\alpha$. Hence $\mathbf{U}_\alpha G_\alpha = \mathbf{U}_\alpha G_\alpha{}^\circ \subseteq (\mathbf{U}_\alpha G_\alpha)^\circ \subseteq \mathbf{U}_\alpha G_\alpha$. Therefore $\mathbf{U}_\alpha G_\alpha = (\mathbf{U}_\alpha G_\alpha)^\circ$, whence $\mathbf{U}_\alpha G_\alpha$ is $^\circ$-open. $\mathfrak{T}^\circ$ thus satisfies *G1* for a topology. But *G2* is a direct consequence of *O3* and *O4*, so that $\mathfrak{T}^\circ$ is a topology on X.

We leave it to the reader to show that if we now define an interior operator on $\langle X, \mathfrak{T}^\circ\rangle$ in accordance with the mapping $A \to A^\circ$, the operator so obtained is precisely $^\circ$. Conversely, if we begin with an arbitrary topological space $\langle X, \mathfrak{T}\rangle$, define an interior operator by $^\circ$: $A \to A^\circ$ and then consider the family of $^\circ$-open sets, this topology will coincide with the original topology. Thus the relationship between topological space and interior spaces is bijective, so that they may be considered as alternative characterizations of the same concept.

In the next section, we shall study the dual operator for arbitrary lattices.

A 2-3. CLOSED SETS, CLOSURE OPERATORS

We note that the definition of a topology is not self-dual in that it requires completeness with respect to union, but not with respect to intersection. The complement of an open set is therefore not necessarily open; *i.e.*, a topology is not necessarily closed under complementation, so that it not necessarily a field of sets, or a Boolean algebra. For example, on the real line, the interval $(-\infty, a)$ is open, but its complement $[a, +\infty)$ is not. Again in the cofinite topology, the complement of a cofinite set is finite and not cofinite. However, since any lattice theoretic concept can be dualized, we are led to the study of the concepts dual to open sets and interior operators. We call a set **closed** if its complement is open. Conditions *G1-G4* for open sets dualize to the following conditions on closed sets:

F1: The intersection of any family of closed sets is closed;

F2: *The union of any finite family of closed sets is closed;*
F3: *The empty set is closed;*
F4: *The space X is closed.*

The dual to the interior operation is the operation $A \to A^-$ where A^- is the smallest closed set containing A. It is characterized by the four conditions:

K1: $A \subseteq A^-$;
K2: $A^{--} = A^-$;
K3: $(A \cup B)^- = A^- \cup B^-$.
K4: $\emptyset^- = \emptyset$.

These laws are known as the Kuratowski axioms for a closure operator on a topological space. Dual to Theorem A2-2, we see that they characterize a topological space, by defining a closed set as one satisfying $A^- = A$, and then an open set as the complement of a closed set. We generalize these results somewhat in the next section to arbitrary lattices with somewhat weaker closure operations.

A 2-4. CLOSED-OPEN SETS

In our discussion of open and closed sets, we noted that a set may be neither open nor closed, open but not closed, closed but not open, or it may be both open and closed. Thus on the real line (0, 1] is neither open nor closed, (0, 1) is open but not closed, [0, 1] is closed but not open, while the empty set is both open and closed. The complement $F = G'$ of an open set G is closed (by definition), but the family $\mathfrak{F}$ of all closed sets is not the complement within $\mathfrak{P}$ ($\mathfrak{P}(X)$) of the family $\mathfrak{T}$ of open sets. We now call a set *closed-open* if it is both closed and open, so that the family $\mathfrak{C}$ of closed-open sets is exactly $\mathfrak{F} \cap \mathfrak{T}$. $\mathfrak{C}$ is always non-empty, since $\emptyset$ and X are always closed-open. Furthermore, in both the trivial topology and the discrete topology on X, every open set is closed-open, so that $\mathfrak{C} = \mathfrak{T}$. The nice thing about $\mathfrak{C}$ from the lattice theoretic point of view is that it is closed under complementation, so that it is a Boolean algebra under set theoretic union, intersection and complementation. Furthermore, as a lattice, it is complete with respect to both union and intersection. One of the principal goals of Chapter 6 is to show that the family of closed-open sets of a topological space can serve as a prototype for any Boolean algebra. This is the topological form of the Stone representation theorem.

A 2-5. NEIGHBORHOODS

The concepts of open and closed sets and their accompanying operators, interior and closure, show that there are many different ways of approaching the concept of a topological space. An alternative approach is through the concept of limit, which in many ways is closer to the elementary approach through the calculus. This is perhaps the most natural approach when dealing with metric spaces, and can be generalized to arbitrary topological spaces via the concept of a filter. Since a filter is a lattice theoretic concept, as we have already seen, it would be natural to develop this approach further at this point. However, we prefer to introduce the notion of a neighborhood and use it to characterize topology first, leaving the filter approach as secondary. The most fundamental concept which led to the rise of topology is that of continuity of a function. The intuitive way to specify continuity of a function f at a point x is to require that given a "neighborhood" of $f(x)$, there exists a "neighborhood" of x which maps into the given "neighborhood" of $f(x)$. By a **neighborhood**, we mean any set N which has a non-empty interior; *i.e.*, $N^\circ \neq \emptyset$. In other words, N is a neighborhood if and only if it contains a non-empty open set. However, a neighborhood itself need not be open. For example, the closed interval $[0, 1]$ on the real line has the interior $(0, 1)$, and is therefore a neighborhood. Note that 1 is *in* this neighborhood, yet we do not consider it to be a neighborhood *of* 1; *i.e.*, a neighborhood need not be a neighborhood of each of its points. We say that a neighborhood ***N is a neighborhood of a point x if and only if*** $x \in N^\circ$. Since every neighborhood has a non-empty interior, every neighborhood is a neighborhood of some point. We are particularly interested in the family $\mathfrak{N}_x$ of all neighborhoods of a fixed point x. We call $\mathfrak{N}_x$ the **neighborhood filter of** x. This is justified by verifying the two conditions for a filter. If N_x is a neighborhood of x and $N_x \subseteq M$, then M is also a neighborhood of x, while if N_x and M_x are both neighborhoods of x, then $N_x \cap M_x$ is a neighborhood of x (exercises). We note further that, since X is always open, X is a neighborhood of every point x of X. Therefore, every neighborhood filter is a non-empty filter. We can characterize the elements of $\mathfrak{N}_x$ as those sets N for which there exists an open set G such that $x \in G \subseteq N$. We write N_x to indicate that N is a neighborhood of x. If G_x is open, then we call it an **open neighborhood**. Every topological space therefore determines a mapping η from the points of x into the lattice of filters of $\mathfrak{P}(X)$ given by $\eta: x \to \mathfrak{N}_x$. This mapping is called the **neighborhood map** associated with the topology $\mathfrak{T}$ on X, and designated by $\eta_{\mathfrak{T}}$. In terms of $\eta_{\mathfrak{T}}$, open sets are characterized as in:

Theorem A 2-3. *A set G is open if and only if G is a neighborhood of each of its points; i.e.,* $G \in \mathfrak{T} \Leftrightarrow G \in \mathfrak{N}_x \ \forall\ x \in G$.

Proof. (*i*) If G is open and $x \in G$, then $G \in \mathfrak{N}_x$, since $x \in G^\circ$.

(*ii*) Let $G \in \mathfrak{N}_x \ \forall\ x \in G$. Then for each $x \in G$, there exists G_x open, such that $x \in G_x \subseteq G$. Hence $\bigcup_x G_x \subseteq G$, where $\bigcup_x G_x$ is open by *G1*. But every x is some G_x, so that $G \subseteq \bigcup_x G_x$. Therefore, $G = \bigcup_x G_x$, whence G is open.

We can once again reverse the procedure and characterize a topological space in terms of a neighborhood map satisfying suitable properties. We define ***a* neighborhood space** $\langle X, \eta \rangle$ as a pair in which X is any set and η is a map from X into $\mathfrak{F}(\mathfrak{P}(X))$, the lattice of non-empty filters of $\mathfrak{P}(X)$, satisfying:

$N1$: $N \in \eta(x) \longleftrightarrow \exists\, G$ such that $x \in G \subseteq N$ where $G \in \eta(y)\ \forall\ y \in G$.

Condition $N1$ is simply the statement that N is a neighborhood of x if and only if there exists an open set G such that $x \in G \subseteq N$. A neighborhood space therefore associates a filter to each point x of the space, the neighborhood filter $\eta(x)$ of x. The elements of $\eta(x)$ are called the **η-neighborhoods** of x. A set is called **η-open** if and only if it is a neighborhood of each of its points. We now leave it as an exercise to show that the family of η-open sets forms a topology on X. Hence every neighborhood space determines a topological space under the above definition of η-open. Furthermore, the neighborhood filter $\mathfrak{N}_x$ of a point x in the associated topological space is exactly the filter $\eta(x)$ of the neighborhood space. Conversely, if we start with a topological space $\langle X, \mathfrak{T} \rangle$ and determine its neighborhood map η: $x \to \mathfrak{N}_x$, and then use this neighborhood map to define a neighborhood space on X, then the η-open sets will be exactly the open sets under the original topology $\mathfrak{T}$. Therefore, the relationship between topological spaces and neighborhood space is bijective, so that they may serve as alternative characterizations of topologies (*cf:* Abbott 3).

A 2-6. THE LATTICE OF TOPOLOGIES, WEAK AND STRONG TOPOLOGIES

Thus far, we have been primarily concerned with a single topology $\mathfrak{T}$ on a given space X. However, the examples given at the beginning show that there may be many distinct topologies definable on the same space, so that a topological space is known only when its carrier set is known and its lattice of open sets is specified. In particular, since a topology on X is sub-lattice of the power set lattice $\mathfrak{P}(X)$, the different topologies on X may be partially ordered under the relation "sub-lattice of"; *i.e.*, set inclusion. If $\mathfrak{S}$ and $\mathfrak{T}$ are two topologies defined on X, such that $\mathfrak{S} \subseteq \mathfrak{T}$, then we say $\mathfrak{T}$ is **stronger (finer)** then $\mathfrak{S}$ or $\mathfrak{S}$ is **weaker (coarser)** than $\mathfrak{T}$. The trivial topology $\mathfrak{T}_0$ is the **weakest** topology on X, while the discrete topology $\mathfrak{T}_1$ is the **strongest**. In general, a finer topology has more open sets and is better able to distinguish between points or sets, a notion to be made more precise shortly.

The collection of topologies on X is not only partially ordered, but is closed under (set) intersection. Thus if $\mathfrak{S}$ and $\mathfrak{T}$ are two topologies on X, then their intersection is also a topology. First, let $G_\alpha \in \mathfrak{S} \cap \mathfrak{T}$. Then $G_\alpha \in \mathfrak{S}$ and $G_\alpha \in \mathfrak{T}$. Hence, since $\mathfrak{S}$ and $\mathfrak{T}$ are topologies, $\bigcup_\alpha G_\alpha \in \mathfrak{S}$ and $\bigcup_\alpha G_\alpha \in \mathfrak{T}$, from which it follows that $\bigcup_\alpha G_\alpha \in \mathfrak{S} \cap \mathfrak{T}$. A similar result holds for finite intersections of the G_α, so that $\mathfrak{S} \cap \mathfrak{T}$ satisfies $G1$ and $G2$ for a topology. Clearly the same argument applies to an arbitrary family of topologies on X, so that the collection $\mathfrak{L}(\mathfrak{T})$ of all topologies on X is complete with respect to intersection. We may therefore apply the corollary to Theorem 6-9 and conclude that $\mathfrak{L}(\mathfrak{T})$ is a complete lattice. Within this lattice the order is set inclusion, meet is set intersection, the least element is $\mathfrak{T}_0$ and the greatest element is $\mathfrak{T}_1$, but the union is not necessarily set union. Rather, the union of two topologies $\mathfrak{S}$ and $\mathfrak{T}$ is the weakest topology containing both $\mathfrak{S}$ and $\mathfrak{T}$. We designate it by $\mathfrak{S} \sqcup \mathfrak{T}$. More generally, the union of a family of topologies $\mathfrak{T}_\alpha$ is the weakest topology on X which is stronger than all the individual topologies. We designate it by $\sqcup_\alpha \mathfrak{T}_\alpha$ to distinguish it from set union.

In general, if $\mathfrak{X}$ is any family of sets in $\mathfrak{P}(X)$, then the intersection of all topologies containing every set in $\mathfrak{X}$ is a topology, the weakest topology containing $\mathfrak{X}$. We call it the topology generated by $\mathfrak{X}$ and designate it by $\mathfrak{T}(\mathfrak{X})$. In this notation, $\sqcup_\alpha \mathfrak{T}_\alpha = \mathfrak{T}(\mathbf{U}_\alpha \mathfrak{T}_\alpha)$; *i.e.*, the union of a family of topologies is the topology generated by their set union.

A 2-7. BASES AND SUBBASES

We can give a more explicit description of the topology generated by a family of subsets $\mathfrak{X}$ in the following way. First, we note that $\mathfrak{T}(\mathfrak{X})$ must contain all finite intersections of elements of $\mathfrak{X}$. It must also contain every arbitrary union of such finite intersections. The family of all such unions of finite intersections of members of $\mathfrak{X}$ will be closed under finite intersection and arbitrary union (apply the distributive laws). Therefore, the topology generated by $\mathfrak{X}$ consists of all subsets of X which are unions of finite intersections of elements of $\mathfrak{X}$. We call $\mathfrak{S}$ a subbase of $\mathfrak{T}(\mathfrak{X})$ and the set $\mathfrak{B}$ of all finite intersections of members of $\mathfrak{S}$ a base of $\mathfrak{T}(\mathfrak{X})$. More generally, a **base** $\mathfrak{B}$ of a topology $\mathfrak{T}$ is a subfamily of $\mathfrak{P}(\mathfrak{X})$ such that every member of $\mathfrak{T}$ is the union of members of $\mathfrak{B}$. Similarly, a **subbase** of a topology $\mathfrak{T}$ is a subfamily $\mathfrak{S}$ of $\mathfrak{T}$ such that every member of $\mathfrak{T}$ is a union of finite intersections of elements of $\mathfrak{S}$. In other words, $\mathfrak{S}$ is a subbase of $\mathfrak{T}$ if the family of finite intersections of members of $\mathfrak{S}$ is a base of $\mathfrak{T}$. In general any family $\mathfrak{X}$ of subsets of X is a subbase of some topology, namely, the topology generated by $\mathfrak{X}$. On the other hand, a family $\mathfrak{B}$ is a base only if it is already closed with respect to finite intersections.

As an example, we consider the real line $\mathbf{R}$ under the usual topology. A set is open if and only if it is the union of open intervals, namely, the union of all those open intervals contained in it. Hence the family of open intervals of the form (a, b), $a, b \in \mathbf{R}$ is a base for the usual topology. Furthermore, the family of infinite half-open intervals of the form either $(-\infty, b)$ or $(a, +\infty)$ is a subbase of $\mathfrak{T}$, since every open interval is the intersection of two such intervals.

More generally, in a metric space $\langle X, \rho\rangle$ the family of open spheres $S_{x,\epsilon}$ is a base of the topology induced by the metric ρ.

In the cofinite topology on X, the dual atoms of $\mathfrak{P}(X)$; *i.e.*, set complements of singleton sets, form a subbase of $\mathfrak{T}$. The corresponding base is then exactly $\mathfrak{T}$ itself.

A 2-8. CARTESIAN PRODUCTS

We can use the notions of base and subbase to define a topology on the cartesian product of a family of spaces $\{X_\alpha, \mathfrak{T}_\alpha\rangle\}_\alpha$ in terms of the topologies on the factor spaces. We first consider a finite family of topological spaces $\langle X_\alpha, \mathfrak{T}_\alpha\rangle$ and form the cartesian product of the carrier sets $X = \Pi_\alpha^n X_\alpha$ as defined in Chapter 2. We now consider a particular index α_0 and fix an open set G_{α_0} in $\mathfrak{T}_{\alpha_0}$. We then consider all n-tuples; *i.e.*, members of $\Pi_\alpha^n X_\alpha$, in which the α_0 coordinate is restricted to G_{α_0}, while the other coordinates are unrestricted. The family of all such sets with different α_0 and G_{α_0} then forms a subbase of a topology on X. We call this topology $\mathfrak{T}_\pi$ the product topology on X and $\langle X, \mathfrak{T}_\pi\rangle$ the topological product of the $\langle X_\alpha, \mathfrak{T}_\alpha\rangle$.

For example, if all the X_α are equal to $\mathbf{R}$, then X is $\mathbf{R}^n$, the set of all n-vectors. If $\mathfrak{T}$ is the usual topology on $\mathbf{R}$, then a subbasic open set in $\langle X, \mathfrak{T}\rangle$ is of the form $(-\infty, a)$ or $(a, +\infty)$. We now consider half spaces within $\mathbf{R}^n$ defined by $x_{i_0} > a$ or $x_{i_0} < a$ for fixed a and i_0. Use of the distributive laws now show that these half spaces form a subbase for the product topology on $\mathbf{R}^n$. For example, if $n = 2$, then the half planes are defined either by $x_1 < a$, or $x_1 > a$, or $x_2 < a$ or $x_2 > a$. Intersections of half planes $x_1 < b$ and $x_1 > a$ give infinite vertical strips, while intersections of vertical and horizontal strips form open rectangles. Other cases are left to the imagination of the reader. The open sets of $\mathbf{R}^2$ under the product topology are then of the form of unions of these basic open sets.

Thus far, we have asumed the number of factors to be finite. In the general case of an arbitrary indexed family of topological spaces, the elements of the carrier space $X = \Pi_\alpha X_\alpha$ consist of functions defined on the index set with values in the X_α. We again take as subbasic open sets those sets which have a single coordinate restricted to lie in a given open set of the corresponding coordinate space. Finite intersections of these subbasic open sets then have a *finite number* of coordinates restricted. For example, we can form basic open sets by considering a finite number of indices, $\alpha_1, \alpha_2, \ldots \alpha_n$ together with open sets $G_{\alpha_1}, G_{\alpha_2}, \ldots, G_{\alpha_n}$ where $G_{\alpha_i} \in \mathfrak{T}_{\alpha_i}$. A basic open set is then one of the form $B = \{\langle x_\alpha\rangle_\alpha \,|\, x_{\alpha_i} \in G_{\alpha_i}\}$.

A second example of considerable use in Chapter 6 is obtained by considering as factors the spaces $\langle \mathbf{2}, \mathfrak{T}\rangle$ where $\mathbf{2} = \{0, 1\}$ is the two element set and $\mathfrak{T}$ is its discrete topology, $\mathfrak{T} = \mathfrak{P}(\mathbf{2})$. For a finite index set, the product space is the set $\mathbf{2}^n$ with the discrete topology. For a denumerable index set, the product space is $\mathbf{2}^{\aleph_0}$ which consists of all infinite sequences $\langle x_1, x_2, \ldots \rangle$ where $x_i = 0$ or 1. The subbasic open sets consist of all sequences with fixed value $x_{i_0} = 0$ or 1 in the i_0th position. The basic open sets are those with fixed values in a finite set of positions, $i_1, i_2, \ldots, i_n$. The space $C = \mathbf{2}^{\aleph_0}$ with the product topology is called a **Cantor Space**. More generally, we may replace $\aleph_0$ by any cardinal α and C by any set of the form $\mathbf{2}^X$ where X is any set of cardinal α. The subbasic open sets are then all functions from X into $\mathbf{2}$, with fixed value at some specified point x of X, while basic open sets have fixed values at some finite set of points, $x_1, x_2, \ldots, x_n$. Returning to the specific case of $\aleph_0$, there is a natural injection of C into the real numbers between 0 and 1. If $\langle x_1, x_2, x_3, \ldots \rangle$ is an element of $C = \mathbf{2}^{\aleph_0}$, then we may map this sequence onto the ternary decimal $y_1 + y_2/3 + y_3/3^2 + \cdots$ where $y_i = 0$ if $x_i = 0$ and $y_i = 2$ if $x_i = 1$. This maps the elements of C onto those ternary decimals involving only 0 or 2. The set of such decimals is called the **Cantor middle third set**. It may be described alternatively in the following fashion. Consider the interval [0, 1] and remove the middle third (1/3, 2/3). From each of the two remaining thirds, again remove the middle third; *i.e.*, remove (1/9, 2/9) and (7/9, 8/9). Repeat by removing the middle third of each remaining interval. The set of all points not removed by this process is the middle third set. The end points of the removed intervals are the ternary decimals involving only 0 or 1 and terminating, while the remaining points are limits of sequences of such points. We leave it to the reader to verify that the middle third set is indeed the set of ternary decimals involving only 0 or 1. We also let the reader show that this set is closed (in the space [0, 1]), and has the power of the continuum. In the next section we relate the product topology on C to the topology of the real unit interval [0, 1].

A 2-9. SUBSPACES AND RELATIVE TOPOLOGIES

In our discussion so far, we have been concerned with topologies on a fixed carrier space X. We now wish to consider topologies on a subset of X. If $\langle X, \mathfrak{T} \rangle$ is a topological space with space X and topology $\mathfrak{T}$, then we wish to show how the topology $\mathfrak{T}$ induces a topology $\mathfrak{T}_Y$ on any subset Y of X. The resulting concept is that of a subspace. It is somewhat analogous to a subalgebra in universal algebra, but the two concepts are by no means identical. In a topological space $\langle X, \mathfrak{T} \rangle$ we have a space X with a structure defined on it which is the topology. But the topology is not a set of operations, so that $\langle X, \mathfrak{T} \rangle$ is not an algebra. Instead, the topology is itself the carrier of an algebra, namely the lattice structure inherited from the power set algebra $\mathfrak{P}(X)$

on $\mathfrak{T}$ as a subalgebra. Furthermore, even $\mathfrak{T}$ with its lattice structure is not a finitary algebra, since we assume closure under infinite unions. Therefore, the concept of subspace cannot be obtained by specialization from that of subalgebra.

If $\langle X, \mathfrak{T}\rangle$ is a topological space, and Y is any subset of X, then the family of subsets of Y obtained as intersections of open sets (elements of $\mathfrak{T}$) in X with Y is a topology on Y, $\mathfrak{T}_Y$; *i.e.*, $\mathfrak{T}_Y = \{G_y \mid G_y = G \cap Y \text{ for some } G \in \mathfrak{T}\}$. This result follows simply by applying the distributive law to $Y \cap \bigcup_\alpha G_\alpha = \bigcup_\alpha (Y \cap G_\alpha)$ and $Y \cap \bigcap_\alpha^n G = \bigcap_\alpha^n (Y \cap G_\alpha)$ to verify $G1$ and $G2$ for a topology. The space $\langle Y, \mathfrak{T}_Y\rangle$ is called a **subspace** of $\langle X, \mathfrak{T}\rangle$ and $\mathfrak{T}_Y$ is called the **relative topology** on Y inherited from $\mathfrak{T}$ on X.

For example, if $X = \mathbf{R}$ is the real line and $Y = [0, 1]$ is the closed unit interval, then Y becomes a topological subspace under the topology in which a set is open in Y if it is the intersection of an open set in X with Y. The interval $(1/2, 1]$ is open in the subspace Y, even though it was not open in X.

If now $\mathfrak{B}$ is a base for the topology $\mathfrak{T}$ of X, then the family of intersections of members of $\mathfrak{B}$ with Y will form a base for the subspace topology on Y (exercise). Similarly, if $\mathfrak{S}$ is a subbase for $\mathfrak{T}$ in X, then the family of intersections of members of $\mathfrak{S}$ with Y is a subbase of $\mathfrak{T}_Y$. For example, in the Cantor middle third set considered as a subspace of $[0, 1]$, a subbase is obtained by considering all intervals of the form $[0, b)$ or $(a, 1]$ and considering those points of C lying in such intervals. The reader may now show that this relative topology on $C = \mathbf{2}^\alpha$ = Cantor middle third set is the same as the product topology on C as defined in the previous subsection.

A 2-10. SEPARATION AXIOMS

We have seen that in the lattice of topologies of a space there are varying degrees of fineness for a topology ranging from the trivial topology to the discrete topology. In the first case, it is impossible to distinguish between distinct points x and y by means of the open sets that contain them, while in the second case every set can be distinguished from every other set in terms of open sets. Between these extremes there are various conditions that may be imposed on the topology to insure the existence of enough open sets to be able to distinguish different sets in terms of their neighborhood systems. These conditions are known as separation axioms. We shall discuss a few of them which we will need to refer to later.

The weakest separation axiom is the following:

T$_0$: *If $x \neq y$ are two distinct points of X, then there exists an open set $G \in \mathfrak{T}$ containing either x or y but not both.*

Topological spaces satisfying T_0 are called ***T_0*-spaces.** In a T_0-space, the set of open sets which contain x is distinct from the set of open sets which contain y. Hence the neighborhood filters of x and y are distinct; *i.e.*, the neighborhood map $\eta: x \to \mathfrak{N}_x$ is an injection of X into $\mathfrak{P}(X)$. However, it is still possible that $\mathfrak{N}_x \subseteq \mathfrak{N}_y$; *i.e.*, that every neighborhood of y contain x. To rule out this possibility, we may add the stronger separation axiom as follows:

$\mathbf{T}_1$: *If $x \neq y$ are two distinct points of X, then there exist open sets G_x and G_y containing x and y respectively, such that $x \notin G_y$ and $y \notin G_x$.*

We call a space satisfying T_1 a **T_1-space**. This axiom has an alternative form in terms of closed sets given by the following theorem.

Theorem A 2-4. *A topological space $\langle X, \mathfrak{T}\rangle$ is a T_1-space if and only if every singleton set $\{x\}$ is closed.*

Proof. (*i*) Let $\langle X, \mathfrak{T}\rangle$ be a T_1-space and let $x \in X$. Then for each $y \in x$, $y \neq x$, there exists G_y such that $y \in G_y, x \notin G_y$. Letting $G = \bigcup_{x \neq y} G_y$, we obtain an open set such that $x \notin G$, but $y \in G \ \forall\ y \neq x$; *i.e.*, $G = \{x\}'$. Hence $\{x\} = G'$ is closed.

(*ii*) Let $\langle X, \mathfrak{T}\rangle$ be a topological space in which every singleton set is closed. Then for any $y \neq x$, $G_y = \{x\}'$ is an open set containing y, but not x. Therefore $\langle X, \mathfrak{T}\rangle$ is a T_1-space.

In lattice theory terms, the axiom T_1 simply states that every dual atom of $\mathfrak{P}(X)$ is in $\mathfrak{T}$. Hence $\mathfrak{T}$ is a dual atomic lattice.

In terms of neighborhoods, a space is a T_1-space if the intersection of all the neighborhoods of a point is simply $\{x\}$ itself; *i.e.*, $\{x\} = \bigcap \{N_x \mid N_x \in \mathfrak{N}_x\}$. This condition should not de confused with the condition that $\mathfrak{N}_x = [\{x\}]\uparrow$. The latter states that the neighborhood filter for x is the principal filter generated by $\{x\}$. In this case, $\{x\}$ is a neighborhood of x and we call x an *isolated point* of X.

A further strengthening of the separation properties of a space is obtained by requiring that distinct points have disjoint neighborhoods. In terms of open sets, this requirement can be stated in the following form:

$\mathbf{T}_2$: *If x and y are distinct points of X, then there exist open sets G_x and G_y such that $x \in G_x$, $y \in G_y$ and $G_x \cap G_y = \emptyset$.*

Again, we call a space a **T_2-space** if it satisfies axiom T_2. Such a space is also called a **Hausdorff space**. Of all the separation axioms, this one is probably the most important and plays a key role in the representation theory of Chapter 6. The principal result needed for Hausdorff spaces in Chapter 6 is contained in the following theorem.

Theorem A 2-5. *If $\langle X_\alpha, \mathfrak{T}_\alpha\rangle$ is a family of Hausdorff spaces, then the product space $\langle \Pi_\alpha X_\alpha, \mathfrak{T}_\pi\rangle$ under the product topology is a Hausdorff space.*

Proof. Let $x = \langle x_\alpha \rangle_\alpha$ and $y = \langle y_\alpha \rangle_\alpha$ be two distinct points of $\Pi_\alpha X_\alpha$. Then there exists some fixed index i_o for which $x_{i_o} \neq y_{i_o}$. Since the component space $\langle X_{i_o}, \mathfrak{T}_{i_o} \rangle$ is a Hausdorff space, there exist open sets $G_{x_{i_o}}$ and $G_{y_{i_o}}$ such that $x_{i_o} \in G_{x_{i_o}}$, $y_{i_o} \in G_{y_{i_o}}$ and $G_{x_{i_o}} \cap G_{y_{i_o}} = \emptyset$. But then these open sets determine subbasic open sets in the product topology, G_x and G_y, such that the i_o-th coordinates are restricted to $G_{x_{i_o}}$ and $G_{y_{i_o}}$ respectively. Hence, $x \in G_x$, $y \in G_y$ and $G_x \cap G_y = \emptyset$ as required.

There are further separation axioms which serve to distinguish points from closed sets, as well as closed sets from each other by means of open sets. However, spaces satisfying these stronger axioms are not needed in our discussion of the representation theory for Boolean algebra and are omitted here.

A 2-11. CONNECTEDNESS

In the preceding section, we discussed methods of imposing restrictions on topological spaces so as to be able to distinguish various sets by means of the open sets which contain them. In this section, we discuss a different kind of separation in which a given space is separated into disjoint components consisting of closed-open sets. First, we say that two sets A and B of a space X are **separated** if $A \cap B^- = A^- \cap B = \emptyset$; *i.e.*, neither intersects the closure of the other. A space is called **disconnected** if it can be partioned into the union of two non-empty separated sets; *i.e.*, $X = A \cup B$ where $A, B \neq \emptyset$ and $A \cap B^- = A^- \cap B = \emptyset$. X is called **connected** if it is not disconnected. *A subset Y of X is disconnected or connected according as it is disconnected or connected as a subspace under the relative topology $\mathfrak{T}_Y$. Two points x and y are said to be connected in X if they lie in some connected subset of X.*

The following theorem gives three alternate characterization of disconnectedness.

Theorem A 2-6. *A space $\langle X, \mathfrak{T} \rangle$ is disconnected if and only if any of the following equivalent conditions holds:*

(i) $X = A \cup B$ where $A, B \neq \emptyset$ and A and B are both open;
(ii) $X = A \cup B$ where $A, B \neq \emptyset$ and A and B are both closed;
(iii) there exists a proper non-empty closed-open subset in X.

Proof. If X is disconnected, then $X = A \cup B$ where $A, B \neq \emptyset$ and $A \cap B^- = A^- \cap B = \emptyset$. Since $B \subseteq B^-$ and $A \cup B = X$, it follows that $A \cup B^- = X$. Hence $A' = B^-$ from which A is open. Similarly, B is open. Again, $B \subseteq B^-$ and $A \cap B^- = \emptyset$ implies $A \cap B = \emptyset$, so that $A = B'$, whence A is closed. Similarly, B is closed. Hence X is the union of two non-empty sets which are both simultaneously open and closed. This proves (*i*), (*ii*) and (*iii*). The converse is left as an exercise.

If now $\langle X, \mathfrak{T}\rangle$ is any topological space, then a maximal connected subset is called a **component** of X; *i.e.*, a component is a connected subset which is not properly contained in any other connected subset. A space is connected if and only if its only component is the entire space. At the other end of the spectrum is a space which is **totally disconnected** in the sense that all of its points are components; *i.e.*, there are no connected subsets which contain two distinct points. Therefore, no two points are connected. As an example, every discrete space is totally disconnected. A less trivial example is the space of rationals considered as a subspace of the real line under the usual topology. This space is totally disconnected but not discrete.

For our purposes, the most important case is that of a Hausdorff space. A sufficient condition that a Hausdorff space be totally disconnected is that it have a base of closed-open sets, as given in the following theorem.

Theorem A 2-7. *If $\langle X, \mathfrak{T}\rangle$ is a Hausdorff space which has a base of closed-open sets, then $\langle X, \mathfrak{T}\rangle$ is totally disconnected.*

Proof. We shall show that no connected subset can contain two distinct points. If, on the contrary, $x \neq y$ are two distinct points in a connected set A, then we can apply the Hausdorff axiom. This asserts that there exist open neighborhoods of x and y which are disjoint; *i.e.*, there exists an open set G_x such that $y \notin G_x$. But every open set is the union of basic open sets. Hence there exists a basic closed-open set B_x such that $x \in B_x \subseteq G_x$ and $y \notin B_x$. Since B_x is closed-open, so is its complement, B'_x. Hence the sets $A \cap B_x$ and $A \cap B'_x$ are both closed-open in the relative topology $\mathfrak{T}_A$. Furthermore, they are complements within A and are both non-empty, But this shows that A is disconnected, contrary to hypothesis.

In the next section we exhibit a partial converse to this theorem.

A 2-12. COMPACT SPACES

Our final concept from topology which is needed in the main text is the concept of compactness. We first introduce this concept into an arbitrary lattice, and then apply it to the topology of a space. An element a of a complete lattice is called **compact** if $a \leq \bigcup_\alpha g_\alpha$ for any set $\{g_\alpha\}_\alpha$ implies there is a finite subset of the g_α's $\{g_1, g_2, \ldots, g_n\}$ such that $a \leq \bigcup_{i=1}^n g_1$. If a is contained in the union of a set of elements $\{g_\alpha\}_\alpha$, we say that the g_α's from a **covering** for a. Using this terminology, an element is compact if, whenever it is covered by an arbitrary covering, there exists a finite subset which is also a covering.

In a topological space, a set A is called **compact** if any covering of A by *open sets* contains a finite subcover; *i.e.*, $A \subseteq \bigcup_\alpha G_\alpha$ implies $A \subseteq \bigcup_{i=1}^{n} G_i$. The space X itself is compact, if every open cover of X contains a finite subcover.

We first note that every closed subset of a compact space is compact. For if F is any closed set and $F \subseteq \bigcup_\alpha G_\alpha$ where the the G_α are open, the F' is open so that the augmented family of open sets $\{G_\alpha, F'\}_\alpha$ is an open cover for X. Hence by the compactness of X, there exist sets $G_1, G_1, \ldots, G_n, F'$ which cover X. But then $G_1, G_2, \ldots, G_n$ is a cover for F, which is a finite subcover of $\{G_\alpha\}_\alpha$. Therefore F is compact.

We can now reëxamine the concept of total disconnectedness in the case of a compact Hausdorff space. We then have the following converse of Theorem A2-7.

Theorem A 2-8. *A compact Hasudorff space is totally disconnected if and only if it has a base of closed-open sets.*

Proof. We must prove that if $\langle X, \mathfrak{T}\rangle$ is a compact Hausdorff space, then it has a base of closed-open sets. We let $\mathfrak{B}$ be the family of all closed-open sets in X. Let G be any open set, and let $x \in G$. If $G = X$, then G is closed-open, since X is. Otherwise, $G' \neq \emptyset$. Furthermore, $G' = F$ is closed. But as a closed subset of a compact space, F is itself compact. Next for any $y \in F$, there exist closed-open sets B_y such that $x \notin B_y$ but $y \in B_y$. The B_y's then form an open cover of F. Hence by the compactness, there exists a finite subcover, $B_{y_1}, B_{y_2}, \ldots, B_{y_n}$ of F. Let $B = \bigcup_{i=1}^{n} B_{y_i}$. Then B is closed-open and $x \notin B$. Hence B' is also closed-open, but $x \in B'$. Furthermore, since $F \subseteq \bigcup_{i=1}^{n} B_{y_i} = B$, it follows that $B' \subseteq F' = G$; *i.e.*, B' is a closed-open subset such that $x \in B' \subseteq G$. By letting x range over all of G, G is the union of closed-open sets. Hence the closed-open sets form a basis of $\mathfrak{T}$.

Compact, totally disconnected, Hausdorff spaces are the most important spaces from the point of view of applications to the theory of representations of Boolean algebras. They are therefore called **Boolean spaces**. The simplest and one of the most important examples is the space $\mathbf{2} = \{0, 1\}$ with the discrete topology. Next the topological product of such spaces are themselves also Boolean spaces. These are called **Cantor spaces** and play an important role in Chapter 6. The principal theorem now needed to complete the theory is to show that the product of an arbitrary number of compact spaces is itself compact. This most significant result is due to Tychonoff, and is known as Tychonoff's theorem. We conclude with a statement of the theorem, but omit the proof.

Theorem A 2-9. *The product of any number of compact spaces is compact.*

BIBLIOGRAPHY

Set Theory:

ABIAN, A., *The Theory of Sets and Transfinite Arithmetic*, W. B. Saunders Co., Philadelphia, 1965.

ALEXANDROFF, P. S., *Einführung in die Mengenlehre und die Theorie der Reelen Function*, Veb Deutscher Verlag der Wissenschaften, Berlin, 1967 (4 th ed.).

BERNAYS, P., and A. A. FRAENKEL, *Axiomatic Set Theory*, North Holland Publishing Co., Amsterdam, 1958.

BOURBAKI, N. *Théorie des Ensembles*, Hermann, Paris, 1960.

CANTOR, G., *Contributions to the Founding of the Theory of Transfinite Numbers*, Dover Publications Inc., New York, 1915.

COHEN, P. J., *Set Theory and the Continuum Hypothesis*, W. A. Benjamin Inc., New York-Amsterdam, 1966.

DEDEKIND, R., *Was Sind und was Sollen die Zahlen?*, Vieweg Braunschweig, 1888.

FRAENKEL, A. A., *Abstract Set Theory*, North Holland Publishing Co., Amsterdam, 1966.

FRAENKEL, A. A., and Y. BAR-HILLEL, *Foundations of Set Theory*, North Holland Publishing Co., Amsterdam, 1958.

HALMOS, P. R., *Naive Set Theory*, D. Van Nostrand Co., Princeton, 1960.

HATCHER, W. S., *Foundations of Mathematics*, W. B. Saunders Co., Philadelphia, 1968.

HAUSDORFF, F., *Mengenlehre*, Dover Publications Inc., New York, 1964.

HAYDEN, S. and J. F. KENNISON, *Zermelo Fraenkel Set Theory*, Charles E. Merrill Publ. Co., Columbus, 1968.

JOHNSON, R. L., and W. Zehna, *Elements of Set Theory*, Allyn and Bacon Inc., Boston, 1962.

KAMKE, E., *Theory of Sets*, Dover Publications Inc., New York, 1950.

MORSE, A. P., *A Theory of Sets*, Academic Press, New York and London, 1965.

NAGEL, E. and J. R. NEWMAN, *Gödel's Proof*, New York University Press, New York, 1958.

PEANO, G., *Arithmetices Principia*, Bocca Turin, 1889.

RUBIN, H. and J. RUBIN, *Equivalents of the Axiom of Choice*, North Holland Publishing Co., Amsterdam, 1963.

RUBIN, JEAN, *Set Theory for the Mathematician*, Holden-Day, San Francisco, 1967.

RUSSELL. B., *The Principles of Mathematics*, London, 1937 (2nd ed.).

RUSSELL. B., and A. N. WHITEHEAD, *Principia Mathematica*, Cambridge University Press, Cambridge, 1950.

SCHMIDT, J., *Mengenlehre*, Bibliographisches Institut Mannheim, Mannheim, 1966.

SIERPINSKI, W., 1. *Leçons sur les Nombres Transfini*, Paris, 1928.
2. *Cardinal and Ordinal Numbers*, Warsaw, 1958.

STOLL, R. R., *Set Theory and Logic*, W. H. Freeman and Co., San Francisco and London, 1963.

SUPPES, P., *Axiomatic Set Theory*, D. Van Nostrand Co., Princeton, 1960.

ZENA, P. W., *Sets with Applications*, Allyn and Bacon Inc., Boston, 1966.

Universal Algebra:

COHN, P. M., *Universal Algebra*, Harper and Row, New York, Evanston and London, 1965.

FUCHS, L., *Partially Ordered Algebraic Systems*, Pergamon Press, Oxford-London-New York-Paris, 1963.

GRÄTZER, G., *Universal Algebra*, D. Van Nostrand Co., Princeton, 1969.

MACLANE, S. and G. BIRKHOFF, *Algebra*, The Macmillan Co., New York, 1967.

PIERCE, R. S., *Introduction to the Theory of Abstract Algebras*, Holt, Rinehart and Winston, New York, 1968.

SCHMIDT, J., *Grundbegriffe der Algebra*, Mathematisches Institut Bonn, Bonn, 1966.

Lattice Theory:

ABBOTT, J. C., *Trends in Lattice Theory*, D. Van Nostrand Co., Princeton, 1969.

BIRKHOFF, G., *Lattice Theory*, Am. Math. Soc. Coll. Publ., Providence, R. I., 1967 (3rd ed.)

DONNELLAN, T., *Lattice Theory*, Pergamon Press, Oxford, 1968.

DUBISCH, R., *Lattices to Logic*, Blaisdell Publishing Co., New York-London-Toronto, 1963.

DUBREIL-JACOTIN, M., L. L. LESIEUR, and R. CROISET., *Leçons sur la Théorie des Treillis*, Gautier-Villars, Paris, 1953.

GERICKE, H., *Theorie der Verbände*, Bibliographisches Institut Mannheim, Mannheim, 1963.

HERMES, H., *Einführung in die Verbandstheorie*, Springer-Verlag, Berlin-Gottingen-Heidleberg, 1955.

LIEBER, L. R., *Lattice Theory*, Galois Institute of Mathematics and Art, Brooklyn, N. Y., 1959.

ORE, O., *Theory of Graphs*, AMS Colloquium Publ., 1964.

RASIOWA, H., and R. SIKORSKI, *The Mathematics of Metamathematics*, Panstwowe Wydawnictwo naukowe Warsaw, 1963.

RUDEANU, S., *Axiomele Latticilor si ale Algebrelor Booleene*, Editura Academiei Republici Populare Romine, Bucharest, 1963.

RUTHERFORD, D. E., *Introduction to Lattice Theory*, Oliver and Boyd, Edinburgh and London, 1965.

SZÁSZ, G., *Einführung in die Verbandstheorie*, Akadémiai Kiadó, Budapest, 1962.

"*Lattice Theory,*" *Proc. Sympos. Pure Math., 2,* Am. Math. Soc., Providence, R. I., 1961.

Boolean Algebra:

ADELFIO, S. A., Jr., and Nolan, C. F., *Principles and Applications of Boolean Algebra,* Hayden Book Publishing Co., New York, 1964.

ARNOLD, B. H., *Logic and Boolean Algebra,* Prentice-Hall Inc., Englewood Cliffs, N. J., 1962.

BOOLE, G., *An Investigation into the Laws of Thought,* Open Court Publ. Co., Chicago, 1854/1940.

BOWRAN, A. P., *A Boolean Algebra,* Macmillan and Co., London, 1965.

FLEGG. H. G., *Boolean Algebra and Its Applications,* John Wiley and Sons, Inc., New York, 1964.

GOODSTEIN, R. L., *Boolean Algebra,* Pergamon Press, Oxford-London, 1966.

HALMOS, P. R., *Lectures on Boolean Algebras,* D. Van Nostrand Co., Princeton, 1963.

HOHN, F. E., *Applied Boolean Algebra,* The Macmillan Co., New York, 1960.

SAMPATH KUMARACHAR, E., *Some Studies in Boolean Algebra,* Karnatak University, Dharwar, 1967.

SIKORSKI, R., *Boolean Algebras,* Springer-Verlag, Berlin-Göttingen-New York, 1964 (Eng. ed.).

WHITESITT, J. E., *Boolean Algebra and Its Applications,* Addison-Wesley Publ., Co., Reading, Mass., 1961.

Topology:

BOURBAKI, N., *Topology, I and II,* Addison-Wesley Publ. Co., Reading Mass., 1968. (Eng. Ed.).

DUGUNDJI, J., *Topology,* Allyn and Bacon, Inc., Boston, 1966.

KELLEY, J. L., *General Topology,* D. Van Nostrand Co., Princeton, 1955.

KOWALSKY, H. J., *Topological Spaces,* Academic Press, New York-London, 1964 (Eng. ed.).

SIMMONS, G. F., *Introduction to Topology and Modern Analysis,* McGraw-Hill Book Co, Inc., New York, 1963.

THRON, W. J., *Topological Structures,* Holt, Rinehart and Winston, New York, 1966.

VAIDYANATHASWAMY, R., *Set Topology,* Chelsea Publ. Co., New York, 1960 (2nd ed.).

Papers:

ABBOTT, J. C., 1. "Remarks on an Algebraic Structure for a Topology," *Proc. of the Second Prague Top. Sym., CSAV (II),* 1966, pp. 17-21.

2. "Semi-Boolean Algebra," *Matematicki Vesnik*, 4 (19), Cb. 1967, pp. 177-198.

3. "Implicational Algebras," *Bull. Math. de la Soc. Sci. Math. de la R. S. de Roumanie*, Tom 11 (59) nr. 1, 1967

ABBOTT, J. C. and P. R. KLEINDORFER, "A New Characterization of Boolean Algebra," *Am. Math. Monthly*, (68) 1961, p. 697.

BERNSTEIN, B. A. "A Set of Four Postulates for Boolean Algebra" *Trans. Am. Math. Soc.* (36) 1934, pp. 876-84.

BYRNE, L., "Two Brief Formulations of Boolean Algebra" *Bull. Am. Math. Soc.*, (52) 1946, pp. 269-72.

COHEN, P. J., "The Independence of the Continuum Hypothesis" *Proc. Nat. Acad. of Sci.*, (50) 1963, pp. 143-48, and (51) 1964, pp. 105-110.

DEDEKIND, R., "Uber die von drei Moduln Erzeugte Dualgruppe," *Math., Ann.*, (53) 1900, pp. 371-403.

FRINK, O., "Pseudo-complements in a Semi-lattice," *Duke Math. Jr* (29) 1962, pp. 505-514.

FREUDENTHAL, H., "Logique Mathématique Appliquée," Gauthier-Villars, Paris, 1958.

GÖDEL, K. "The Consistency of the Axiom of Choice and the Generalized Continuum Hypothesis with the Axioms of Set Theory," Princeton University Press, Princeton, N. J., 1940.

HUNTINGTON, E. V., 1. "Sets of Independent Postulates for the Algebra of Logic," *Trans. Am. Math. Soc.*, (5), 1904, pp. 288-309.

2. "Postulates for the Algebra of Logic," *Trans. Am. Math. Soc.*, (35) 1933, pp. 274-304.

LOOMIS, L., "On the Representation of σ-complete Boolean Algebras", *Bull. Am. Math. Soc.*, (53) 1947, pp. 757-60.

MACNEILLE, H., "Partially Ordered Sets," *Trans. Am. Math. Soc.* (42) (1937), pp. 416-60.

MENGER, K., "Function Algebra and Propositional Calculus," from *Self Organizing Systems*, Spartan Books, Washington, pp. 525. (1962).

NEMITZ, W. C., "Implicative Semi-Lattices," *Trans. Am. Math. Soc.*, (117) 1965, pp. 128-42.

SCOTT, D., 1. "A Proof of the Independence of the Continuum Hypothesis," *Math Systems Theory*, 1:89-111, 1967.

2. "The Theorem on maximal ideals in lattices and the axiom of choice," *Bull. Am. Math. Soc.*, (60), 1954, pp. 83 ff.

3. "Definitions by abstraction in axiomatic set theory," *Bull. Am. Math. Soc.*, (61), 1955, p. 442.

SHEFFER, H. M., "Postulates for Boolean Algebras" *Trans. Am. Math. Soc.*, (14) 1913, 481-88.

STONE, M. H., "The Theory of Representations for Boolean Algebras," *Trans. Am. Math. Soc.*, (40) 1936, pp. 37-111.

TARSKI, A., "Sur Quelques Théorèmes qui équivalent à l'axiome du choix," *Fund. Math.*, (5) 1924, pp. 147-154.

ZERMELO, E., 1. "Beweis dass jede Menge wohlgeordnet werden kann" *Math. Ann.* (59) 1904, pp. 514–516.

2. "Untersuchungen uber die Grundlagen der Mengenlehre," *Math. Ann.* (65) 1908, pp. 261–281.

ZORN, M., "A Remark on Method in Transfinite Algebra," *Bull Amer. Math. Soc.* (41) 1935, pp. 667–670.

SPECIAL SYMBOLS

Page numbers listed below indicate the location where the symbol is first introduced or where the principal definition is given.

$\in$	"element of", 4
$\notin$	"not an element of", 4
ϕ	empty set (chapter 1), 4, 12
$\emptyset$	empty set (chapters 2-7), 23
$\longleftrightarrow$	"if and only if", 4
$\{t \mid p(t)\}$	set builder, 4
$\Rightarrow$	"implies", 10
$\exists$	"there exists", 10
$\forall$	"for all", 10
$\vee$	"either...or", 10
$\wedge$	"both...and", 10
$\cap, \sqcap, \boldsymbol{\cap}$	intersection, meet, 12, 129, 58
$\cup, \sqcup, \boldsymbol{\cup}$	union, 13, 129, 58
$\subseteq$	inclusion, 9
$\subset$	proper inclusion, 9
$\{x, y\}$	pair set, 14
$\{x\}$	singleton set, 14
n^*	successor of, 14
$\mathfrak{P}(x)$	power set, 17
$\langle x, y\rangle$	ordered pair, 22
$X \times Y$	cartesian product, 23
N	natural numbers, 25
P	positive integers, 33
E	even integers, 65
O	odd integers, 65
Z	integers, 25
Q	rational numbers, 25
R	real numbers, 24
C	complex numbers, 24
ρ , σ	relations, 25
D_ρ	domain of, 26
R_ρ	range of, 26
ϕ	null relation, 27
μ	universal relation, 27
Δ_X	identity on X, 27
$\rho\vert_X$	restricted to X, 27
ρ^*, ρ_*	induced power set relations, 28
ρ^{-1}	inverse relation, 28
f , $\xrightarrow{f}$	function, mapping, 31
$\equiv$, $\sim$	equivalence relation, 35
π	projection map, 46
Π	cartesian product, 46
$\sim$	"not", 48
$\vert\vert$	joint denial, 49
$\vert$	Shoeffer stroke, 49
Δ	symmetric difference, 49

INDEX